D1240189

Statistical Adjustment

⌐ of Data ¬

BY

W. EDWARDS DEMING, Ph.D.

BUREAU OF THE CENSUS

WASHINGTON

Dover Publications, Inc.
New York   New York

Published in Canada by General Publishing Company, Ltd., 30 Lesmill Road, Don Mills, Toronto, Ontario.
Published in the United Kingdom by Constable and Company, Ltd., 10 Orange Street, London WC 2.

This Dover edition, first published in 1964, is an unabridged and corrected republication of the work published by John Wiley and Sons, Inc., in 1943.

Library of Congress Catalog Card Number: 64-24416

Manufactured in the United States of America

Dover Publications, Inc.
180 Varick Street
New York 14, N. Y.

PREFACE

The central thought in writing this book has been the adjustment of data, with emphasis on scattered portions of the topic that are difficult to find elsewhere, and which in my opinion are destined to assume increased importance in the future. Some of the topics that in the past have been thought to be important in statistics and least squares are conspicuously absent here, or receive only scant mention. It must be confessed that this circumstance arises partly by choice.

The intention has been to produce a book for reference, and also for a text. Some differential calculus is used in the development of the general theory in Chapter IV, but it is not necessary to be able to follow this development in order to apply the recommended procedures, or to interpret the results of the calculations. The main prerequisite is knowledge and experience in the subject matter.

The reader must not expect to find in this book an account of statistical methods for all occasions. It supplements: it does not supplant. There has not been in my mind any hope of covering the entire field of least squares. For instance, recent contributions from Hotelling, Wald, and Churchill Eisenhart have regretfully been omitted. An attempt to include them would have meant an unpredictable delay in publication.

Possibly the reader will see here the interpretation of adjusted values in a new light, owing to my appreciation of the powerful stimulus of Shewhart's contributions to statistical procedures and the philosophy of science. The student is first introduced to some basic statistical concepts, and in particular he is asked to view a method of adjustment as a way of arriving at a figure *that can be used for a given purpose* — in other words, for action. An abundance of procedures and skeleton table forms for numerical calculation is provided for immediate adaptation to many kinds of problems met in practice.   It can be said that all of the recommended procedures have been tested in use, many of them in mass production.   For the first time, a method for adjusting the observations (finding the calculated points corresponding to the observed points) is provided for the circumstance in which both the x and y coordinates are subject to error.   The insidious phenomenon of the instability of equations is introduced, even though inadequately, and the reader can at least claim acquaintance with it.

The successful introduction of sampling into the 1940 Census of Population, aside from being a manifestation of wisdom and foresight on the part of Dr. Philip M. Hauser, Assistant Director of the Census, and Dr. Leon E. Truesdell, Chief Statistician for Population, brought with it a host of unsolved statistical problems. One of these was the adjustment of sample frequencies to known marginal totals, solutions to which are given in Chapter VII. With the subsequent rapid growth of sampling in the conduct of many social and economic surveys of local and national scope, the inclusion of such methods may turn out to be timely.

Different kinds of problems of adjustment (e.g., geodesy on the one hand and curve fitting on the other) are here unified and brought under one general principle and one solution.   The distinctions between different kinds of problems are left where they belong, namely, in the conditions that the adjusted values are subjected to (Ch. IV).   Unfortunately and inadvertently, intellectual gulfs have grown up between writers in statistics, least squares, and curve fitting.   Each of the three groups has gone its own way, rediscovering developments long since discovered by the others, or — what is worse — not rediscovering them.   Here the reader will find contributions from all three groups, and he will perceive that they are complementary.

The methods of this book were developed over a period of sixteen years in the government service, during which I have had the pleasure of assisting colleagues in many branches of science. The manuscript originated in notes kept during my statistical practice, and to meet the need of text material for classes taught in the Graduate School of the Department of Agriculture.   A mimeographed edition of portions of this book appeared in 1938 under the title *Least Squares* as a publication of the Graduate School. Many of the calculations and procedures were worked out by my wife, Lola S. Deming. A number of helpful comments came from Professor W. G. Cochran, who kindly read the galley proof. Extensive contributions in the text, and help in reading proof, have come from several of my colleagues and assistants in the Census, notably Mr. Samuel W. Greenhouse, now with the armed forces, and Mr. Jacob E. Lieberman.

W.E.D.

WASHINGTON
August 1943

CONTENTS

PART A: SOME SIMPLE ADJUSTMENTS

PART B: THE LEAST SQUARES SOLUTION OF MORE COM-
PLICATED PROBLEMS

equations. 29. Short expression for S. The normal equations are really normal. The matrix of the coefficients is positive definite.

PART C: CONDITIONS WITHOUT PARAMETERS

30. Adaptation of the general solution to conditions without parameters. 31. Example: the plane triangle. 32. The plane triangle continued. The weights of the adjusted angles, and any function of them.

33. Steps in the formation of the normal equations. 34. Numerical example: a surveying problem. 35. Conclusions from the solution of the normal equations. 36. Shorter method of computing the weights of a large number of functions.

37. Statement of the problem. 38. Cell frequencies and sampling errors. 39. Nature of the adjustment. 40. A closer look at the problem. 41. The least squares requirement. 42. The two-dimensional problem. 43. A numerical example of the two-dimensional Case II. 44. The three-dimensional problem. 45. A simplified procedure — iterative proportions. 46. Iterative proportions in three dimensions. 47. Simplification when only one cell requires adjustment. 48. The Stephan method. 49. The Bruyère method. 50. Some remarks on the accuracy of an adjustment.

PART D: CONDITIONS CONTAINING PARAMETERS

51. Some general remarks on the purpose of curve fitting. 52. Graphical considerations. 53. The conditions. 54. The L coefficients. 55. The normal equations for curve fitting. 56. Adjusting the observations, or finding the calculated

PART A

SOME SIMPLE ADJUSTMENTS

CHAPTER I

ON THE MEANING OF ADJUSTMENT

1. Some remarks on the problem of adjustment. Before learning how to use least squares, or any other method of adjustment, one might rightfully ask what is accomplished by procedures of adjustment, and what is the purpose of using them?

In the first place it must be recognized that any measurement is the result of doing something — applying some operation. Some procedure is carried out, and some number is written down as a result. In the second place it must be understood that the purpose of taking the measurement is to use it for doing something. *The object of taking data is to provide a basis for action.*

If you were to measure a table with the idea of ordering a plate glass top for it, you would use a rule, tape, or yardstick, and measure it. The procedure of laying down the rule, counting the number of feet, estimating the number of inches and fractions of the last foot, and recording the figure, constitutes the operation of measurement. The action, in this case, consists of ordering a plate glass of a certain size. The measurement provides a basis for the action. If the measurement is wrong by so great an amount that the glass is unfit for the purpose intended when it arrives, then the figure has led us to the wrong action.

You might repeat the operation of measurement, especially if the length is required to the nearest sixteenth of an inch. Whatever the exactness required, the problem is fundamentally the same. One takes a measurement — that is, one carries out an operation — and thus gets a certain result (a number), and writes

1

it down.   Why should he repeat the operation?   The answer may
be contained in one or both of two statements: (a) to get a better
value for the purpose intended, by *adjusting the observations;*
(b) to gain some assurance that he is following the procedure
intended.   The latter is often more important, though also more
difficult.   Methods of adjustment assist us in both questions.

As has been said above, the object of taking data is to provide
a basis for action, and an *adjusted value is a derived number that can
be used for the purpose intended,* if it is possible to be had from the
data presented for adjustment.

The principle of least squares provides a method for getting an
adjusted value.   It can be applied whether or not the data are
worth adjusting, but the results are useful only when the data are
good in the first place; no purely mathematical procedure can
make a good figure out of any number of bad ones.   Data not in
statistical control — i.e., not random, are not usefully adjusted.
It is important to know when data are worth adjusting.   A partial
answer will be arrived at in this section.

Suppose that one were to repeat the operation of measurement
n times, thus getting n numbers for the length of the table, denoted
as $x_1, x_2, x_3, \cdots, x_n$.   The problem is to adjust these observations,

Observation number	Observed value
1	x_1
2	x_2
3	x_3
.	.
.	.
.	.
n	x_n

i.e., to derive from them a number that can be used as the length of
the table, for ordering the glass.   Assuming that the procedure is
being followed correctly, one must answer the question: would the
mean of the n measurements be better than any one of the measurements drawn at random?   Would the median of these n observed
values be better than the mean?   Would it be still better to

average the greatest and least of the *n* observed values? Why not just take any one of the observed values and use it? We shall proceed to some considerations that may help to provide useful answers to these questions. A statistician is expected to make better adjustments than anyone else. That is his business. However, the statistician must insist that he be rated, not on some individual adjustment, but in a *population of adjustments*, that is, on a " long run " of adjustments. If, in the long run he has a greater percentage of satisfactory results than anyone else could have gotten, then his method of adjustment is better. In isolated instances, his results may not be so good as those obtained by someone else, yet his method may be better in the sense just stated.

Any measurement or any adjusted value is a *prediction* in the sense that the number that we are going to use for the length of a table is about what we should expect anyone else to get if he were to measure the table. As a matter of fact, every empirical scientific statement is a prediction, because, no matter how many times it has been confirmed in the past, it is always subject to future confirmation by experiment. Any measurement is but one term in a sequence of terms (results) that actually or theoretically might yet be taken by repeated applications of the operation of measurement. It is important to realize that it is not the one measurement, alone, but its relation to the rest of the sequence that is of interest. We should not risk designating a measurement a measurement if we did not think that it could be duplicated within stated limits by future measurements, and that future action would bear out the usefulness of the number so designated.

2. Randomness and the importance of order. In attempting to answer the questions that have been raised in the preceding paragraphs, let us make a chart, showing the results of repeating our operation of measurement. Let us plot the observed values as ordinates and the observation numbers as the abscissas. Suppose the chart has the appearance of Fig. 1. The observations show a trend. Under such circumstances should we take the average, median, or any other function of these observations for an adjusted value? The answer is *no*. Something is wrong with the procedure

or the measuring instrument. The first thing to do is to find out
what the trouble is.

Let it be noted that the trend is recognizable only when there are
a number of measurements. If only one or two measurements had
been taken, the trend and the existence of any difficulty would not
have been recognized, and the glass ordered would not fit.

Now let us do something else. Suppose that each number in the
above table is written on a poker chip. Let these chips be physi-
cally similar, put into a bowl and thoroughly stirred, and then

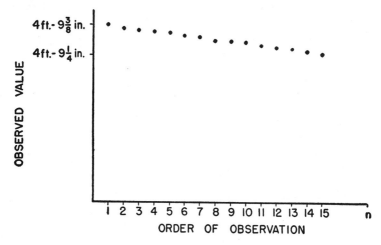

FIG. 1. A chart showing the observed value plotted against the observation
number. The observations exhibit a trend.

drawn one at a time with shuffling between draws. With care,
this operation of getting numbers will be a *random operation*, and
will accordingly produce a *random sequence*. One actual random
operation gave the sequence of numbers shown in Fig. 2.

Just what is the difference between Figs. 1 and 2? The numbers
plotted are the same, i.e., for every number shown in one chart,
there is the same number in the other. What is different, then?
The *order* of the observations is different. The original order has
been destroyed by drawing the numbers from a bowl, and there is
no more trend. On this account alone, the *actions* that would be

taken on the basis of the two charts are entirely different. The action based on the series of n measurements shown in Fig. 1 would be first to try to find out what is the trouble with the procedure of measurement that produced the n observations. Ordering the glass would come second: we should defer ordering it until we get better (more useful) measurements. On the other hand, if Fig. 2 had been the result of the actual measurements, we could go ahead and order the glass at once. It is not alone the observed values that count; *their relation to one another in the order of production is*

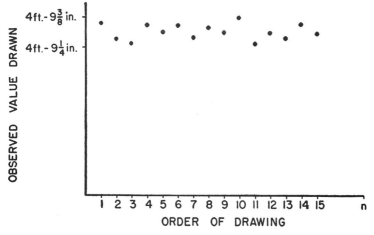

FIG. 2. The observations here exhibit randomness. These are the same numbers as shown in Fig. 1, but their order has been made random by drawing them from a bowl.

also important.

When the trend of Fig. 1 occurs in actual observation with a measuring instrument, we immediately suspect something is wrong, and we try to find the difficulty. But if a trend like this were to occur under the ideal conditions of sampling (drawing the numbers from a bowl), we have no suspicions, but simply accept this result as one of the things that is going to happen once in a while.

Let it be noted that trends and other patterns resulting from repeated observations occur not only in physical measurements, but also in the social sciences. For instance, in a survey that is repeated monthly, if a person repeatedly answers the same questionnaire, his answer may vary from time to time, and may even show a trend, even though his status in life, measured by usual standards, has not changed appreciably. Repetition alone may be the cause of more careful attention to the details of the questions, gradually bringing about a different evaluation of the same circumstances, resulting in a trend. Moreover, repetition of a question month by month may actually produce a trend; for instance, if a housewife weighs out her flour week by week in order to record for some survey the amount she uses, she may become flour conscious and gradually use more or less than she did before.

Results like the points in Fig. 2 show *stability*, or *randomness*, and *can be statistically adjusted* to get a figure that can be used. It is to be noted that a rather large number of measurements is required before one can say that the operation of measurement is random.   Visual inspection of the chart is often sufficient, but the more dependable Shewhart criterion of randomness[1] can be used if desired.   The main thing is to have enough observations, and to plot them.   With enough experience in using a particular method of measurement it may not be necessary to do this.   The point is that before the observations can be adjusted, they must arise from a random operation.

The adjustment itself may be a very simple procedure.   It might consist of merely picking out any one of the n observations in Fig. 2 by lot, as one might be willing to do if (after randomness is assured) the measurements are all seen to lie within a band that is narrower than the requirement.   Even if one of the n observations is picked out by lot, the other observations of the sequence are not thrown away;   they all provide information.   Together they perform two functions: (i) they help to demonstrate the randomness of the operation of measurement, and (ii) they show

---

[1] The Shewhart criterion of randomness is described in his book entitled *Economic Control of Quality of Manufactured Product* (Van Nostrand, 1931); also in his book *Statistical Method from the Viewpoint of Quality Control* (The Graduate School, Department of Agriculture, 1939).   It is described and used in the pamphlet entitled " Control Chart Method of Controlling Quality during Production " (American Standards Association, 29 West 39th St., New York, 1942).

that the band of variation is so small that any one of them alone
will suffice. The method of adjustment might of course be slightly more
complicated. One might take the mean, or the median, of the n
observations. The mean is in fact the least squares adjustment,
as we shall learn in Chapter II. One could also conceivably split
the difference between the greatest and least of the observations
to get an adjusted value.

The advantage of these slightly more complicated methods of
adjustments is that if they are carried out for repeated sets of n
measurements, the adjusted values so produced will fall within a
narrower band than the band corresponding to the original observations. For most random operations, the least squares adjustments will show the narrowest band of all, and this is a very practical argument in favor of least squares.

3. Performing a simple adjustment. Simple problems are always best for illustration: if we can understand simple problems,
there is some hope that we can under-
stand more complicated ones. One
of the best to look at from the standpoint of adjustment is a plane triangle in which the three angles have
been observed by some angular measuring instrument, such as a transit
or a protractor. In the triangle of
Fig. 3 the three angles have been
measured once each, with the results
shown in the table. The observed
angles add up to 179° 30'. Suppose
we demand that the angles be adjusted so that their sum is 180° exactly. Two methods of adjustment
might at times suggest themselves.

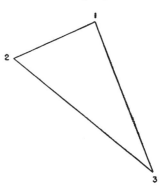

FIG. 3. The three angles of a
triangle have been measured.
The sum of the adjusted angles
is forced to be 180°.

Method 1. Distribute the 30' deficiency amongst the three
angles in proportion to size.

Method 2. Distribute the 30' deficiency equally amongst the
three angles.

| Angle | Observed | Adjusted | |
		Method 1	Method 2
1	120° 07'	120° 27'	120° 17'
2	38 23	38 29	38 33
3	21 0	21 04	21 10
Sum	179° 30'	180° 0'	180° 0'

The two methods of adjustment give the results shown in the table. Which do you prefer? Either is simple enough, and your preference will be easily settled, depending on the circumstances. If the protractor is correctly graduated, then the measurements of an angle may be randomly distributed about its true value, resembling in a fashion those in Fig. 2. Under such circumstances one would prefer Method 2. If on the other hand the protractor had been stretched in its manufacture so that the 180° index actually extends through more than half a circumference, then, though the measurements of any angle be randomly distributed, they will be distributed around a value that is too small. Under such circumstances, angular measurements need to be corrected by small additions, proportionate to the size of the angle measured. This is what Method 1 calls for. We can not say that either of the two methods is better; each has its place, depending on the circumstances. (Cf. Sec. 5 also.)

As we shall see later (Sec. 31), Method 2 is the least squares adjustment under the assumption that the protractor is correctly graduated. Thus, the method of least squares seems to lead to a simple and common sense procedure. It will be so wherever the problem is simple enough to visualize. In a later chapter we shall return to the problem of the triangle, in which the least squares procedure will be worked out for more complicated situations, in which the angles have been measured more than once, or an unequal number of times, and the sides may have been measured also (Sec. 34; pp. 74 ff.).

Another simple example is a line that has been divided into segments, and some action is to be based on their lengths. The observed lengths of the segments do not add to the observed length of the whole line, and an adjustment is required. A very simple procedure would be to apportion the excess or deficiency equally amongst the segments and the whole line: if the segments are in excess, their observed values will each be decreased by a certain amount, and the observed value of the whole line will be increased by the same amount, this amount being the excess divided by $n + 1$, where n is the number of segments. This adjustment is very easily applied. It actually is the least squares adjustment. More complicated problems of this type occur when the segments are not all measured the same number of times, or are measured with instruments of different precisions. Such problems will form the object of later attention, but we pause here to note

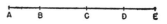

Fig. 4. The line AE and its four segments have been measured. The sum of the adjusted segments must equal the adjusted over-all length.

that in this simple case the least squares procedure provides an easy and satisfactory adjustment. (See Exercise 2, p. 86.)

In more complicated problems, it is not so easy to picture what happens in the adjustment, but we shall be able to apply the same principles in working them out. Problems of curve fitting are essentially the same nature as the geometric illustrations just given: in each problem the adjustment consists of altering the observed values in order to satisfy certain conditions that we decide to impose on the adjusted values.

4. Least squares adjustments often easy. It is sometimes supposed that the method of least squares is more difficult than most methods to carry out. This is not always so; least squares is often the simplest and most satisfying of all known methods. In many problems, normal equations are not required. It all depends on what conditions are to be imposed, or how rigidly the user insists on fulfilling them. There are some problems in which least squares provides the only known method at any price, as for instance, complicated problems in triangulation and geodesy; also the adjustment of the observations in curve fitting when the weights vary and more particularly when both coordinates are subject to errors of observation. We have already seen some examples in which the least squares adjustment is simple and direct; for instance, it was noted in connexion with the adjustment of the observations in Fig. 2 that the least squares adjustment happens to be identical with the mean of the n observations — and calculating a mean is usually a simple enough procedure. We saw likewise that in the adjustment of the triangle by Method 2, the least squares adjustment turned out to be merely the equal distribution of the deficiency amongst the three angles. The least squares adjustment of the segments of the line in the last section is moreover simple enough, again being merely an equal distribution of the deficiency or excess of the segments. Students who have fitted polynomials in the form of orthogonal polynomials will realize that the method of least squares, though perhaps not simple, is at least a routine matter, not involving the solution of normal equations. There is another illustration, contained in Chapter VII, in which tables of frequencies obtained by sample surveys are adjusted to expected marginal totals that are obtained from other considerations, such as a complete count; here again the adjustment can be made rapidly without the solution of normal equations. One could go on and point out many other problems in which the least squares adjustment is about as simple to carry out as any that could be devised, in view of the conditions imposed on the adjusted values.

5. Statistical methods and correction for biases. There is another kind of adjustment, which might be referred to as an adjustment for bias. Laboratory instruments are often calibrated against a standard, and a correction factor applied to the measurements. Similar corrections are often required in canvasses in the social sciences. A mailed questionnaire, for example, usually requires corrections, because not everyone responds, and those that do not, form a class distinct from those that do. Moreover, the responses in a mailed questionnaire will be different from the responses in an interview questionnaire, even for questions worded identically. Increasing the size of the sample, or the number of observations, will decrease the sampling errors, but not the biases. A statistical adjustment is applied primarily to effect compromises with statistical fluctuations (sampling errors and errors of observation). A bias is never discovered or measured, nor has any meaning, unless two or more distinct methods of observation or experimentation are compared with each other. Statistical adjustments of data, together with the Shewhart statistical methods of quality control, are powerful tools in the detection of biases, difference in performance, deterioration or other changes in quality, the standardization of quality, and a host of important related problems.

Simultaneous adjustment for bias and statistical fluctuations can often be made, as when sample frequencies constituting observations on the breakdown of a certain class of the population are adjusted to the known total of that class (Ch. VII), or when a line is forced to pass through the origin because theory and other related knowledge of the subject tell us that it should (Sec. 15, p. 31). In the triangle problem of Section 3, Method 1 simultaneously corrects for a stretched or compressed scale, and for statistical fluctuations of the measurements; but we should not be in position to choose between Methods 1 and 2 without knowing somehow or other from other experience with it whether the protractor scale *i.* is uniformly stretched or compressed, or *ii.* can be considered perfect.

6. Repeated experimental results necessary for establishing a scientific law. It would be splendid if all action required in social, economic, and industrial planning could be based on scientific laws; but actually, so many of the laws remain yet to be discovered that most action must necessarily be taken on the basis of knowledge of the subject matter in related fields. Of course, it is true that action is often prompted by prejudices and whims, even when a scientific basis for action exists, but this is a failing of human nature, hardly a problem in mathematics or statistics.

No one experiment by itself establishes a law, or a valid basis for action. It is the consistency of repeated results under a variety of conditions that establishes a law. The method of least squares can be applied to a single set of data, but no matter how carefully the least squares adjustment is carried out, the curve so fitted, or the observations so adjusted, do not have scientific validity unless there is other evidence at hand to show under what conditions the same or similar results will be obtained, and how these conditions are to be brought about and controlled.[2]

A long series of experiments may provide the additional evidence that is needed, particularly if the different experiments of the series are performed under a variety of conditions (different temperatures, climatic conditions, economic levels, etc.). If the data in each experiment are random or nearly so (see Fig. 2 and discussion), and if the adjusted coordinates or the adjusted parameters in the fitted curve turn out to have about the same values, time after time, without fail, a scientific law may be considered established, and the conditions under which it holds may be stated.

Thus, to be more specific, it is not the standard error of a slope, as estimated from a single set of data, but rather the persistent smallness of the standard error, or the persistent recurrence of the slope, in experiment after experiment, under a variety of conditions, that really attains scientific significance. By this we mean that *useful predictions* can be made regarding future slopes, and that we can say under what conditions these slopes will be maintained. Repeated patterns lie at the basis of scientific significance. *Repeated and repeatable* good fits, and *repeated and repeatable* statistical significance, establish a scientific law. In science one is usually if not always studying the underlying system of forces (social, economic, mechanical, chemical, or whatever), in order to take action on the cause system, to regulate *future* product. Measurements or surveys already carried out on some one particular batch of product (population of people, lot of industrial product, etc.), provide part but only part of the chain of evidence that is required for predictions with regard to data of the future. The

---

[2] " . . . it being justly esteemed an unpardonable temerity to judge the whole course of nature from one single experiment, however accurate or certain." From Hume's *An Enquiry Concerning Human Understanding* (London, 1748), section vii, part 2.

" But to argue, without analysis of the instances, from the mere fact that a given event has a frequency of 10 percent in the thousand instances under observation, or even in a million instances, that . . . it is likely to have a frequency near to 1/10 in a further set of observations, is . . . hardly an argument at all." J. M. Keynes, *Treatise on Probability* (Macmillan, 1929), p. 407.

operationally verifiable meaning of a scientific law is a prediction of future results, not a statement of past results.

Every experiment in a series should be designed and performed with care and judgment, even if many more experiments are required. Likewise, the data of each experiment should be summarized in the most efficient manner for comparison with the other sets of data. The importance of statistical theories and the design of experiments can not be overemphasized. Under conditions of randomness, the method of least squares usually provides a good summary of an experiment by preserving most of the information in the data, provided the right curve is being fitted. In some problems the method of least squares is simple and easy to apply; in others it is difficult (Sec. 4). In some kinds of problems, no other method is known. What method of adjustment to use (least squares, free hand curves, etc.) is as much a matter of economics as science, and must be decided on the basis of time, costs, and results. It is more important to insist on having a series of experiments carried out under a variety of conditions, than to insist on using any particular method of adjustment.

7. The nature of an adjustment. A student of statistical theory may well wonder how the adjustment of data differs from other statistical calculations, and in particular the calculations that are performed in problems of estimation. A problem of adjustment might be identified as a problem in estimation in which the end product is a set of *adjusted values*, which have been forced (adjusted) to satisfy certain conditions.

It is these conditions that distinguish one problem from another. In the triangle problem of Section 3, and later on in Sections 31 and 34, the sum of the adjusted angles is forced to be 180°. In adjusting the line and line segments of Section 3, the sum of the adjusted segments must equal the adjusted total length of the line. In curve fitting (Figs. 16 and 17, pp. 132 and 133) there are likewise conditions to be fulfilled, because the adjusted observations are forced to lie on a so-called calculated curve. The principle of least squares (Ch. II) remains the same in all these problems, but the different kinds of conditions imposed on the adjusted values lead to different procedures in certain preliminary stages of the solution.

CHAPTER II

SIMPLE ILLUSTRATIONS OF CURVE FITTING

8. The principle of least squares. Before going into the general problem of the adjustment of observations (Ch. IV), it will be helpful to apply least squares to some simple applications in curve fitting. Fortunately, simple problems afford nearly as much opportunity for thought in the field of statistical inference as the more complicated ones do. In all of them, simple or complicated, *the principle of least squares* requires the *minimizing of the sum of the weighted squares of the residuals.* This sum may be written as

$$S = \sum w \, res^2 \tag{1}$$

The summation (denoted by $\sum$) of the weighted squares of the residuals is to be taken over all the observations that are subject to error. S is called the " sum of squares," or, more explicitly, the " sum of the weighted squares." Weight will be defined in Section 11.

In curve fitting, either or both of the x and y observations may be subject to error. Accordingly, S will be written explicitly for the x residuals alone, or the y residuals alone, or both, depending on the experimental conditions. For instance, later on, when both the x and y coordinates are in error we shall write

$$S = \sum (w_x V_x^2 + w_y V_y^2) \tag{2}$$

Here V_x is an x residual, and V_y is a y residual (see Fig. 17 on p. 133). If only y is subject to error, the first term on the right is to be omitted, and if only x is subject to error, the second term is to be omitted. In this chapter we shall be content to deal with a few simple problems in which only one coordinate has error.

The *principle* of least squares is the minimizing of S. The *method* of least squares is a rule or set of rules for proceeding with the actual computation.   Here we shall try to learn both, and how to interpret the results.   We may now define χ^2 by the equation

$$\chi^2 = \frac{S}{\sigma^2} \tag{3}$$

The symbol σ denotes the standard error of observations of unit weight (Sec. 11). Now since σ is a constant in any one problem, χ^2 is a minimum when S is a minimum; hence we may think of least squares not only as the minimizing of S, but also of χ^2. Least squares may also be considered the minimizing of the estimate $\sigma(ext)$, to be introduced in Section 13. Another way of looking at the problem is to say that the principle of least squares is the *maximizing* of $P(\chi)$, and that we seek the solution that gives the greatest probability on the chi-test.

Remark. It is interesting to recall Gauss' *Theoria Motus* statement of the principle of least squares, in particular his recognition of the occasional need for compounding errors of different dimensions (seconds of arc, seconds of time, length, weight, etc.). In curve fitting, this compounding is exemplified as explained above, namely, by taking account of the errors in both the x and y coordinates, when both are subject to error, just as one would take account of the errors in both the angles and the sides of a triangle (Sec. 34). The following quotation from Gauss is taken from his *Theoria Motus Corporum Coelestium* (Hamburg, 1809), Art. 179. His h is *weight*, written in Eq. 2 and elsewhere as w. His sum $hhvv + h'h'v'v' + h''h''v''v'' + \cdots$ is the S of Eq. 1.

"... quamobrem systema maxime probabile valorum pro quantitatibus p, q, r, s, etc., id erit, ubi aggregatum $hhvv + h'h'v'v' + h''h''v''v'' +$ etc., i.e., *ubi summa quadratorum differentiarum inter valores revera observatos et computatos per numeros qui praecisionis gradum metiuntur multiplicatarum fit minimum.* Hoc pacto ne necessarium quidem est, ut functiones V, V', V'', etc., ad quantitates homogeneas referantur, sed heterogeneas quoque (e.g., minuta secunda arcuum et temporis) repraesentare poterunt, si modo rationem errorum, qui in singulis aeque facile committi potuerunt, aestimare licet."

This was Gauss' enunciation of the principle of least squares in 1809. In 1823, in his *Theoria Combinationis Observationum Erroribus Minimis Obnoxiae*, he took the view that one seeks values for the adjusted observations and parameters which render the variance of the parameters a minimum. Both points of view are arbitrary, and are justifiable only in experience. Fortunately, both points of view lead to the same identical least squares solution. An article by A. C. Aitken and H. Silverstone, " On the estimation of statistical parameters " (*Proc. Royal Soc. Edinburgh*, vol. lxi, 1942: pp. 186–194), is instructive.

9. The simplest example of curve fitting — the single sample.
Let a single sample of n controlled[1] (random) observations be

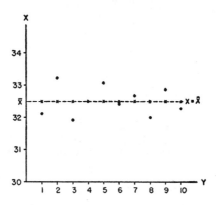

Fig. 5.   Ten observations
$$x_1, x_2, \cdots, x_{10}$$

of equal precision (equal weight) are made on an unknown magnitude α. The true points are connected by the simple relation $x = \alpha$, hence $x = a$ is the curve to be fitted.   The least squares value of a turns out to be $\bar{x}$, the mean of the ten observations. $x = \alpha$ is the " true curve," and $x = \bar{x}$ is the " calculated curve."   The calculated points are shown by the crosses; they all lie on the calculated curve.   This is the simplest problem in curve fitting.
Compare with Fig. 6, page 25, and with Fig. 16, page 132.

made on some magnitude, such as the length of a table.   Suppose that it is desired to derive an adjusted value a, from these observa-

[1] For a partial explanation of controlled observations and randomness, see the first chapter.

tions. We look upon the problem as one in fitting the curve

$$x = a \qquad (4)$$

to the n observations. This is the simplest of all curves; it is merely a horizontal line (Fig. 5). It contains but one *adjustable constant* or parameter, namely, a. This parameter a is now to be determined. The method of least squares will be illustrated. The problem is to minimize S, the sum of the weighted squares of the residuals. The observations are all of equal weight, since by supposition they appear to have been drawn all from the same bowl. We shall therefore let all the weights be unity. If x denotes an observation, then $x - a$ is the corresponding *residual*, since, by definition,

Residual = Observed − Calculated

The square of the residual will be $(x - a)^2$; hence the sum

$$S \equiv \sum (x - a)^2 \qquad (5)$$

will be the quantity to be minimized. The sign $\sum$ means that the squares of all the residuals are to be summed.

> Here the y coordinates of the points are merely the ordinal numbers of the observations (1st, 2d, 3d, etc.). The y coordinates are of course without error here, so only x residuals appear in the expression for S.

Now the n observations, having once been made, can not be changed. They are constants. The only variable in Eq. 5 is the adjustable parameter a. By giving various values to a, S is made to take on various values. There will be a minimum, and it will occur when the derivative

$$\frac{dS}{da} = -2 \sum (x - a) \qquad (6)$$

vanishes, that is to say, when

$$\sum (x - a) = 0 \quad \text{or} \quad \sum x - na = 0$$

The least squares value of a is accordingly

$$a = \frac{1}{n} \sum x \equiv \bar{x} = \text{the mean} \qquad (7)$$

So the horizontal line $x = \bar{x}$ in Fig. 5 gives the smallest possible value to the sum of the squares of the residuals, and hence to χ^2. The line $x = \bar{x}$ is the " calculated curve "; it is the " curve " $x = a$ fitted by least squares. On this line lie all the " calculated points," these being the least squares estimates of the observed points. (In this problem, the calculated points all have the same ordinate, namely, $\bar{x}$. Compare Fig. 5 with Fig. 17, p. 133.)

The fit of this line may be judged by comparing the value of $\chi^2/(n-1)$ with σ^2. This is done by looking up $P(\chi)$ for the observed value of χ^2 corresponding to $n-1$ degrees of freedom. This subject will be touched upon again in Section 13 and elsewhere. Tables for the use of the chi-test will be found in R. A. Fisher's *Statistical Methods for Research Workers* (Oliver and Boyd).

Note that the value of σ is not required for the application of least squares, because whatever σ is, χ^2 is a minimum when S is a minimum. σ did not occur in Eq. 6. σ is required, nevertheless, for the use of the chi-test for the fit of the curve. It is presumed to be obtained from previous experience with the measuring instrument. By the time enough data are gathered to attain and test for randomness, σ will be known closely enough.

Note also that if s denotes the standard deviation of the n measurements, then $\chi^2 = ns^2/\sigma^2$, and the minimized value of S is ns^2. For a new sample of n observations there will be a new mean, $\bar{x}$, a new line, and a new χ^2. Any one value of $\bar{x}$ can form a basis for action only if there is evidence that future values of $\bar{x}$ would be closely the same. This evidence must come from experience with the procedure of measurement.

10. The same problem with unequal weights. (*a*) *Direct solution.* In the preceding section, all the observations had equal weight,[2] they were " drawn from the same bowl " (Ch. I). Suppose now that the n observations $x_1, x_2, \cdots, x_n$ have weights w_1,

[2] The meaning of weight will be learned in the next section.

$w_2, \cdots, w_n$, perhaps not all equal. The observations are now drawn from bowls having the same mean, but perhaps various standard deviations. The procedure is formally very similar to what it was before. We are now to make the sum of the *weighted* squares of the residuals a minimum, so we write

$$S = \sum w_i(x_i - a)^2 \qquad (8)$$

the ith residual being, as before, $x_i - a$. Here, the weight w_i is introduced because the weights are not all unity. As before, S is to be a minimum with respect to a. The derivative

$$\frac{dS}{da} = -2 \sum w_i(x_i - a)$$

when set equal to zero gives

$$\sum w_i(x_i - a) = 0$$

or

$$a \sum w_i = \sum w_i x_i \qquad (9)$$

whence

$$a = \frac{\sum w_i x_i}{\sum w_i} \equiv \bar{x} \qquad (10)$$

where $\bar{x}$ is now the *weighted mean* of the n observations. In the event that $w_1 = w_2 = \cdots = w_n$, this result reduces to the previous value of a in Eq. 7. In other words, the problem of the preceding section (equal weights) was a special case of this one.

The minimized value of S is here

$$S = \sum w_i(x_i - \bar{x})^2 = \sum w_i x_i^2 - \bar{x}^2 \sum w_i \text{ (See p. 151.)} \quad (11)$$

(b) *Tabular solution.* In Section 61 we shall see a systematic procedure for the solution of normal equations and for calculating the "reciprocal matrix," in which are found the variance and product variance[3] coefficients; also we shall see the minimized value of S calculated right along with the solution of the normal equations. In simple problems like the one just considered, there is only one normal equation (Eq. 9) and it is of course very easily

---

[3] Following Aitken, the term product variance is used here rather than covariance.

solved (see Eq. 10). Nevertheless, it is interesting to see how the routine process that is to be shown in Section 61 applies here. Let us therefore set up the following tabulation, and perform the steps indicated below. The subscript i in the summations has been omitted for the sake of brevity.

Row	a	=	1	C
I	$\sum w$		$\sum wx$	1
2			$\sum wx^2$	0
3			$-\dfrac{(\sum wx)^2}{\sum w}$	$\cdots$
II			$\sum wx^2 - \dfrac{(\sum wx)^2}{\sum w}$	$\cdots$

An ellipsis $(\cdots)$ in the tabular array denotes a space wherein a number would ordinarily be entered in numerical calculation, but in which it is not worth while to show the entry in symbols.

Row I is the main equation; it is equivalent to Eq. 9. Each letter across the heading of the tabulation is to be multiplied by the coefficient standing below it in Row I. Row 2 contains the sum of the weighted squares of the x values, measured from zero. The C column is filled in as shown. Row 3 comes by multiplying Row I through by $-\sum wx/\sum w$. Row II comes by adding Rows 2 and 3. In the " 1 " column of Row II is found the quantity

$$S = \sum wx^2 - \frac{(\sum wx)^2}{\sum w} \quad \text{or} \quad \sum wx^2 - \bar{x}^2 \sum w$$

as already derived in Eq. 11. S is here seen as the initial sum of weighted squares, $\sum wx^2$ in Row 2, reduced by the amount $(\sum wx)^2/\sum w$ to take account of the fact that the residuals are finally measured from the fitted line $x = a$, instead of from 0. It is interesting to perceive that this minimized value of S has come forth *without the intermediate step* of computing each residual after adjustment, then squaring it, and then adding them all together. Similar short cuts, due to Gauss, will be found also in the more complex problem, as will be seen later. (See Secs. 29, 59, and 61; also compare with Sec. 15b.)

Row I solved for a gives

$$a = \frac{\sum wx}{\sum w}$$

in agreement with Eq. 10. However, if we use the C column in place of the " 1 " column in solving for a, we get $1/\sum w$. Interpreted, this means that

$$\frac{1}{w_a} = \frac{1}{\sum w} \tag{12}$$

This solution can be looked upon as the one and only term in the reciprocal matrix (to be encountered later in extended form; Sec. 61). This one term is the variance coefficient of a, which interpreted means that

$$\sigma_a{}^2 = (\text{S.E. of } a)^2 = \frac{\sigma^2}{w_a} = \frac{\sigma^2}{\sum w} \tag{12'}$$

The standard error of a thus decreases as the weights of the individual observations increase. This equation will be understood better after the discussion on weights has been read (next section).

11. A digression to define weights. By definition, the *weight* w_f of the function f is inversely proportional to the variance $\sigma_f{}^2$ of f. That is to say, $1/w_f$ is the *variance coefficient* of f. In symbols,

$$w_f = \frac{\sigma^2}{\sigma_f{}^2} \quad \text{or} \quad \sigma_f{}^2 = \frac{\sigma^2}{w_f} \tag{13}$$

σ^2 is simply a proportionality factor, and is evidently *the variance of a function of unit weight*. If σ^2 be arbitrarily doubled, and w_f also doubled, $\sigma_f{}^2$ is unaffected in value.

For example, let f be $\bar{x}$, the mean of the n observations x_1, x_2, $\cdots$, x_n, which are random variates taken from a universe of standard deviation σ, hence *each of unit weight*. Then, since the variance of $\bar{x}$ is σ^2/n, substitution of $\bar{x}$ for f in Eq. 13 gives

$$w_{\bar{x}} = \frac{\sigma^2}{\dfrac{\sigma^2}{n}} = n \quad \text{or} \quad \sigma_{\bar{x}}{}^2 = \frac{\sigma^2}{n} \tag{14}$$

whence we see that n is the weight of $\bar{x}$, and $1/n$ its variance coefficient.   Or, if the n original observations were each of weight w instead of unity (as we could as well say, since weights are relative and not absolute, depending as they do on the arbitrary factor σ^2), then the variance of single observations would be σ^2/w, and the variance of $\bar{x}$ would be one nth as much.   In this case, therefore, Eq. 13 gives

$$w_{\bar{x}} = \frac{\sigma^2}{\dfrac{\sigma^2}{nw}} = nw \quad \text{or} \quad \sigma_{\bar{x}}^2 = \frac{\sigma^2}{nw} \tag{15}$$

saying that nw is now the weight, and $1/nw$ the variance coefficient, of $\bar{x}$.   So, as before, the weight of $\bar{x}$ is just n times the weight of a single observation.

" The primal conception of a weight is that of a repeated observation."[4]   In Fisher's terminology, the mean $\bar{x}$ of n observations contains n times as much *information* as a single observation.

Concerning two functions f_1 and f_2, it can be said at once from Eq. 13 that

$$w_1 : w_2 = \sigma_2^2 : \sigma_1^2 \tag{16}$$

which says that the weights of two functions are inversely proportional to their variances.

Exercise 1.   If V_i denotes the residual at point i, w_i the weight of the observation, then $\chi^2 = (1/\sigma^2) \sum wV^2$.   Show that this may be written

$$\chi^2 = \sum \left(\frac{V}{\dfrac{\sigma}{\sqrt{w}}} \right)^2$$

which says that χ^2 is the sum of the squares of the residuals, each residual (V_i) being measured in units of the standard error $\sigma/\sqrt{w}$ of the corresponding observation (compare with Eq. 20, next section).   In other words, χ^2 is the sum of the squares of the *standardized residuals*. χ^2 is therefore independent of the units used in

[4] E. B. Wilson and Ruth R. Puffer, " Least squares and laws of population growth," *Proc. Amer. Acad. Arts and Sci.* (Boston), vol. 68, August 1933.

measurement; a change from feet to inches or centimeters, or from pounds to ounces or grams, changes the residuals, but *not* the standardized residuals, nor χ^2.

Exercise 2. When both x and y observations are subject to error, one may wish to designate the summation explicitly as

$$\chi^2 = \frac{1}{\sigma^2} \sum (w_x V_x^2 + w_y V_y^2)$$

as has already been indicated in Section 8.   Show that this may be written

$$\chi^2 = \sum \left\{ \left(\frac{V_x}{\dfrac{\sigma}{\sqrt{w_x}}} \right)^2 + \left(\frac{V_y}{\dfrac{\sigma}{\sqrt{w_y}}} \right)^2 \right\}$$

which again says that χ^2 is the sum of the squares of all the residuals, each one being measured in units of the standard error of the corresponding observation on the x or y coordinate.   So χ^2 is, as before, the sum of the squares of the *standardized residuals*. The remarks in the preceding exercise still hold.

Exercise 3. S, or the sum of the weighted squares of the residuals, like χ^2, is also invariant to changes in units (as from pounds to ounces, etc.).   But S is dependent on the arbitrary choice of σ, whereas χ^2 is not.   One weight in the whole set is arbitrary, and the others are related to it through Eq. 13; fixing this one weight is equivalent to fixing σ. S can be doubled by doubling all the weights, but this has no effect on χ^2 because σ^2 would also be doubled.   The least squares solution for a (and other parameters, if any, as in more complicated problems) is independent of σ^2; the parameter or parameters that minimize S for one set of weights will also minimize it if all the weights are doubled.

> For another interpretation of S in curve fitting, see Exercise 3 of Section 58, page 145, where S is seen to be equal to the sum of $WF_0'^2$. Other exercises dealing with weights occur at the end of Chapter III.

12. A more complicated problem — several samples.   (*a*) *All observations have the same precision.*   Let us suppose that n observations of equal weight (equal precision), and all on the same unknown, as for example those of Section 9, are arbitrarily sub-divided into m samples of $n_1, n_2, \cdots, n_m$ observations. We shall say that

X_1 is the mean of n_1 single observations.
X_2 " " " " n_2 " "   .
        .   .   .
        .   .   .
        .   .   .
X_m " " " " n_m " "   .

Now if single observations have unit weight, then it will follow from Eqs. 14 or 15 that the weights of the m means are

$$w_1 = n_1, w_2 = n_2, \cdots, w_m = n_m$$

We may now consider the m sample means to be m observations of weights respectively $n_1, \cdots, n_m$, to which the results of Section 10 apply. The value of a that minimizes χ^2 is then

$$X = \frac{\sum wX}{\sum w} = \frac{n_1X_1 + n_2X_2 + \cdots + n_mX_m}{n_1 + n_2 + \cdots + n_m} \qquad (17)$$

which follows from Eq. 10. This value of X is the *weighted mean* of the m samples. Actually, it is also the mean of the entire group of $n_1 + n_2 + \cdots + n_m$ single observations, since they are all of the same weight (unity). Our result implies that when the residuals (V_i) are reckoned from this value of X, the sum S or $\sum wV^2$ is a minimum. By Eq. 11, page 19, its value is

$$S = \sum n_i(X_i - X)^2 = \sum n_iX_i^2 - nX^2$$

A schematic representation of the observations, residuals, and errors, and their relationships to the weighted mean, is shown in Fig. 6.

Exercise 1. Show that when the residuals (V_i) are measured from the value of X shown in Eq. 17, the weighted sum of the residuals is zero. That is, $\sum wV = 0$.

It is not to be inferred that $\sum wV = 0$ in all least squares adjust-ments; see Remark 4 on page 182.

Exercise 2. The value of X is independent of the mode of dividing up the n observations, that is, the subgroups of $n_1, n_2,$

$\cdots$, and n_m observations can be formed from the n observations in any manner whatever.

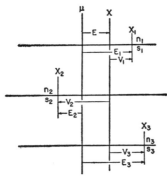

FIG. 6.   Three series of observations on a magnitude μ.

n_1 observations have mean X_1 and standard deviation s_1
n_2 " " " X_2 " " " s_2
n_3 " " " X_3 " " " s_3

X is the weighted mean of the three series. The errors and residuals in the individual means X_1, X_2, X_3 are denoted by E_1, E_2, E_3 and V_1, V_2, V_3 respectively. The error in the weighted mean X is denoted by E. As the figure happens to be drawn, E, E_1, E_3, V_1, and V_3 are positive, and E_2 and V_2 are negative, as the arrows indicate. This case of curve fitting is intermediate between the simplest problem shown on page 16 and more difficult ones described in Chapter VIII.

Exercise 3.   On the contrary, the value of S does depend on how the n observations are subdivided, and similarly for χ^2. (*Note:* χ^2 is just S divided by σ^2.)

(*b*) *The precisions of the single observations differ from one sample to another.* Suppose that

X_1 is the mean of n_1 observations from a population of standard deviation σ_1. Then the variance of X_1 will be $\sigma_1{}^2/n_1$.

.

.

.

X_m is the mean of n_m observations from a population of standard deviation σ_m. Then the variance of X_m is $\sigma_m{}^2/n_m$.

$\sigma_1, \sigma_2, \cdots, \sigma_m$ need not all be equal. For the weights of X_1, X_2, etc., we may take

$$
\left.
\begin{aligned}
w_1 &= \frac{\sigma^2}{\dfrac{\sigma_1{}^2}{n_1}} = \frac{n_1\sigma^2}{\sigma_1{}^2} \quad \text{for the weight of } X_1 \\[2em]
w_2 &= \frac{\sigma^2}{\dfrac{\sigma_2{}^2}{n_2}} = \frac{n_2\sigma^2}{\sigma_2{}^2} \quad \text{`` ``} \qquad \text{``} \qquad \text{`` } X_2 \\[1em]
&\;\;\vdots \qquad\qquad\qquad\qquad\qquad\qquad\quad \vdots \\[1em]
w_m &= \frac{\sigma^2}{\dfrac{\sigma_m{}^2}{n_m}} = \frac{n_m\sigma^2}{\sigma_m{}^2} \quad \text{`` ``} \qquad \text{``} \qquad \text{`` } X_m
\end{aligned}
\right\} \tag{18}
$$

σ^2 is arbitrary, because the weights are purely relative. Again, as in Sections 9 and 10, the problem is to fit the curve

$$ x = a \tag{4} $$

The answer is already contained in Eq. 10 on p. 19, which applied to the present problem gives

$$
a = \frac{\sum wX}{\sum w} = \frac{\dfrac{n_1 X_1}{\sigma_1{}^2} + \dfrac{n_2 X_2}{\sigma_2{}^2} + \cdots + \dfrac{n_m X_m}{\sigma_m{}^2}}{\dfrac{n_1}{\sigma_1{}^2} + \dfrac{n_2}{\sigma_2{}^2} + \cdots + \dfrac{n_m}{\sigma_m{}^2}} = X \tag{19}
$$

The quantity X just defined is the *weighted mean* of the m samples. Residuals (V_i) reckoned from it make S or $\sum w_i(X_i - X)^2$ a minimum.

> The problem of part (b) reduces to that of part (a) if $\sigma_1 = \sigma_2 = \cdots = \sigma_m$. It is interesting to see that σ does not appear in the fraction of Eq. 19, i.e., X is independent of σ. If σ^2 were doubled, all weights would be doubled, but X would be unaltered. Likewise χ^2 in Eq. 20 would be unaltered. (See the exercises in Sec. 11.)

Exercise 4. Show that when the residuals are measured from X as defined in Eq. 19,

$$\sum wV = 0$$

as was true also in part (a) of this section.   (See Exercise 1, p. 24.) Note that χ^2 can be written

$$\chi^2 = \sum \frac{(\text{Discrepancy between } X_i \text{ and } X)^2}{\text{Variance of } X_i \text{ about true mean}} \tag{20}$$

See Exercise 1 of Section 11, page 22.

13. The estimates of σ, internal and external. Because of the distribution[5] of χ^2 when the actual sampling (the experimental work) is described by the mathematical model here assumed, namely, normally distributed observations, the mean value of χ^2 in the long run is equal to k, the number of independent residuals or " degrees of freedom."[6]   In any one experiment, χ^2 may be larger or smaller than the average.   For the problems of parts (a) and (b), the number is $m - 1$ because there is one relation (Eqs. 17 or 19) between the m residuals and X.   The unbiased[7] estimate of σ^2 made by *external consistency*[8] is found by calculating what value of σ forces χ^2 to take its mean value k.   In other words, the esti-

[5] Karl Pearson, *Phil. Mag.*, vol. 50, 1900: pp. 157–175.   A paper dealing more specifically with curve fitting of the kind here considered will be found in the *J. Amer. Stat. Assoc.*, vol. 29, 1934: pp. 372–382; see also *Phil. Mag.*, vol. 19, 1935: pp. 389–402.

[6] The correction for the number of unknowns evaluated (one in this case) and the equivalent of setting the mean value of χ^2 equal to S divided by the number of observed quantities diminished by the number of unknowns evaluated were set forth by Gauss in his *Theoria Combinationis Observationum Erroribus Minimis Obnoxiae*, Pars posterior (Göttingen, 1823; vol. 4 of his *Werke*), Art. 38.   This correction is sometimes credited to Bessel, but the reference just given, which was kindly furnished by Dr. G. J. Lidstone, places the originality with Gauss.

[7] Unbiased in the sense that its mean value is σ^2.

[8] The terms external and internal consistency were introduced by Birge (*Phys. Rev.*, vol. 40, 1932: pp. 207–227).   The comparison of the two estimates (Sec. 13) is an application of the " analysis of variance," the essential features of which have long been recognized by physical scientists; see, for example, A. de Forest Palmer, *Theory of Measurements* (McGraw-Hill, 1912) pp. 66–71.

mated σ satisfies Eq. 3, page 15, whence comes the estimate

$$\sigma^2(ext) = \frac{S}{k} \qquad (21)$$

From this equation, for the problem of Section 12b, we get

$$\sigma^2(ext) = \frac{\Sigma \, wV^2}{k} = \frac{1}{m-1} \Sigma \frac{n_i \sigma^2}{\sigma_i^2} (X_i - X)^2 \qquad (22)$$

This estimate is made from the external consistency of the data, i.e., from the fit of the " curve " $X = a$. What we do in making the estimate $\sigma(ext)$ is to say arbitrarily that χ^2 does equal k. This is equivalent to saying that $P(\chi)$ is about $\frac{1}{2}$ — not exactly $\frac{1}{2}$ because of the skewness of the χ^2 distribution, which, however, gradually disappears with increasing k.

If we are not positive that all m samples came from populations having coincident means, we should have as an alternate hypothesis that the m population means μ_1, μ_2, $\cdots$, μ_m are not all identical. Now if one or more of them really are not equal to the others, $\sigma^2(ext)$ is raised, on the average, to some value higher than σ^2; consequently in examining the hypothesis that $\mu_1 = \mu_2 = \cdots = \mu_m$, we should be interested in knowing if $\sigma^2(ext)$ is significantly greater than σ^2, or, what is the same thing, if χ^2 is significantly higher than k. This can be ascertained by looking up $P(\chi)$ in tables of chi-square. Of course, χ^2 can not be computed or compared with k unless σ is known. Or, to use Fisher's table of z, one would set

$$z = \tfrac{1}{2} \ln \frac{\sigma^2(ext)}{\sigma^2} \qquad (23)$$

and look up $P(z)$ with Fisher's n_1 as $m - 1$, and with n_2 equal to infinity, since σ^2 is here assumed known. In regard to the interpretation of $P(z)$, see the small type in the next section. Tables and examples in the use of $P(\chi)$ and $P(z)$ will be found in Fisher's *Statistical Methods for Research Workers* (Oliver and Boyd); also in several other texts.

Now the

$$\text{Wt. of } X \equiv w_X = \Sigma \frac{n_i \sigma^2}{\sigma_i^2} \qquad (24)$$

and the

$$(\text{Est'd S.E. of } X)_{ext}^{2} = \frac{\sigma^2(ext)}{w_X} = \frac{1}{(m-1)w_X} \sum wV^2$$

$$= \frac{1}{(m-1)w_X} S \qquad (25)$$

There is also the estimate of σ made from the *internal consistency*[9] of the data, i.e., from the consistency of the observations within samples. This is[10]

$$\sigma^2(int) = \frac{n_1 s_1{}^2 + n_2 s_2{}^2 + \cdots + n_m s_m{}^2}{n_1 + n_2 + \cdots + n_m - m} \qquad (26)$$

whence the

$$(\text{Est'd S.E. of } X)_{int}^{2} = \frac{\sigma^2(int)}{w_X} \qquad (27)$$

wherein w_X has the value given in Eq. 24. $s_1, s_2, \cdots, s_m$ are the standard deviations of the m samples.

> The estimate by internal consistency is possible only if there are points in which there is more than one observation. When there is but one observation at each point, the estimate of σ by internal consistency is not a possibility.

14. Comparison of the two estimates — analysis of variance. As was mentioned in the preceding section, the estimate $\sigma(ext)$ is valid only if the m populations have coincident means; if any two of the means $\mu_1, \mu_2, \cdots, \mu_m$ are unequal, $\sigma^2(ext)$ is, on the average, raised above σ^2. But, in contrast, the estimate $\sigma(int)$ is unaffected by inequalities among the means of the populations; so long as σ remains the constant standard deviation of all of them, the average value of $\sigma^2(int)$ is still σ^2. It follows that a statistical test of the hypothesis $\mu_1 = \mu_2 = \cdots = \mu_m$ is to examine the ratio of the two

---

[9] See the reference to Birge on page 27.

[10] See, for example, Eq. 67 in Deming and Birge's *Statistical Theory of Errors* (The Graduate School, The Department of Agriculture, Washington, 1934, 1938), p. 158.

estimates. To do this, we may follow Fisher and take

$$z = \tfrac{1}{2} \ln \frac{\sigma^2(ext)}{\sigma^2(int)} \tag{28}$$

and look in his tables to see if z is " significantly " different from 0. (In doing this, we use $m - 1$ for Fisher's n_1, and $n_1 + n_2 + \cdots + n_m - m$ for his n_2.) If z is found to be so large that it lies beyond the 1 percent limit, we say there is " statistical evidence " that the data are not homogeneous, or that not all the μ_i are equal; in other words, that the curve

$$X_i = a \tag{29}$$

is *not a good fit.*

> *Remark.* Such a calculation of " significance " takes account only of the numerical data of this one experiment. An estimate of σ is not to be regarded as a number that can be used in place of σ unless the observations have demonstrated randomness (Ch. I), and not unless the number of degrees of freedom (the denominator in Eqs. 21 or 26) amounts to 15 or 20, and preferably more. A broad background of experience is necessary before one can say whether his experiment is carried out by demonstrably random methods. Moreover, even in the state of randomness, it must be borne in mind that unless the number of degrees of freedom is very large, a new experiment will give new values of both $\sigma(ext)$ and $\sigma(int)$, also of $P(\chi)$ and $P(z)$. Ordinarily, there will be a series of experiments, and a corresponding series of P values. It is the *consistency* of the P values of the series, under a wide variety of conditions, and not the smallness of any one P value by itself that determines a basis for action, particularly when we are dealing with a cause system underlying a scientific law (Ch. I). In the absence of a large number of experiments, related knowledge of the subject and scientific judgment must be relied on to a great extent in framing a course of action. Statistical " significance " by itself is not a rational basis for action.

15. Another simple problem — the slope of a line that is known to pass through the origin. (*a*) *The* y *coordinates subject to error;* x *free of error.* The equation to be fitted to the points in Fig. 7 is

$$y = bx \tag{30}$$

Let y_i denote the observed ordinate at the ith point; then $y_i - bx_i$ is the residual at that point. It is a vertical, or y residual, because the error is all in y, by assumption. If w_i denotes the weight of y_i, then the sum

$$S = \sum w_i(y_i - bx_i)^2 \quad (31)$$

is to be minimized. We differentiate this with respect to b and obtain

$$\frac{dS}{db} = -2\sum w_i x_i(y_i - bx_i) \quad (32)$$

Set equal to zero, this gives

$$b \sum wx^2 = \sum wxy \quad (33)$$

whence

$$b = \frac{\sum wxy}{\sum wx^2} \quad (34)$$

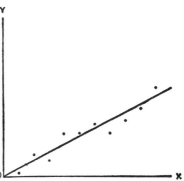

Fig. 7. A line known to pass through the origin. The slope is to be estimated from the observed points.

The subscripts are omitted for convenience. w means the weight of a y observation, as before.

Note that here, neither $\sum res$ nor $\sum w \cdot res$ is necessarily zero, but that $\sum w \cdot x \cdot res = 0$. The student should demonstrate these statements. (Cf. Remark 4, p. 182, for an extension of this note.)

Special cases. i. Suppose that the weight of y is inversely proportional to x; i.e., the square of the standard error of y is proportional to x. Then Eq. 34 gives

$$b = \frac{\sum y}{\sum x} \quad (35)$$

Here, $\sum res = 0$, as the student should prove.

The result obtained in Eq. 35 has application in many problems in the social sciences. Sample surveys of (e.g.) vacancy are often taken in a city or metropolitan district, by picking out certain blocks, or segments of blocks, and noting at every dwelling unit therein (or sometimes at every kth dwelling unit) whether that dwelling unit is vacant or occupied. If in Block i, or Segment i, it is found that there are x_i dwelling units, of which y_i are vacant, then when the survey is completed, the estimated vacancy rate (fraction vacant) for the entire city may be taken as

$$b = \frac{\sum y_i}{\sum x_i}$$

$$= \frac{\text{Total number of vacant dwelling units in the sample}}{\text{Total number of dwelling units in the sample}} \quad (35')$$

This estimate will be close enough for purposes of action, if the sample is not too small. Often a 5 or 10 percent sample of all the dwelling units in a city or metropolitan district is sufficient.

The justification for using Eq. 35 to obtain an estimate of the vacancy rate lies in the observation that, except when the vacancy rate is inordinately high, the vacant dwelling units are usually scattered throughout the city at random. (This observation was first made by Messrs. J. Stevens Stock and Lester R. Frankel of Washington, in their sample surveys of rent and housing.)[11]

Another application of Eq. 35 is to the hatchability of eggs: the more eggs set, the more hatch y (except for random scattered infertility), but also the greater the error in y, in absolute numbers.

Eq. 35 is used in Example IV at the end of the book, for a sample inventory of canned goods.

ii. Suppose that all the y weights are equal; i.e., all y observations have the same standard error. Then Eq. 34 gives

$$b = \frac{\sum xy}{\sum x^2} \quad (36)$$

This is perhaps a more usual case than the preceding one, particularly in engineering, physics, and chemistry.

iii. Suppose that the weight of an observation on y is inversely proportional to x^2. By putting $w = 1/x^2$, we find from Eq. 34 that

$$b = \frac{\sum \dfrac{y}{x}}{\sum 1} = \frac{1}{n} \sum \frac{y}{x} = \text{average } \frac{y}{x} \quad (37)$$

The letter n here stands for the number of points. Each observed point gives an observed slope y/x, and the least squares estimate obtained from all the points is in this case simply the average of all n observed slopes.

---

[11] Private communication to the author.

The distinction between Eqs. 35, 36, and 37 should be noted carefully. In Eq. 35 a point has more influence on b if it is far outlying, this influence being closely proportional to the distance of the point from the origin. In Eq. 36 the influence of a point is further accentuated by its distance from the origin. In Eq. 37 the advantage of distance is completely removed, the final result being merely the average slope of the n rays joining the origin with the observed points.

(b) *The tabular solution of* b, *and its weight, and the sum* S. This will be similar to the tabulation in Section 10b (q.v.). We enter in Row I, from Eq. 33, the coefficient of b under b, and the right-hand member under the " 1." Enter the weighted sum of squares of y in Row 2. Fill in the C column with 1 and 0 as shown.

Row	b	=	1	C	
I	$\sum wx^2$		$\sum wxy$	1	
2			$\sum wy^2$	0	How obtained (cf. Sec. 10b)
3			$-\dfrac{(\sum wxy)^2}{\sum wx^2}$	$\cdots$	(By multiplying Row I through by $-\sum wxy/\sum wx^2$)
II			$\sum wy^2 - \dfrac{(\sum wxy)^2}{\sum wx^2}$	$\cdots$	(By adding Rows 2 and 3)

An ellipsis ($\cdots$) in the tabular array denotes a space wherein a number would ordinarily be entered in numerical calculation, but in which it is not worth while to show the entry in symbols.

Row I solved with the " 1 " column gives b as in Eq. 34. Row I solved with the C column gives $b = 1/\sum wx^2$, which means that

$$\text{The weight of } b = w_b = \sum wx^2 \tag{38}$$

Row II shows the minimized value of S in the " 1 " column, which is to say that

$$S \quad \text{or} \quad \sum w(y - bx)^2 = \sum wy^2 - \frac{(\sum wxy)^2}{\sum wx^2} \tag{39}$$

Thus S is calculated in the tabular solution without the necessity of first solving for b and the individual residuals. The initial sum of squares, $\sum wy^2$ in Row 2, is seen to be reduced by the amount $(\sum wxy)^2/\sum wx^2$, the residuals being finally measured from the fitted line, instead of the x axis.

Here the external estimate of σ will be found by writing

$$\sigma^2(ext) = \frac{S}{m-1} \qquad \text{(Cf. Sec. 13.)} \qquad (40)$$

whence the

$$(\text{Est'd S.E. of } b)_{ext}{}^2 = \frac{S}{(m-1)w_b} = \frac{S}{(m-1)\sum wx^2} \qquad (41)$$

16. The t test for the slope. In order to apply the Student t test to see if there is statistical evidence that the calculated value of b is "significantly different" from some theoretical value, say B, we should write

$$t = \frac{|B - b|}{\text{Est'd S.E. of } b} \qquad (42)$$

and make the Student t test, using Fisher's n equal to our $m - 1$. The region of rejection in the t distribution is to be chosen with due regard to admissible alternative slopes, which may be greater or less than B. In the denominator of Eq. 42 we may use the estimate made by external consistency, or that made by internal consistency (Sec. 13). If $\sigma(int)$ were used in place of $\sigma(ext)$ in Eq. 41, then we should have

$$(\text{Est'd S.E. of } b)_{int}{}^2 = \frac{\sigma^2(int)}{w_b} = \frac{\sigma^2(int)}{\sum wx^2} \qquad (43)$$

This would replace the denominator of Eq. 42, and the number of degrees of freedom (Fisher's n) would be the total number of observations diminished by the number m.

With regard to the interpretation of statistical tests, see the remark at the end of Section 14, page 30.

17. The x coordinates subject to error, y free of error. w_i will now denote the weight of x_i. In place of Eq. 31 we now have

$$S = \sum w_i \left(x_i - \frac{y_i}{b}\right)^2 \tag{44}$$

since here the y residuals are zero, and S is made up by squaring the x residuals. By differentiation

$$\frac{dS}{db} = + \frac{2}{b^2} \sum w_i y_i \left(x_i - \frac{y_i}{b}\right) \tag{45}$$

Set equal to zero this gives

$$b \sum wxy = \sum wy^2, \quad \text{or} \quad b = \frac{\sum wy^2}{\sum wxy} \tag{46}$$

Note the distinction between Eqs. 34 and 46. w in Eq. 46 is the weight of x, not y.

> For another derivation of Eq. 46, see Hint 1 in Exercise 12,
> page 46.

EXERCISES

Exercise 1. If b in Eq. 46 be distinguished as b', prove that between Eqs. 34 and 46 there exists the relation

$$\frac{b}{b'} = \frac{\sum w_y xy \sum w_x xy}{\sum w_y x^2 \sum w_x y^2}$$

Exercise 2. Find the curve $y = bx$, also w_b, from the following data.

x	y_{obs}	w_y
1	0.52	1
2	0.96	1
3	1.50	2
5	2.65	1

y alone is subject to error. Use the tabular arrangement on page 33.

Exercise 3. Find the curve $y = b'x$, also $w_{b'}$, referring to p. 47.

x_{obs}	y	w_x
1.05	0.5	1
1.90	1.0	1
3.08	1.5	2
4.86	2.5	1

x alone is subject to error. Again use the tabular arrangement, but *be careful.*

PART B

THE LEAST SQUARES SOLUTION OF MORE COMPLICATED PROBLEMS

CHAPTER III

THE PROPAGATION OF ERROR

18. Small errors in functions of one variable. If $f(x)$ is a function of x, the linear term in Taylor's series can often be used to express with sufficient accuracy the effect on $f(x)$ of a small error in x. Thus, if Δx is the error in x, and Δf the resulting error in $f(x)$, Δf and Δx may be closely enough related by the equation

$$\Delta f = f'(x)\, \Delta x \tag{1}$$

This is the equation for the *propagation of error* in a function of a single variable. $f'(x)$ is the first derivative of $f(x)$, evaluated at the point $x, f(x)$. In practice, the true value of x is not known, but it is usually sufficient to evaluate $f'(x)$ at a near-by point, such as a point whose coordinates are determined experimentally. $f'(x)$ remains constant while Δx and Δf vary.

The above equation says that the error in $f(x)$ will be proportional to the error in x. The derivative $f'(x)$ is the factor of proportionality. The equation is not exact, i.e., the error in f is *not* strictly proportional to the error in x, except when $f(x)$ is a linear function of x. It is close enough for actual use provided the error Δx is small enough, or when the higher derivatives of $f(x)$ are small enough. Fortunately, in practice much experimental work, and most of the functions used, satisfy these requirements.

The relation between the error in $f(x)$, and the approximation afforded by Eq. 1, is shown in Fig. 8.

In a linear function, such as

$$f(x) = a + bx \qquad (2)$$

the higher derivatives $f''(x)$, $f'''(x)$, etc., are zero absolutely, and Eq. 1 reduces to

$$\Delta f = b \, \Delta x \qquad (3)$$

which is exact for any error in x, however large. The error in $f(x)$ will now be exactly proportional to the error in x.

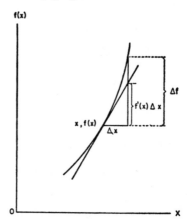

FIG. 8. Showing the relation between the errors in x and $f(x)$, and the approximation contained in the equation

$$\Delta f = f'(x) \, \Delta x$$

Δx is the error in x, Δf the error in the function $f(x)$. The approximation in Eq. 1 is made by using the tangent to the curve in place of the curve itself.

19. Small errors in functions of several variables. Taylor's series can be extended to obtain expressions for small errors in functions of several variables. Thus, if F is a function of x, y, z, and if they are in error by the amounts Δx, Δy, Δz, then F will be in error by some amount ΔF, which can be expressed closely enough as

$$\Delta F = F_x \, \Delta x + F_y \, \Delta y + F_z \, \Delta z \qquad (4)$$

provided the errors Δx, Δy, and Δz are small enough, or when the higher derivatives are small enough. Here F_x, F_y, F_z denote the derivatives

$$F_x = \frac{\partial F}{\partial x}, \quad F_y = \frac{\partial F}{\partial y}, \quad F_z = \frac{\partial F}{\partial z} \tag{5}$$

which in practice are to be evaluated at the point x, y, z, or as near this point as is experimentally possible.

Eq. 4 is the formula for the *propagation of error* in three variables. It can be extended to more variables simply by adding more terms of the same kind.

Eq. 4 is written only through the first powers of Δx, Δy, and Δz, because the rest of the Taylor series (involving the squares and higher powers and cross-products of Δx, Δy, and Δz) will be negligible if Δx, Δy, and Δz are not too large, or if the higher derivatives are small enough. In practice, the possible errors Δx, Δy, and Δz are limited in magnitude, and Eq. 4 is usually a good enough approximation for ordinary situations. In the event that F is linear in x, y, and z (as in Exercise 2 at the end of the chapter), there are no terms at all except the linear terms (i.e., there are no neglected terms), and Δx, Δy, and Δz may then be ever so large without invalidating Eqs. 4, 7, 8, and 9. (Compare with the explanation in the preceding section for a function of a single variable, particularly the text accompanying Eqs. 2 and 3.)

20. The propagation of mean square error or variance.   Eq. 4 leads to a relation between the mean square errors or the variances of x, y, z, and F, and hence also a relation between their standard errors and their weights.   If we square each side of Eq. 4 we get

$$\Delta F^2 = (F_x \, \Delta x)^2 + (F_y \, \Delta y)^2 + (F_z \, \Delta z)^2 + 2F_x F_y \, \Delta x \, \Delta y$$
$$+ 2F_x F_z \, \Delta x \, \Delta z + 2F_y F_z \, \Delta y \, \Delta z \tag{6}$$

Now let Δx, Δy, and Δz take on all possible values[1] within their allowable ranges of variation. The derivatives F_x, F_y, F_z, being

---

[1] In practice, the assumption that Δx, Δy, Δz are not large, and that Eqs. 4 and 6 may be cut off with the 1st power of Δx, Δy, Δz, to the neglect of higher powers, usually causes no difficulty.   Doubt on this point can in any example be resolved at the expense of a second adjustment: see the footnote on page 180, and the reference to Gauss.   Similarly, the assumption that σ_x, σ_y, σ_z exist causes no difficulty in practice.

evaluated at x, y, z, are constants while Δx, Δy, and Δz vary. Then let each term in Eq. 6 be replaced by its average value; the result is

$$\sigma_F{}^2 = (F_x\sigma_x)^2 + (F_y\sigma_y)^2 + (F_z\sigma_z)^2$$
$$+ 2(F_xF_y\sigma_x\sigma_y r_{xy} + F_xF_z\sigma_x\sigma_z r_{xz} + F_yF_z\sigma_y\sigma_z r_{yz}) \quad (7)$$

where $\sigma_x{}^2$ = variance of x, r_{xy} the correlation between Δx and Δy, etc. This formula (also the simplified form in Eq. 8 when it applies) is called the *propagation of mean square error*, or the *propagation of variance*.

The terms in parenthesis are zero if the errors in x, y, and z are independent, i.e., uncorrelated. In such a situation Eq. 7 reduces to

$$\sigma_F{}^2 = (F_x\sigma_x)^2 + (F_y\sigma_y)^2 + (F_z\sigma_z)^2 \quad (8)$$

or, by Eq. 13 of Chapter II,

$$\frac{1}{w_F} = \frac{F_xF_x}{w_x} + \frac{F_yF_y}{w_y} + \frac{F_zF_z}{w_z} \quad (9)$$

This equation could be called the propagation of weight, if it needed a name. It will be seen to be of great importance in the solution of the general problem in least squares. One may refer to Exercises 11 and 12 at the end of this chapter; also Eq. 14 of Ch. IV, p. 55; Remark 1 of Sec. 28, p. 56; Eq. 8 of Ch. VIII, p. 134; Exercises 3 and 4 of Sec. 58, on page 145; and Remark 3 in Exercise 4 of Ch. X, p. 181.

21. The standard error of a mean. It is interesting to see that if F be taken as the mean ($\bar{x}$) of the n independent observations x_1, x_2, $\cdots$, x_n each of standard error σ, then Eq. 8 leads to the well-known expression

$$\sigma_{\bar{x}}{}^2 = \frac{\sigma^2}{n} \quad \text{(Cf. Eq. 14 on p. 21.)}$$

as was taken for granted on page 21. This, however, does not tell us that if the individual observations are normally distributed, the mean $\bar{x}$ is also — this fact must be obtained otherwise. Eqs. 7, 8, and 9 are in fact independent of any assumption concerning the distributions of the errors in x, y, z, and F, provided the standard errors σ_x, etc., actually exist, as was stipulated in the footnote on page 39.

22. A numerical example of small errors. To see how the Taylor series operates, we may try it with the particular function

$$F = 4x^2 + \sin xy + z \tag{10}$$

where the product xy is in radians. Let us evaluate F at the point

$$x = 2$$
$$y = 0.95$$
$$z = 10$$

We find

$$F_0 = 4 \times 2^2 + \sin 1.9 + 10$$
$$= 16 + 0.9463 + 10 = 26.9463 \tag{11}$$

Now let x decrease by the amount 0.1, y increase by 0.05, and z increase by 0.2. These increments may be considered as small errors, and we wish to see what effect they have on F. The new values of x, y, and z are 1.9, 1.0, and 10.2, and the new value of F is

$$F_1 = 4 \times 1.9^2 + \sin 1.9 + 10.2$$
$$= 25.5863 \tag{12}$$

The change in F is

$$\Delta F = F_1 - F_0 = 25.5863 - 26.9463 = -1.3600 \tag{13}$$

To compare this (exact) value of ΔF with the approximation afforded by Eq. 4, we first take the derivatives,

$$\left. \begin{array}{l} F_x = 8x + y \cos xy \\ F_y = x \cos xy \\ F_z = 1 \end{array} \right\} \tag{14}$$

and then evaluate them at the point $x = 2$, $y = 0.95$, $z = 10$. They turn out to be numerically

$$\left. \begin{array}{l} F_x = 15.6929 \\ F_y = -0.6466 \\ F_z = 1 \end{array} \right\} \tag{15}$$

whence by Eq. 4, we calculate the approximation

$$\Delta F = -15.6929 \times 0.1 - 0.6466 \times 0.05 + 1 \times 0.2$$
$$= -1.4016 \tag{16}$$

This is to be compared with the exact value of ΔF, computed in Eq. 13.   Other functions, and other values of Δx, Δy, Δz, would give different degrees of approximation.   In the development of the general problem in least squares, we shall be compelled to accept the approximations afforded by Eqs. 4, 7, 8, and 9.   Fortunately, for. purposes of action, the results are usually close enough.

EXERCISES

In the following exercises, independence of the observations is assumed, as in Eq. 8.

Exercise 1.   (a) The mean square error of the sum or difference of two numbers having equal precisions is twice the mean square error of either alone (assumed independent).

(b) The root mean square error (standard error) of a sum or difference of two numbers having equal precisions is $\sqrt{2}$ times the standard error of either alone.

(c) The root mean square error of the sum of n observations of equal standard error, σ, is $\sigma\sqrt{n}$.

(d) A surveying party chains a distance of L feet.   Show that the standard error of the measurement is proportional to $\sqrt{L}$.

Exercise 2.   (a) If u is a linear function of the independent variables x, y, and z, say

$$u = ax + by + cz$$

then the root mean square errors are related by the equation

$$\sigma_u{}^2 = a^2\sigma_x{}^2 + b^2\sigma_y{}^2 + c^2\sigma_z{}^2$$

A special case is contained in Exercise 1a.

(b) If F is a linear function of the n independent variates $x_1, x_2, \cdots, x_n$ of the form

$$F = a_1x_1 + a_2x_2 + \cdots + a_nx_n$$

and if the variates x_1, x_2, $\cdots$, x_n are distributed with variances $\sigma_1{}^2$, $\sigma_2{}^2$, $\cdots$, $\sigma_n{}^2$, then F is distributed with variance

$$\sigma_F{}^2 = a_1{}^2\sigma_1{}^2 + a_2{}^2\sigma_2{}^2 + a_3{}^2\sigma_3{}^2 + \cdots + a_n{}^2\sigma_n{}^2$$

Exercise 3.   (a) If $u = axyz$, then

$$\sigma_u{}^2 = u^2 \left\{ \left(\frac{\sigma_x}{x}\right)^2 + \left(\frac{\sigma_y}{y}\right)^2 + \left(\frac{\sigma_z}{z}\right)^2 \right\}$$

or

$$\left(\frac{\sigma_u}{u}\right)^2 = \left(\frac{\sigma_x}{x}\right)^2 + \left(\frac{\sigma_y}{y}\right)^2 + \left(\frac{\sigma_z}{z}\right)^2$$

which interpreted says that the squares of the *percentage* or *relative* mean square errors are additive (or the squares of the coefficients of variations are additive).

(b) The result of part (a) can be written

$$\sigma_U{}^2 = \sigma_X{}^2 + \sigma_Y{}^2 + \sigma_Z{}^2$$

where $U = \log_k u$, $X = \log_k x$, etc., k being any base whatever.

Exercise 4.   If $u = axy/vz$, then

$$\left(\frac{\sigma_u}{u}\right)^2 = \left(\frac{\sigma_x}{x}\right)^2 + \left(\frac{\sigma_y}{y}\right)^2 + \left(\frac{\sigma_v}{v}\right)^2 + \left(\frac{\sigma_z}{z}\right)^2$$

The squares of the percentage errors are again additive.

Exercise 5.   If $u = ax^\alpha y^\beta z^\gamma$, then

$$\left(\frac{\sigma_u}{u}\right)^2 = \left(\frac{\alpha\sigma_x}{x}\right)^2 + \left(\frac{\beta\sigma_y}{y}\right)^2 + \left(\frac{\gamma\sigma_z}{z}\right)^2$$

Here the percentage errors are increased by the factors α, β, γ. (Exercises 3 and 4 are special cases of this.)

Exercise 6.   For the conditions of Exercises 4 and 5 the relations between the weights are respectively

$$\frac{1}{u^2 w_u} = \frac{1}{x^2 w_x} + \frac{1}{y^2 w_y} + \frac{1}{v^2 w_v} + \frac{1}{z^2 w_z}$$

and

$$\frac{1}{u^2 w_u} = \frac{\alpha^2}{x^2 w_x} + \frac{\beta^2}{y^2 w_y} + \frac{\gamma^2}{z^2 w_z}$$

Exercise 7.   (a) If $A = \pi r^2$ (A the area and r the radius, d the diameter, of a circle), then if an error Δr be committed in measuring r, or Δd in d, the corresponding error in the area is closely

$$\Delta A = 2\pi r\, \Delta r = \frac{2A}{r}\, \Delta r$$

whence

$$\frac{\Delta A}{A} = 2\,\frac{\Delta r}{r} = 2\,\frac{\Delta d}{d}$$

An error of 1 percent in either the radius or the diameter thus means about 2 percent error in the area.   Also

$$\frac{\sigma_A}{A} = 2\,\frac{\sigma_r}{r} \quad \text{and} \quad A^2 w_A = \tfrac{1}{4}r^2 w_r = \tfrac{1}{4}d^2 w_d$$

(This is a special case of Exercise 5.)

(b) The measurements on the sides of a rectangle, a and b, are subject to the errors Δa and Δb.   Show that these errors are related to the area A by the equation

$$\frac{\Delta A}{A} = \frac{\Delta a}{a} + \frac{\Delta b}{b} \qquad \text{(The percentage errors are thus additive.)}$$

(c) The same equation is satisfied by the area of an ellipse, a and b being the axes or semi-axes.

Exercise 8.   (a) If y is in error by the amount δy, then $\ln y$ is in error by approximately $\delta y/y$, if δy is not too big.[2]

(b) If logarithms to the base 10 are used, the error in $\log y$ is approximately $0.434\ \delta y/y$.

(c) In particular, let y change from 15 to 16, as in Fig. 9.   Then calculate the increment in $\log y$ by the approximate formula just derived, and compare it with the exact value of the increment.   In other words, carry out the calculations mentioned in the legend of Fig. 9.

---

[2] The abbreviation *ln* is used here for " logarithme naturel," as is common in Europe, and among chemists everywhere.   The abbreviation *log* will be used for a logarithm to base 10.

(d) Let $Y = \ln y$; then

$$\sigma_Y{}^2 = \frac{\sigma_y{}^2}{y^2}$$

and

$$w_Y = y^2 w_y$$

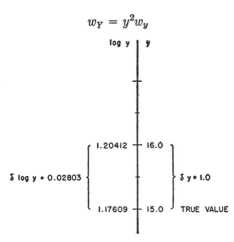

FIG. 9. Illustrating the relation between an error in y and an error in log y. Here y changes by unity, and log y changes by 0.02803. The approximate relation $\delta \log y = 0.434\ \delta y/y$ gives 0.02895, which is to be compared with the exact value 0.02803. Smaller changes (smaller values of δy) show better agreement, but even for this rather large value of δy the approximate relation would be adequate for many purposes.   (See Exercise 8c, p. 44.)

(This result is important; see Exercise 18 in Ch. X, p. 201.)

(e) If $Y = \log y$, then

$$\sigma_Y{}^2 = \left(0.4343 \frac{\sigma_y}{y}\right)^2$$

and

$$\frac{1}{w_Y} = 0.434^2 \frac{1}{y^2 w_y}$$

Exercise 9.   Let $u = ae^{bx}$, then

$$\sigma_u{}^2 = b^2 u^2 \sigma_x{}^2 \quad \text{or} \quad \sigma_U{}^2 = b^2 \sigma_x{}^2$$

where

$$U = \ln u$$

Exercise 10.   The period of a simple pendulum is $T = 2\pi\sqrt{(L/g)}$. Show that if the length L is too long by one-tenth of a percent, the clock will lose about 44 seconds per day.

Exercise 11.   (a) Prove that if F is a function of x, and x a function of t, then

$$\frac{F_x F_x}{w_x} = \frac{F_t F_t}{w_t}$$

where F_x denotes dF/dx, and F_t denotes dF/dt.

(b) Prove from Eq. 9 that

$$w_x = \left(\frac{dt}{dx}\right)^2 w_t$$

$$\text{Var } x = \left(\frac{dx}{dt}\right)^2 \text{Var } t \quad \text{(Var denotes variance.)}$$

$$\sigma_x = \left|\frac{dx}{dt}\right| \sigma_t \qquad \begin{array}{l} (\sigma_x \text{ denotes the standard error} \\ \text{of } x; \; \sigma_t \text{ the standard error of } t.) \end{array}$$

Exercise 12.   Prove that when the line

$$y = b'x$$

is fitted to points for which x is subject to error and y free of error (as in Sec. 17), it turns out that the weight of b' is

$$w_{b'} = \frac{1}{b'^3} \sum w_x xy = \frac{1}{b'^4} \sum w_x y^2$$

Hint 1: From Section 15a, wherein y was subject to error, and x free of error, we had

$$b = \frac{\sum w_y xy}{\sum w_y x^2} \quad \text{(Eq. 34, p. 31)}$$

$$w_b = \sum w_y x^2 \quad \text{(Eq. 38, p. 33)}$$

Now look at Fig. 7 on page 31. Viewed from the back it will appear like Fig. 10, and the equation of the line will be

$$x = \frac{1}{b'} y \quad (y \text{ now free of error})$$

From the equations just written for b and its weight, we may now interchange x and y in the formula for b and write

$$\frac{1}{b'} = \frac{\sum w_x xy}{\sum w_x y^2} \quad \text{(Cf. Eq. 46, p. 35.)}$$

$$\frac{w_1}{b'} = \sum w_x y^2$$

whence by the result of the preceding exercise, part (b),

$$w_{b'} = \left\{ \frac{d}{db'} \frac{1}{b'} \right\}^2 \frac{w_1}{b'}$$

$$= \frac{1}{b'^4} \sum w_x y^2 = \frac{1}{b'^3} \sum w_x xy \quad \text{Q.E.D.}$$

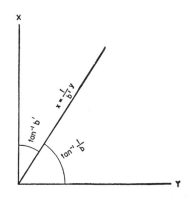

FIG. 10. This figure illustrates Exercise 12. It is the same as Fig. 7 when viewed from the back.

Hint 2: (Due to my colleague Morris H. Hansen.)   Write

$$b' = \frac{\sum w_x y^2}{w_{x1} x_1 y_1 + w_{x2} x_2 y_2 + \cdots + w_{xn} x_n y_n} \quad \text{(Cf. Eq. 46, p. 35.)}$$

$$\frac{db'}{dx_i} = -b' \frac{w_{xi} y_i}{\sum w_{xi} x_i y_i}$$

Now make use of Eq. 8 on page 40 and get

$$\sigma_{b'}^2 = \sum \left(\frac{db'}{dx_i} \right)^2 \sigma_{xi}^2 = \sigma^2 \sum \left(\frac{db'}{dx_i} \right)^2 \frac{1}{w_{xi}}$$

$$w_{b'} = \frac{\sigma^2}{\sigma_{b'}^2} = \frac{(\sum w_{xi} x_i y_i)^2}{b'^2 \sum w_{xi} y_i^2} = \frac{1}{b'^3} \sum w_x xy \quad \text{Q.E.D.}$$

Exercise 13. (a) Recompute the approximation to ΔF in Section 22 by using the derivatives F_x, F_y, F_z evaluated at $x + \Delta x = 1.9$, $y + \Delta y = 1.0$, $z + \Delta z = 10.2$, instead of at the initial values of x, y, z. (*Answer:* $\Delta F = -1.3184$. Note that the result is very close to that shown by Eq. 16.)

(b) Show that when the derivative in Eq. 1 is evaluated at $x + \Delta x$, instead of at x, the result for Δf differs only in squares and higher powers of Δx from the value obtained for Δf by evaluating the derivative at x.

(c) Prove a similar statement for Eq. 4 when the derivatives are evaluated at $x + \Delta x$, $y + \Delta y$, $z + \Delta z$. (In practice we are obliged to evaluate the derivatives at the observed points, not the adjusted points. Fortunately the distinction in the results is usually negligible.)

Exercise 14. If V_i is the ith residual from the line in Sec. 15, page 30, that is, if

$$V_i = y_i - bx_i$$

Then, since

$$b = r\sigma_y/\sigma_x$$

it follows that

$$V_i = y_i - r(\sigma_y/\sigma_x)x_i$$

Show that the variance of V is

$$\text{Var } V = \sigma^2_{(ext)} = \sigma_y^2(1 - r^2)$$

Hint: Since x and y are correlated, use Eq. 7 and find that

$$\text{Var } V = \sigma_y^2 + (-r\sigma_y/\sigma_x)^2\sigma_x^2 + 2(-r\sigma_y/\sigma_x)r\sigma_x\sigma_y$$
$$= \sigma_y^2(1 - r^2)$$

See Exercise 3b on page 177, where $\sum V_i^2$ is given explicitly.

CHAPTER IV

THE GENERAL PROBLEM IN LEAST SQUARES

23. Outline of the problem.[1] As a result of any experiment or sample survey there will be observations, and when the adjustment is completed, to each observed value there will be a corresponding adjusted value. It is useful to introduce the concept of a true value, which is merely the average value that would result from repeating the experiment a large number of times in a state of randomness. In curve fitting, one can visualize the relation between the observed, adjusted, and true coordinates, and it may be helpful to the reader to turn forward at this time to Figs. 16 and 17 on pages 132 and 133.

In formulating the general problem we shall deal with the quantities listed in the table below —

Observed quantities:	X_1,	X_2,	$\cdots$,	X_n;	Y_1,	Y_2,	$\cdots$,	Y_n
Their adjusted (or calculated) values:	x_1,	x_2,	$\cdots$,	x_n;	y_1,	y_2,	$\cdots$,	y_n
Their weights:	w_{x1},	w_{x2},	$\cdots$,	w_{xn};	w_{y1},	w_{y2},	$\cdots$,	w_{yn}
Their true values:	ξ_1,	ξ_2,	$\cdots$,	ξ_n;	η_1,	η_2,	$\cdots$,	η_n
The residuals (obs'd — calc'd):	V_{x1},	V_{x2},	$\cdots$,	V_{xn};	V_{y1},	V_{y2},	$\cdots$,	V_{yn}

In geometrical problems, and other problems not involving parameters, the observations need not be considered as coordinates of observed points.

The assumption will be made here that there is no correlation between the errors in the observations. This assumption covers a wide class of problems, but does fail to cover some.

[1] The development from here on is an amplification of three papers that appeared in the *Phil. Mag.* The references are vol. 11, 1931: pp. 146–158; vol. 17, 1934: pp. 804–829; vol. 19, 1935: pp. 389–402.

The residuals (V) are defined by equations typified by

$$\left. \begin{array}{l} V_{xi} = X_i - x_i \\ V_{yi} = Y_i - y_i \end{array} \right\} \qquad \text{(Res. = obs'd - calc'd)} \qquad (1)$$

It is the residuals that are actually calculated first, and in actual use, these equations are therefore reversed. Once the residuals are found, the adjusted quantities are calculated by subtracting each residual in turn from the corresponding observation, according to Eqs. 6 ahead.

24. The conditions. The principle of least squares requires that the sum of the weighted squares of the residuals,[2]

$$S = \sum w \cdot res^2 \qquad (2)$$

shall be made a minimum with respect to the adjusted values $x_1, x_2, \cdots, x_n, y_1, y_2, \cdots, y_n$. But this is not a simple problem in the maximum and minimum of functions, for here the adjusted values are related to one another. For example, in the case of measurements on the three angles of a plane triangle, we required that $x_1 + x_2 + x_3 = 180°$ (see p. 7). In curve fitting, the problem is further complicated by the fact that the conditions on the adjusted values (x_i) involve the estimates a, b, c of the unknown parameters α, β, γ. In the problem of Section 10, for instance, the adjusted values of the x coordinates of the n points were all required to be equal to a, which was then evaluated as $\bar{x}$ (Fig. 5) to make the sum of the squares of the residuals a minimum.

So to take care of the general case we shall suppose that the adjusted values x_i and y_i are subject to ν conditions, to be symbolized as

$$\left. \begin{array}{l} F^1(x_1, x_2, \cdots, y_n; \quad a, b, c) = 0 \\ F^2(\qquad `` \qquad\qquad ) = 0 \\ \phantom{F^2}\cdot \qquad\qquad\qquad\qquad\quad \cdot \\ \phantom{F^2}\cdot \qquad\qquad\qquad\qquad\quad \cdot \\ \phantom{F^2}\cdot \qquad\qquad\qquad\qquad\quad \cdot \\ F^\nu( \qquad `` \qquad\qquad) = 0 \end{array} \right\} \begin{array}{c} \nu \text{ equations} \\ \text{for} \\ \nu \text{ conditions} \end{array} \qquad (3)$$

[2] The sign $\sum$ will denote summation over all observations, x and y both, if both are observed.

The superscript on each F distinguishes that condition from another. Different sorts of problems are characterized by the different kinds of conditions that the adjusted quantities x_i, y_i, and a, b, c are subjected to. From the theoretical standpoint, the different problems are all conveniently handled alike. This is possible because there is only one principle of least squares, namely, the minimizing of χ^2.

Eqs. 3 will be referred to as the *conditions*, or the *condition equations*. The functions F^1, F^2, etc., on the left, are the *condition functions*. They must be so chosen that when equated to zero they force the conditions that are to be imposed on the adjusted coordinates, angles, lengths, etc.

The assumption behind this development is that the conditions would all be satisfied exactly by the true (unknown) quantities being measured, and the true parameters α, β, γ, all of which, theoretically at least, could be had closely enough by increasing the number of experiments.

25. Notation for the derivatives. The derivatives of the condition functions will be denoted by subscripts, as in Eq. 5 of Chapter III (p. 39). Specifically, the notation will be as follows:

$$F_{x1}{}^h = \frac{\partial F^h}{\partial x_1}, \quad F_{y1}{}^h = \frac{\partial F^h}{\partial y_1}, \quad \text{etc.}$$
$$F_a{}^h = \frac{\partial F^h}{\partial a}, \quad F_b{}^h = \frac{\partial F^h}{\partial b}, \quad \text{etc.} \tag{4}$$

Denoting differentiations by subscripts is very convenient in some work, as it is here. It is a common practice among mathematicians.

The subscript 0 in Eq. 5 below does *not* denote differentiation, but an approximation to the condition function F^h.

These derivatives, like the condition functions themselves, are functions of x_1, x_2, $\cdots$, y_n, a, b, c. In what follows, we shall need numerical values of these derivatives, and fortunately, for most purposes, it will suffice to evaluate them with the observed quantities X_1, X_2, $\cdots$, Y_n, and with the best available approximations a_0, b_0, c_0 obtainable for the parameters, (cf. Ch. III; in particular, Exercise 13). In other words, $F_{x1}{}^h$ is to be a number representing our best guess[3] at the numerical value of this derivative, and similarly for the other derivatives.

We then write

$$F_0{}^h = F^h(X_1, X_2, \cdots, Y_n; \quad a_0, b_0, c_0) \quad h = 1, 2, \cdots, \nu \quad (5)$$
$$\nu \text{ equations}$$

$F_0{}^1$ is a small number, being just the amount by which the condition $F^1 = 0$ fails to be satisfied by the observed values X_1, X_2, $\cdots$, and the approximations a_0, b_0, c_0. Similar statements hold for $F_0{}^2$, $F_0{}^3$, $\cdots$, $F_0{}^\nu$.

> As stated earlier, a_0, b_0, c_0 are approximate values of a, b, c. They can usually be arrived at somehow, as by forcing three of the conditions, i.e., solving for the values of a, b, and c that make three of the condition functions vanish. This is the so-called method of selected points, concerning which more is said in the reduced type at the end of Section 55 (p. 138). Each F_0 would be exactly zero except for errors of observation and the consequent impossibility of choosing a_0, b_0, c_0 to satisfy all the conditions simultaneously.

26. The reduced conditions. Now let the conditions be made linear in the residuals V_{x1}, V_{x2}, $\cdots$, V_{yn}, A, B, C, by expanding Eqs. 3 by Taylor's series, retaining only the first powers of the residuals,[4] and remembering that

$$\left. \begin{array}{l} x_i = X_i - V_{xi} \\ y_i = Y_i - V_{yi} \\ a = a_0 - A \\ b = b_0 - B \\ c = c_0 - C \end{array} \right\} \quad \text{(Calc'd = obs'd − residual)} \quad (6)$$

[3] If our best guess is too far wrong, a second adjustment will be required, but this rarely happens in practice. See the quotation from Gauss on page 180.

[4] The problem of a straight line with no error at all in one of the coordinates (Exercises 1 and 7 in Sec. 65) is one in which there are no squares and higher powers of the residuals to neglect, hence no discrepancies of the kind mentioned (cf. Eq. 3 of Ch. III). The simple example of the triangle in Chapters I and V is another. On rare occasions the residuals may be so large that the neglected terms invalidate the reduced conditions (Eqs. 7), in which event, in general, no systematic solution is available. An exception is the straight line under certain circumstances of weighting; see Exercise 6 of Section 65.

When this is done, the conditions originally expressed by Eqs. 3 take the form

$$\sum_x F_{xi}{}^h V_{xi} + \sum_y F_{yi}{}^h V_{yi} + F_a{}^h A + F_b{}^h B$$
$$+ F_c{}^h C = F_0{}^h, \qquad h = 1, 2, \cdots, \nu$$
$$\nu \text{ equations} \qquad (7)$$

These are called the *reduced conditions*. They are equivalent to Eqs. 3, except for small discrepancies arising from the neglect of higher powers of the residuals in the expansion.

27. The method of Lagrange multipliers.[5] Now if S is at its minimum value, and if any or all of the residuals then undergo small variations (expressed by δ), the variation in S will be zero to within higher powers of the variations in the residuals; in other words

$$\tfrac{1}{2}\delta S = \sum wV\delta V = 0, \quad \text{one equation} \qquad (8)$$

The variations typified by δV are not arbitrary, but must always permit the residuals to satisfy the condition Eqs. 3, or their equivalent, Eqs. 7. So by differentiating Eqs. 7 we find that

$$\sum F_{xi}{}^h \delta V_{xi} + \sum F_{yi}{}^h \delta V_{yi} + F_a{}^h \delta A + F_b{}^h \delta B$$
$$+ F_c{}^h \delta C = 0, \qquad h = 1, 2, \cdots, \nu$$
$$\nu \text{ equations} \qquad (9)$$

Now multiply Eq. 9 through by $-\lambda_h$, an arbitrary multiplier, to get

$$-\lambda_h(\sum F_{xi}{}^h \delta V_{xi} + \sum F_{yi}{}^h \delta V_{yi}) - \lambda_h F_a{}^h \delta A - \lambda_h F_b{}^h \delta B$$
$$- \lambda_h F_c{}^h \delta C = 0, \qquad h = 1, 2, \cdots, \nu$$
$$\nu \text{ equations} \qquad (10)$$

[5] This is the method of Lagrange multipliers; see his *Mécanique analytique* (1811), tome 1, p. 74; or Benjamin Williamson, *Differential Calculus* (Longmans, 1893), Chapter 11. The least squares problem without parameters was worked out by Gauss. He called his multipliers *correlata*, not mentioning Lagrange. Many texts in least squares use the term " correlates " or " correlatives " in this connexion, but apparently none makes any mention of Lagrange. The reference to Gauss is his *Supplementum Theoriae Combinationis Observationum Erroribus Minimis Obnoxiae* (Göttingen, 1826; *Werke*, vol. 4), art. 11.

Add Eqs. 8 and 10 and collect coefficients of the variations δ:

$$\sum (w_{xi}V_{xi} - [\lambda_h F_{xi}{}^h])\delta V_{xi} + \sum (w_{yi}V_{yi} - [\lambda_h F_{yi}{}^h])\delta V_{yi}$$
$$- [\lambda_h F_a{}^h]\delta A - [\lambda_h F_b{}^h]\delta B - [\lambda_h F_c{}^h]\delta C = 0, \quad \text{one equation} \quad (11)$$

In Eq. 11 there are two kinds of summations — there is the summation $\sum$ running over all observations, and there is also the summation over h, in which h runs from 1 to ν, i.e., over all conditions. The latter summation will be denoted by the Gauss brackets [ ].

> Here the number of parameters is taken as 3. If there were p parameters, there would be $2n + p$ variations. For practice, the student should write out Eqs. 8–15 with (e.g.) $n = 3$ and $\nu = 2$ with two parameters. There is no other way to gain familiarity with the development.

Eq. 11 contains $2n + 3$ variations, $\delta V_{x1}, \delta V_{x2}, \delta V_{x3}, \cdots, \delta V_{yn}, \delta A, \delta B, \delta C$. But on account of Eqs. 9, only $2n + 3 - \nu$ of these variations are arbitrary. Let $\lambda_1, \lambda_2, \cdots, \lambda_\nu$ be so chosen that ν of the coefficients in Eq. 11 vanish; then the coefficients of the variations in the remaining $2n + 3 - \nu$ terms must also vanish, because they are used with an equal number of variations, each of which is arbitrary. Then all the coefficients in Eq. 11 vanish, which means that

$$V_{xi} = \frac{1}{w_{xi}} [\lambda_h F_{xi}{}^h] \quad n \text{ equations}; \quad i = 1, 2, \cdots, n \quad (12x)$$

$$V_{yi} = \frac{1}{w_{yi}} [\lambda_h F_{yi}{}^h] \quad n \text{ equations}; \quad i = 1, 2, \cdots, n \quad (12y)$$

$$[\lambda_h F_a{}^h] = 0 \qquad \text{one equation} \qquad (13a)$$

$$[\lambda_h F_b{}^h] = 0 \qquad \text{one equation} \qquad (13b)$$

$$[\lambda_h F_c{}^h] = 0 \qquad \text{one equation} \qquad (13c)$$

Each residual (V_{xi} or V_{yi}) in Eqs. 12 is inversely proportional to the weight w_{xi} or w_{yi} of the corresponding observation. Does this seem reasonable? If any observation is relatively infallible, having $w = \infty$, then its residual is zero; i.e., there is no correction. In curve fitting, for example, it sometimes happens that all the x coordinates are free of error; the corresponding residuals are then 0, and the calculated values of x are the same as the observed.

The ν Lagrange multipliers (λ) are no longer arbitrary; they now have particular values; they have been chosen so as to cause ν of the coefficients in Eq. 11 to vanish (*vide supra*). Their values can be found from Eqs. 13 and 15. We shall now derive Eqs. 15.

28. The general normal equations. Now substitute $(1/w_{xi}) \times [\lambda_h F_{xi}{}^h]$ for V_{xi}, and likewise for y, in the reduced conditions (Eqs. 7). Collect the coefficients of $\lambda_1, \lambda_2, \cdots, \lambda_\nu, A, B, C$, and in so doing set

$$L_{hk} = \frac{F_{x1}{}^h F_{x1}{}^k}{w_{x1}} + \frac{F_{x2}{}^h F_{x2}{}^k}{w_{x2}} + \cdots + \frac{F_{xn}{}^h F_{xn}{}^k}{w_{xn}}$$

$$+ \frac{F_{y1}{}^h F_{y1}{}^k}{w_{y1}} + \frac{F_{y2}{}^h F_{y2}{}^k}{w_{y2}} + \cdots + \frac{F_{yn}{}^h F_{yn}{}^k}{w_{yn}}$$

$$= L_{kh} \tag{14}$$

The following system of equations results. They may be called the " general normal equations." For convenience, only the coefficients are tabled, the unknowns being written across the top. On the left of the equality sign, each coefficient is to be multiplied by the unknown appearing above it, the plus sign between terms being understood. On the right, each F_0 is multiplied by unity, hence the heading " 1 " for that column.

THE GENERAL NORMAL EQUATIONS

λ_1	λ_2	λ_3	$\cdots$	λ_ν	A	B	C	=	1	
L_{11}	L_{21}	L_{31}	$\cdots$	$L_{\nu 1}$	$F_a{}^1$	$F_b{}^1$	$F_c{}^1$		$F_0{}^1$	
L_{12}	L_{22}	L_{32}	$\cdots$	$L_{\nu 2}$	$F_a{}^2$	$F_b{}^2$	$F_c{}^2$		$F_0{}^2$	
L_{13}	L_{23}	L_{33}	$\cdots$	$L_{\nu 3}$	$F_a{}^3$	$F_b{}^3$	$F_c{}^3$		$F_0{}^3$	
.	.	.		.	.	.	.		.	(15)
.	.	.		.	.	.			.	
.	.	.		.	.	.	.		.	
$L_{1\nu}$	$L_{2\nu}$	$L_{3\nu}$	$\cdots$	$L_{\nu\nu}$	$F_a{}^\nu$	$F_b{}^\nu$	$F_c{}^\nu$		$F_0{}^\nu$	
$F_a{}^1$	$F_a{}^2$	$F_a{}^3$	$\cdots$	$F_a{}^\nu$	0	0	0		0	(13a)
$F_b{}^1$	$F_b{}^2$	$F_b{}^3$	$\cdots$	$F_b{}^\nu$	0	0	0		0	(13b)
$F_c{}^1$	$F_c{}^2$	$F_c{}^3$	$\cdots$	$F_c{}^\nu$	0	0	0		0	(13c)

Remark 1. Along the diagonal, $h = k$, and off the diagonal, $h \neq k$. By comparing Eq. 14 with Eqs. 8 and 9 of Chapter III, it can be seen that L_{hh} is the reciprocal of the weight of the condition function F^h. In curve fitting it is in fact sometimes useful to write $1/W$ in place of L, as will frequently be done later. (Cf. also Remark 3 on p. 135.) The term L_{hk} off the diagonal is the product variance of the two condition functions F^h and F^k. It will thus be observed that the diagonal in the general normal equations is made up of the variances of the condition functions, every term of which is positive, and that the terms off the diagonal are product variances, which can sometimes be negative.

Remark 2. Since $L_{hk} = L_{kh}$, as is indicated by Eq. 14, the coefficients of the unknowns in Eqs. 15 are symmetrical about the diagonal. Because of this symmetry, it will be possible, following Gauss, Doolittle, and others, to shorten the numerical computation for finding the unknowns (Secs. 34 and 61). In the abbreviated solution, it is not necessary to enter the coefficients below the diagonal (see Sec. 30).

The general normal equations are $\nu + 3$ in number, and can be solved for the $\nu + 3$ unknowns written across the top. Special methods of solution will be taken up in Sections 34 and 61, but for the present we shall only note that once the residuals A, B, and C are found, the final (adjusted) values of the parameters are obtained by subtracting the residuals from the approximate values, as shown in Eqs. 6.

The solution of the general normal equations yields also numerical values for the Lagrange multipliers $\lambda_1, \lambda_2, \cdots, \lambda_\nu$, which through Eqs. 12 enable the residuals (V) to be calculated. The observations X_i and Y_i are then adjusted by subtracting the residuals, again according to Eqs. 6. The adjusted quantities x_i, along with the adjusted parameters found by Eqs. 6, will satisfy the ν conditions expressed by Eqs. 3 (p. 50), or their equivalent, the reduced conditions, Eqs. 7 (p. 53).

Exercise. Apply Taylor's series to any one of Eqs. 3 to derive the corresponding *reduced condition* shown as Eq. 7.

29. Short expression for S. The normal equations are really normal. The matrix of the coefficients is positive definite. By definition, $S = \sum w \, res^2$. Now by substituting for the residuals in terms of Eqs. 12x and 12y, we find that

$$S = \sum_x \frac{1}{w_{xi}} [\lambda_h F_{xi}{}^h]^2 + \sum_y \frac{1}{w_{yi}} [\lambda_h F_{yi}{}^h]^2$$

$$= \frac{1}{w_{x1}} (\lambda_1 F_{x1}{}^1 + \lambda_2 F_{x1}{}^2 + \cdots + \lambda_\nu F_{x1}{}^\nu)^2$$

$$+ \frac{1}{w_{x2}} (\lambda_1 F_{x2}{}^1 + \lambda_2 F_{x2}{}^2 + \cdots + \lambda_\nu F_{x2}{}^\nu)^2$$

$$+ \cdots + \frac{1}{w_{yn}} (\lambda_1 F_{yn}{}^1 + \lambda_2 F_{yn}{}^2 + \cdots + \lambda_\nu F_{yn}{}^\nu)^2$$

$$= L_{11}\lambda_1{}^2 + L_{22}\lambda_2{}^2 + \cdots + L_{\nu\nu}\lambda_\nu{}^2$$
$$+ 2(L_{12}\lambda_1\lambda_2 + \text{the other cross-product terms})$$

$$=$$

	λ_1	λ_2	λ_3	$\cdots$	λ_ν	A	B	C	
λ_1	L_{11}	L_{21}	L_{31}	$\cdots$	$L_{\nu1}$	$F_a{}^1$	$F_b{}^1$	$F_c{}^1$	
λ_2	L_{12}	L_{22}	L_{32}	$\cdots$	$L_{\nu2}$	$F_a{}^2$	$F_b{}^2$	$F_c{}^2$	
λ_3	L_{13}	L_{23}	L_{33}	$\cdots$	$L_{\nu3}$	$F_a{}^3$	$F_b{}^3$	$F_c{}^3$	
$\cdot$	$\cdot$	$\cdot$	$\cdot$		$\cdot$	$\cdot$	$\cdot$	$\cdot$	(16)
$\cdot$	$\cdot$	$\cdot$	$\cdot$		$\cdot$	$\cdot$	$\cdot$	$\cdot$	
λ_ν	$L_{1\nu}$	$L_{2\nu}$	$L_{3\nu}$	$\cdots$	$L_{\nu\nu}$	$F_a{}^\nu$	$F_b{}^\nu$	$F_c{}^\nu$	
A	$F_a{}^1$	$F_a{}^2$	$F_a{}^3$	$\cdots$	$F_a{}^\nu$	0	0	0	
B	$F_b{}^1$	$F_b{}^2$	$F_b{}^3$	$\cdots$	$F_b{}^\nu$	0	0	0	
C	$F_c{}^1$	$F_c{}^2$	$F_c{}^3$	$\cdots$	$F_c{}^\nu$	0	0	0	

$$= \lambda_1 F_0{}^1 + \lambda_2 F_0{}^2 + \lambda_3 F_0{}^3 + \cdots + \lambda_\nu F_0{}^\nu = [\lambda_h F_0{}^h]$$

by Eqs. 15, page 55. We have thus discovered that

$$S = [\lambda_h F_0{}^h] \tag{17}$$

In this way, S, the minimized sum of the weighted squares of the residuals, is expressible in terms of the Lagrange multipliers; wherefore, so far as S is concerned, it is not necessary to compute the residuals and square them. Later, we shall see that S can be computed by a systematic procedure without even finding the Lagrange multipliers (Secs. 34 and 61). It is a fact that in some problems it is nevertheless advisable to compute the residuals, so that they can be examined individually (cf. Sec. 78).

Gauss derived Eq. 17 for the case of geometric conditions, for which parameters are absent. For other special expressions of S, useful in curve fitting, when parameters are present, see the exercise following this section; also Exercise 3, page 163.

Since $S > 0$, the quadratic form (16) is positive definite[6]; that is, no matter what values be given to $\lambda_1, \lambda_2, \cdots, \lambda_\nu, A, B, C$, the quadratic form (16) can not be negative. The symmetry of the general normal equations (Sec. 28) has already been noted; hence these equations are really normal — i.e., they are not only symmetric, but the quadratic form of the coefficients is positive definite.

Exercise. Show that

$$-S = \frac{\begin{vmatrix} L_{11} & L_{21} & L_{31} & \cdots & L_{\nu 1} & F_a{}^1 & F_b{}^1 & F_c{}^1 & F_0{}^1 \\ L_{12} & L_{22} & L_{32} & \cdots & L_{\nu 2} & F_a{}^2 & F_b{}^2 & F_c{}^2 & F_0{}^2 \\ L_{13} & L_{23} & L_{33} & \cdots & L_{\nu 3} & F_a{}^3 & F_b{}^3 & F_c{}^3 & F_0{}^3 \\ \cdot & \cdot & \cdot & & \cdot & \cdot & \cdot & \cdot & \cdot \\ \cdot & \cdot & \cdot & & \cdot & \cdot & \cdot & \cdot & \cdot \\ \cdot & \cdot & \cdot & & \cdot & \cdot & \cdot & \cdot & \cdot \\ L_{1\nu} & L_{2\nu} & L_{3\nu} & \cdots & L_{\nu\nu} & F_a{}^\nu & F_b{}^\nu & F_c{}^\nu & F_0{}^\nu \\ F_a{}^1 & F_a{}^2 & F_a{}^3 & \cdots & F_a{}^\nu & 0 & 0 & 0 & 0 \\ F_b{}^1 & F_b{}^2 & F_b{}^3 & \cdots & F_b{}^\nu & 0 & 0 & 0 & 0 \\ F_c{}^1 & F_c{}^2 & F_c{}^3 & \cdots & F_c{}^\nu & 0 & 0 & 0 & 0 \\ F_0{}^1 & F_0{}^2 & F_0{}^3 & \cdots & F_0{}^\nu & 0 & 0 & 0 & 0 \end{vmatrix}}{\begin{vmatrix} L_{11} & L_{21} & L_{31} & \cdots & L_{\nu 1} & F_a{}^1 & F_b{}^1 & F_c{}^1 \\ L_{12} & L_{22} & L_{32} & \cdots & L_{\nu 2} & F_a{}^2 & F_b{}^2 & F_c{}^2 \\ L_{13} & L_{23} & L_{33} & \cdots & L_{\nu 3} & F_a{}^3 & F_b{}^3 & F_c{}^3 \\ \cdot & \cdot & \cdot & & \cdot & \cdot & \cdot & \cdot \\ \cdot & \cdot & \cdot & & \cdot & \cdot & \cdot & \cdot \\ \cdot & \cdot & \cdot & & \cdot & \cdot & \cdot & \cdot \\ L_{1\nu} & L_{2\nu} & L_{3\nu} & \cdots & L_{\nu\nu} & F_a{}^\nu & F_b{}^\nu & F_c{}^\nu \\ F_a{}^1 & F_a{}^2 & F_a{}^3 & \cdots & F_a{}^\nu & 0 & 0 & 0 \\ F_b{}^1 & F_b{}^2 & F_b{}^3 & \cdots & F_b{}^\nu & 0 & 0 & 0 \\ F_c{}^1 & F_c{}^2 & F_c{}^3 & \cdots & F_c{}^\nu & 0 & 0 & 0 \end{vmatrix}}$$

[6] Maxime Bôcher, *Higher Algebra* (Macmillan, 1907), page 150.

PART C

CONDITIONS WITHOUT PARAMETERS

CHAPTER V

GEOMETRIC CONDITIONS

30. Adaptation of the general solution to conditions without parameters. When the conditions imposed by Eqs. 3 or 7 (pp. 50 and 53) of the last chapter are geometric, there are no parameters or adjustable constants. The quantities a, b, and c then do not exist, and in the general normal equations (p. 55), all the rows and columns containing A, B, C, $F_a{}^h$, $F_b{}^h$, and $F_c{}^h$ are to be deleted. The Lagrange multipliers (λ) are the only unknowns left, and only the square array of L coefficients remains. The general solution thus reduces to Eqs. 1 shown below.

λ_1	λ_2	λ_3	$\cdots$	λ_ν	$=$	1
L_{11}	L_{12}	L_{13}	$\cdots$	$L_{1\nu}$		$F_0{}^1$
	L_{22}	L_{23}	$\cdots$	$L_{2\nu}$		$F_0{}^2$
		L_{33}	$\cdots$	$L_{3\nu}$		$F_0{}^3$
				$\cdot$		$\cdot$
				$\cdot$		$\cdot$
				$\cdot$		$\cdot$
				$L_{\nu\nu}$		$F_0{}^\nu$

$$(1)$$

Here the coefficients below the diagonal have been omitted, since in the abridged solution soon to be learned, those below the diagonal are not used. The coefficients are to be read " down to the diagonal, then to the right." The unknowns are the ν Lagrange multipliers.

This type of problem (no parameters) was solved by Gauss,[1] and is treated satisfactorily in many textbooks. It arises in

[1] See the reference to Gauss in Section 27, page 53.

geodesy, surveying, and in astronomy, and this accounts for the attentions of Gauss, Bessel, and Encke, who were mainly interested in the problems of adjustment arising in astronomy.

31. Example: the plane triangle. We shall return now to the triangle problem discussed in Section 3 (see Fig. 3, p. 7). The angles are measured with a transit. The weights might arise from the number of repetitions on each angle.

$$\text{Observations:} \quad X_1, X_2, X_3$$

$$\text{Weights:} \quad w_1, w_2, w_3$$

$$\text{Calc'd values:} \quad x_1, x_2, x_3 \quad \text{(to be found)}$$

Here there is only the one condition, namely,

$$x_1 + x_2 + x_3 = 180° \quad \text{(This corresponds to Eq. 3, p. 50.)} \quad (2)$$

so we write

$$F(x_1, x_2, x_3) = x_1 + x_2 + x_3 - 180° \tag{3}$$

(There is only the one condition, so no superscript on the F is needed.) This condition function F will be zero when we are able to insert the adjusted values x_1, x_2, x_3 into it. By inserting the observed values we calculate

$$F_0 = X_1 + X_2 + X_3 - 180° \quad \text{(See Eq. 5, p. 52.)} \tag{4}$$

F_0 is not zero unless $X_1 + X_2 + X_3$ happens to be exactly $180°$, in which case no question of adjustment arises. The derivatives of F are

$$F_1 = F_2 = F_3 = 1 \quad \text{(See Eq. 4, p. 51.)} \tag{5}$$

There is only one L coefficient (why?). It could be called L_{11} but no subscript is needed, so we shall use simply L. It is calculated as follows:

$$L = \frac{F_1 F_1}{w_1} + \frac{F_2 F_2}{w_2} + \frac{F_3 F_3}{w_3} = \frac{1}{w_1} + \frac{1}{w_2} + \frac{1}{w_3} \quad \text{(Eq. 14, p. 55)} \tag{6}$$

There is but one normal equation, namely,

$$L\lambda = F_0 \tag{7}$$

The solution is

$$\lambda = \frac{F_0}{L} \tag{8}$$

The numerator, F_0, is the amount by which the observed angles fail to close. The denominator, L, is $1/w_1 + 1/w_2 + 1/w_3$, which happens to be equal to $1/w_F$ by Eq. 9 on page 40 (propagation of mean square error).

After λ is worked out numerically, we may find the three residuals by Eq. 12, page 54:

$$\left. \begin{aligned} V_1 &= \frac{1}{w_1}\lambda F_1 = \frac{\lambda}{w_1} \\[2mm] V_2 &= \frac{1}{w_2}\lambda F_2 = \frac{\lambda}{w_2} \\[2mm] V_3 &= \frac{1}{w_3}\lambda F_3 = \frac{\lambda}{w_3} \end{aligned} \right\} \tag{9}$$

The adjusted angles are then

$$x_1 = X_1 - V_1; \quad x_2 = X_2 - V_2; \quad x_3 = X_3 - V_3 \tag{10}$$

The sum of the adjusted angles is identically $180°$, for

$$\begin{aligned} x_1 + x_2 + x_3 &= X_1 + X_2 + X_3 - (V_1 + V_2 + V_3) \\[2mm] &= X_1 + X_2 + X_3 \\[2mm] &\quad - \left(\frac{1}{w_1} + \frac{1}{w_2} + \frac{1}{w_3}\right)\frac{X_1 + X_2 + X_3 - 180°}{\dfrac{1}{w_1} + \dfrac{1}{w_2} + \dfrac{1}{w_3}} \\[2mm] &= 180° \text{ exactly} \end{aligned} \tag{11}$$

The equations for V_1, V_2, and V_3 are valid no matter how large F_0 is. This is a case where there are no higher powers of the residuals to be neglected, and is in contrast with the more general statement in footnote 4, page 52.

Note that the residuals are inversely proportional to the

weights of the observations; that is,

$$V_1 : V_2 : V_3 = \frac{1}{w_1} : \frac{1}{w_2} : \frac{1}{w_3} \qquad (12)$$

Thus, in this problem, the adjustment by least squares simply takes the excess or deficiency F_0 (which will ordinarily be a small amount, perhaps a few minutes of arc) and distributes it among the three angles in inverse proportion to their weights (cf. Ch. I, p. 8). The student should reflect on this at length. If the action of least squares seems reasonable in this simple problem, it may be so in more complicated ones, even if we are not so easily able to visualize its working. Even in more complicated problems, the principle is the same (the minimizing of $\sum w \, res^2$ or of χ^2); it is only the conditions to which the adjusted values are subject that differ from one problem to another.

Exercise 1. Show that the condition

$$x_1 + x_2 + x_3 = 180° \qquad (2)$$

determines a plane distant $180°/\sqrt{3}$ from the origin, and cutting equal intercepts from the axes. The calculated point lies on the plane, and the observed point off it. If the weights are all equal, the distance between the observed and calculated points is to be minimized, in which case the line segment joining the observed and calculated points is perpendicular to the plane $x_1 + x_2 + x_3 = 180°$. See Fig. 11.

If the weights of the observed angles are unequal, the distance between the observed and calculated points is not to be minimized, but rather the quantity

$$w_1(X_1 - x_1)^2 + w_2(X_2 - x_2)^2 + w_3(X_3 - x_3)^2 \qquad (13)$$

Exercise 2. Any possible plane triangle is represented by a point on this plane for which x_1, x_2, and x_3 are positive. *Any* method of adjustment would consist of picking off some point on this plane, corresponding to a given observed point X_1, X_2, X_3 off the plane.

Exercise 3. Solve the triangle problem (p. 60) without the Lagrange multiplier.

Hint: Take $S = \sum wV^2 = \sum w(X - x)^2$ \qquad (14)

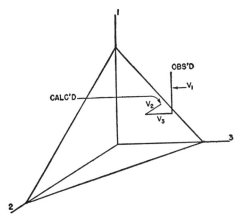

Fig. 11. The three angles of a plane triangle constitute the coordinates of a point. The calculated (or adjusted) angles add to 180°. The point representing the calculated angles lies on a plane distant $180°/\sqrt{3}$ from the origin. The observed point lies beyond the plane if there is an observed excess beyond 180°, but lies on the under side of the plane if there is an observed deficiency. It lies on the plane only by accident, in which case no adjustment is required.

By the one and only condition on the adjusted values, we may take

$$x_3 = 180° - x_1 - x_2 \tag{15}$$

or

$$V_3 = F_0 - V_1 - V_2 \tag{16}$$

where, as before,

$$F_0 = X_1 + X_2 + X_3 - 180°$$

Then

$$S = w_1 V_1{}^2 + w_2 V_2{}^2 + w_3 (F_0 - V_1 - V_2)^2 \tag{17}$$

x_1 and x_2 are independent; so are V_1 and V_2. Hence we may set dS/dV_1 and dS/dV_2 both equal to zero. The result is

$$\left. \begin{aligned} w_1 V_1 - w_3(F_0 - V_1 - V_2) &= 0 \\ w_2 V_2 - w_3(\qquad " \qquad) &= 0 \end{aligned} \right\} \tag{18}$$

It follows that

$$w_1 V_1 = w_2 V_2, \tag{19}$$

and that

$$\left. \begin{aligned}
V_1 &= \frac{1}{w_1} \frac{1}{\dfrac{1}{w_1} + \dfrac{1}{w_2} + \dfrac{1}{w_3}} \, F_0 \\[2ex]
V_2 &= \frac{1}{w_2} \frac{1}{\dfrac{1}{w_1} + \dfrac{1}{w_2} + \dfrac{1}{w_3}} \, F_0 \\[2ex]
V_3 &= \frac{1}{w_3} \frac{1}{\dfrac{1}{w_1} + \dfrac{1}{w_2} + \dfrac{1}{w_3}} \, F_0
\end{aligned} \right\} \qquad (20)$$

which are equivalent to Eqs. 9 on page 61, obtained with the Lagrange multiplier.

> All problems in least squares can theoretically be solved without the use of Lagrange multipliers. Occasionally it may even seem easier to dispense with them, but most problems then become hopelessly involved, as Kummell discovered.[2]

32. The plane triangle continued. The weights of the adjusted angles, and any function of them. Returning to the triangle problem of the last section, suppose we ask for

The weight of angle x_1

and

The weight of the sum of $x_1 + x_2 + x_3$, after adjustment

Of course we know in advance that the weight of this sum must be infinite, since we forced it to be a definite amount, 180°; but it will be interesting to see if this result comes by the routine about to be described. The rules for finding the weights of functions of the adjusted observations are illustrated in what follows, and a more complicated example will be worked out in the next chapter. The theoretical proofs will be found in several books on least squares, for example, O. M. Leland's *Practical Least Squares*

---

[2] Charles H. Kummell, *The Analyst* (Des Moines), vol. 6, 1879: pp. 97–105.

(McGraw-Hill, 1921) and T. W. Wright and J. F. Hayford's *Adjustment of Observations* (Van Nostrand, 1884, 1906).

Let

$$G^1 = x_1 \tag{21}$$

and

$$G^2 = x_1 + x_2 + x_3 \tag{22}$$

G^1 and G^2 are then the functions whose weights are wanted. As many more functions could be added as desired, but here we shall be content to see just the weights of x_1 and of $x_1 + x_2 + x_3$ worked out. The procedure is as follows. We need to form certain sums, and to this end we make up the following table, numerical values ordinarily being inserted in place of the symbols in the body of the table. F is defined by Eq. 3 on page 60.

(1) i	(2) F_i	(3) G_i^1	(4) G_i^2	(5) $\dfrac{F_i}{\sqrt{w_i}}$	(6) $\dfrac{G_i^1}{\sqrt{w_i}}$	(7) $\dfrac{G_i^2}{\sqrt{w_i}}$	(8) Sum
1	1	1	1	$\dfrac{1}{\sqrt{w_1}}$	$\dfrac{1}{\sqrt{w_1}}$	$\dfrac{1}{\sqrt{w_1}}$	
2	1	0	1	$\dfrac{1}{\sqrt{w_2}}$	0	$\dfrac{1}{\sqrt{w_2}}$	for numerical check
3	1	0	1	$\dfrac{1}{\sqrt{w_3}}$	0	$\dfrac{1}{\sqrt{w_3}}$	

Next step, from columns 5, 6, and 7 the sums called for in the normal equations can be evaluated, as shown below.

$$\left[\frac{F_i G_i^1}{w_i}\right] = \frac{1}{w_1}, \quad \left[\frac{F_i G_i^2}{w_i}\right] = L, \quad \text{as defined on page 60}$$

$$\left[\frac{G_i^1 G_i^1}{w_i}\right] = \frac{1}{w_1}, \quad \left[\frac{G_i^2 G_i^2}{w_i}\right] = L \quad \text{``} \quad \text{``} \quad \text{``} \quad \text{``} \quad \text{``}$$

[ ] means summation, as in Section 27 (Gauss' notation). These sums are appended in the C^1 and C^2 columns, and the solution proceeds.

Row	λ	=	1	C^1	C^2
I	L		F_0	$\left[\dfrac{F_iG_i^1}{w_i}\right]=\dfrac{1}{w_1}$	$\left[\dfrac{F_iG_i^2}{w_i}\right]=L$
2			0	$\left[\dfrac{G_i^1G_i^1}{w_i}\right]=\dfrac{1}{w_1}$	$\left[\dfrac{G_i^2G_i^2}{w_i}\right]=L$
	How obtained				
3	Row I $\times\ -\dfrac{F_0}{L}$		$-\dfrac{F_0F_0}{L}$	$\ldots$	$\ldots$
II	$2+3$		$-\dfrac{F_0F_0}{L}$	$\ldots$	$\ldots$
4	Row I $\times\ -\dfrac{1}{w_1L}$			$-\dfrac{1}{Lw_1^2}$	$\ldots$
II^1	$2+4$			$\dfrac{1}{w_1}-\dfrac{1}{Lw_1^2}$	$\ldots$
5	Row I $\times\ -\dfrac{L}{L}$				$-L$
II^2	$2+5$				0

In a numerical solution, a sum column would be introduced at the right for a check, and the spaces filled in by the ellipses would be filled in with numbers (see the note in reduced type on p. 33). For a numerical illustration see pages 82 and 83.

Row I gives $\lambda = F_0/L$, as already found on page 61. Looking next at the " 1 " column in Row II we see $-F_0F_0/L$, which has the value $-\lambda F_0$, and which by Eq. 17 on page 57 is none other than $-S$. Thus, $\sum wV^2$ is computed in a routine manner without first finding the individual residuals V_1, V_2, and V_3.

The variance coefficient of G^1, or the reciprocal of its weight, appears in the C^1 column of Row II^1; and the variance coefficient of G^2, or the reciprocal of its weight, appears in the C^2 column of Row II^2.

Before adjustment, the weight of G^1 was w_1, the weight of the observation X_1: *after* adjustment, the reciprocal of its weight is

$1/w_1 - 1/Lw_1{}^2$.   Now of course

$$\frac{1}{w_1} - \frac{1}{Lw_1{}^2} < \frac{1}{w_1}$$

which means that the weight of x_1 is greater than the weight of X_1. That is, the weight *after* adjustment is *greater than the weight before,* which seems reasonable enough; the observations on the other two angles help to estimate x_1, and to increase our confidence in its value. After the adjustment we feel that we know more about the triangle than before.

In particular if all three angles have the same weight before adjustment, then if $w_1 = w_2 = w_3 = 1$, the weight of x_1 after adjustment is $1/\{1/w_1 - 1/Lw_1{}^2\} = 1/\{1 - 1/3\} = 1.5$, which is 50 percent greater than the weight of X_1. *The adjustment therefore increases the weight by 50 percent.* The same thing is of course true for the other angles.

If the weight of an angle has been increased 50 percent, its standard error has diminished 18 percent, since

$w_{before} : w_{after} = (\text{S.E.}_{after} : \text{S.E.}_{before})^2$ (See Eq. 16, p. 22.)

Next consider the weight of $x_1 + x_2 + x_3$. From Row II^2 in the form above we see that the reciprocal of the weight of this function is zero; in other words, the weight of $x_1 + x_2 + x_3$ is infinite; it is therefore known absolutely. The adjustment *forced* the sum to be 180°, and it is no surprise to find its weight after adjustment to be infinite.

This simple example gives a glimpse of the method for the solution of problems involving rigorous conditions. A guide for systematic computation, and a more complicated example, are given in the next section.

EXERCISES

Exercise 1. Take the values of V_1, V_2, and V_3 found earlier, namely λ/w_1, λ/w_2, and λ/w_3, and show by direct substitution that λF_0, the negative of the extreme left entry in Row II of the tabulation shown above, is actually S, or $w_1V_1{}^2 + w_2V_2{}^2 + w_3V_3{}^2$.

Exercise 2. By the use of Eq. 7, page 40, show that the variance of the sum $x_1 + x_2 + x_3$ of the adjusted angles of a plane triangle is 0; hence its weight is infinite.

Hint: $$x_3 = 180° - x_1 - x_2$$

whence

$$\text{Var } (x_1+x_2+x_3) = \sigma_1{}^2+\sigma_2{}^2+\sigma_3{}^2+2r_{12}\sigma_1\sigma_2+2r_{13}\sigma_1\sigma_3$$
$$+2r_{23}\sigma_2\sigma_3 \tag{a}$$

$$\sigma_1{}^2 = \sigma_2{}^2 + \sigma_3{}^2 + 2r_{23}\sigma_2\sigma_3 \tag{b}$$

$$\sigma_2{}^2 = \sigma_1{}^2 + \sigma_3{}^2 + 2r_{13}\sigma_1\sigma_3 \tag{c}$$

$$\sigma_3{}^2 = \sigma_1{}^2 + \sigma_2{}^2 + 2r_{12}\sigma_1\sigma_2 \tag{d}$$

By combining the last three equations with Eq. *a* it is found that

$$\text{Var } (x_1 + x_2 + x_3) = 0 \tag{e}$$

Exercise 3. Observations $X_1, X_2, \cdots, X_n$, with weights $w_1, w_2, \cdots, w_n$ are taken on n quantities, the adjusted values of which are connected by the one condition

$$x_1 + x_2 + \cdots + x_n = C$$

By making use of the scheme outlined in Section 32 for finding the weight of a function after adjustment, show that the weight U_r of the sum $x_1 + x_2 + \cdots + x_r$, $r < n$, *after adjustment,* is

$$\frac{1}{U_r} = \frac{1}{W_r} - \frac{W}{W_r{}^2}$$

where

$$\frac{1}{W_r} = \frac{1}{w_1} + \frac{1}{w_2} + \cdots + \frac{1}{w_r}$$

and

$$\frac{1}{W} = \frac{1}{w_1} + \frac{1}{w_2} + \cdots + \frac{1}{w_n} = L$$

In particular, if $w_1 = w_2 = \cdots = w_n = 1$,

$$U_r = \frac{n}{r(n-r)}$$

If $n = 3$ and $r = 1$, $U_r = 3/2$, which is the special case of one angle of a triangle, already worked out on page 67. If $n = 4$, as for a quadrilateral, one angle, *after adjustment*, has the weight $4/3$, the sum of any two angles has the weight 1, and the sum of three angles has the weight $4/3$.

This problem has application also in the social sciences, where proportions are observed by sampling methods, and the total count is known from other sources (Ch. VII). For a cell that is not too small (i.e., for one having a sample frequency of possibly 10 or higher), the weight of the observed frequency may be assumed inversely proportional to that frequency, and the variance thereof equal to the cell frequency.

Suppose that n_1 and n_2 are the observed sample frequencies in a two-celled table, the total count of the two cells being known. If $n_1 + n_2 = n$, then n_1/n and n_2/n are the observed proportions. Denote them by p and q. Then $p + q = 1$, $L = 1/w_1 + 1/w_2 = n_1 + n_2 = n$, and the weight U_1 of the cell n_1 *after adjustment* is given by the equation

$$\frac{1}{U_1} = \text{variance of } n_1 = \frac{1}{w_1} - \frac{1}{nw_1{}^2}$$

$$= n_1 - \frac{n_1{}^2}{n} = n_1 q = npq$$

Thus the variance of n_1 is reduced from n_1 to npq by the adjustment. The variance of the proportion p is reduced from p/n to pq/n. The ratio of the variance after adjustment to the variance before adjustment is thus equal to q. The reduction in variance is considerable when q is small, i.e., when p is nearly unity, as happens when n_1 is nearly all of n.

CHAPTER VI

SYSTEMATIC COMPUTATION FOR GEOMETRIC CONDITIONS

33. Steps in the formation of the normal equations. There will be observations, weights, and conditions imposed on the adjusted values.

$$\text{Observations: } X_1, X_2, \cdots, X_n$$

$$\text{Weights: } w_1, w_2, \cdots, w_n$$

$$\text{Conditions: } \left. \begin{array}{l} F^1(x_1, x_2, \cdots, x_n) = 0 \\ F^2(x_1, x_2, \cdots, x_n) = 0 \\ F^3(x_1, x_2, \cdots, x_n) = 0 \\ F^4(x_1, x_2, \cdots, x_n) = 0 \end{array} \right\} \quad \begin{array}{l} \text{(These are Eqs. 3,} \\ \text{p. 50, except that} \quad (1) \\ \text{here there are no} \\ \text{parameters.)} \end{array}$$

1st step. Write down the conditions, i.e., select the appropriate F functions. Decide also on the G functions whose weights are wanted. One then works out the values of F_0, which will usually turn out to be small numbers, since the conditions will be nearly but not quite satisfied by the observations; see for instance page 77.

> By the use of the reciprocal matrix as explained in Section 36, one need not decide on all his G functions at the start; more can be added later without great inconvenience.

The solution will be illustrated with four conditions; i.e., the number ν in Eqs. 3 on page 50 is taken as 4, which will be the number of Lagrange multipliers (λ). Expansion or contraction to more or fewer conditions is easy. (In the simple triangle problem of Sec. 31, p. 60, there was only one condition, and one λ.)

We shall assume here that we want to find the weights of two functions of the adjusted values. Let these functions be designated as

$$G^1(x_1, x_2, \cdots, x_n)$$

$$G^2(x_1, x_2, \cdots, x_n)$$

(In the triangle problem of Sec. 32, G^1 was x_1, and G^2 was $x_1 + x_2 + x_3$; see p. 65.)

2d step. This requires some differential calculus. It consists of writing down the various derivatives that are needed, such as

$$F_1{}^1 \quad \text{or} \quad \frac{\partial F^1}{\partial x_1}, \qquad\qquad F_2{}^1 \quad \text{or} \quad \frac{\partial F^1}{\partial x_2}$$

$$F_3{}^2 \quad \text{or} \quad \frac{\partial F^2}{\partial x_3}, \qquad\qquad F_2{}^3 \quad \text{or} \quad \frac{\partial F^3}{\partial x_2}$$

Etc.

These are used for forming the L coefficients, according to Eq. 14 on page 55. We shall also need the derivatives of the G functions, such as

$$G_1{}^1 \quad \text{or} \quad \frac{\partial G^1}{\partial x_1}, \qquad\qquad G_2{}^1 \quad \text{or} \quad \frac{\partial G^1}{\partial x_2}$$

$$G_3{}^2 \quad \text{or} \quad \frac{\partial G^2}{\partial x_3}, \qquad\qquad G_2{}^3 \quad \text{or} \quad \frac{\partial G^3}{\partial x_2}$$

Etc.

which are to be used in computing the weights of the G functions.

3d step. Work out the numerical values of the derivatives; see, for instance, page 78. In each case, the observed values X_1, $X_2, \cdots, X_n$ are used in place of the adjusted quantities $x_1, x_2, \cdots$, x_n, since approximate values of the derivatives are usually close enough; at least they will have to suffice till we can get better ones. The following table is made up, numerical values being inserted in the spaces. Naturally, more or fewer columns will be needed in various problems, and different computers will work differently even on the same problem. The layout will also vary, depending on what type of calculating machine is available. Only general directions can be given in advance of a specific problem.

TABLE 1 (3D STEP)

i	w_i	$\dfrac{1}{\sqrt{w_i}}$	$F_i{}^1$	$F_i{}^2$	$F_i{}^3$	$F_i{}^4$	$G_i{}^1$	$G_i{}^2$	Sum
1	...	...	...	...	...	...	...	...	...
2	...	...	...	...	...	...	...	...	...
.	.	.	.	.	.	.	.	.	.
.	.	.	.	.	.	.	.	.	.
.	.	.	.	.	.	.	.	.	.
n	...	...	...	...	...	...	...	...	...

The sums at the right in Table 1 are formed exclusive of the entries for the weights. They are useful in checking the formation of Table 2.

4th step. Form Table 2, which is derived from Table 1, by multiplying the F and G derivatives by the corresponding values of $1/\sqrt{w_i}$, as indicated in the headings of Table 2.

TABLE 2

THE MATRIX FOR THE FORMATION OF THE NORMAL EQUATIONS (4TH STEP)

i	$\dfrac{F_i{}^1}{\sqrt{w_i}}$	$\dfrac{F_i{}^2}{\sqrt{w_i}}$	$\dfrac{F_i{}^3}{\sqrt{w_i}}$	$\dfrac{F_i{}^4}{\sqrt{w_i}}$	$\dfrac{G_i{}^1}{\sqrt{w_i}}$	$\dfrac{G_i{}^2}{\sqrt{w_i}}$	Sum s_i
1	...	...	...	...	...	...	...
2	...	...	...	...	...	...	...
.	.	.	.	.	.	.	.
.	.	.	.	.	.	.	.
.	.	.	.	.	.	.	.
n	...	...	...	...	...	...	...
Sum	...	...	...	...	...	...	... $\sqrt{}$

Table 2 is termed a matrix because from it is formed the normal equations. Moreover, in matrix notation, the formation of the normal equations is the product $M'M$, M being the matrix of Table 2, and M' its " transpose."

The sums shown at the right and across the bottom of Table 2 are used for checking the formation of the normal equations. The sums themselves are checked by adding them down and across, to see that they add to the same grand total either way (the " corner check ").

There are various procedures that one can follow in computing Table 2 from Table 1. With automatic multiplication, the computer may prefer to use $1/\sqrt{w_i}$ as a constant factor in row i, reading off the individual products

$(F_i^1/\sqrt{w_i}$, etc.) and entering them in Table 2, cumulating the sum $F_i^1 + F_i^2 + F_i^3 + F_i^4 + G_i^1 + G_i^2$ of the multipliers to check with the sums already entered in Table 1.

With a machine having two multiplier registers, one for cumulating the quotients, and the other for reading individual quotients, the computer may cumulate a sum in either the horizontal or vertical without extra effort. If the machine moreover permits the dividend to be altered independently of the keyboard, one may set $\sqrt{w_i}$ on the keyboard and use it for a divisor throughout an entire horizontal row of Table 1, entering the individual quotients in Table 2, and at the same time cumulating the sum s_i to be entered at the right.

The use of punch card equipment for forming normal equations may save time and expense on large projects.

5th step. The coefficients in the normal equations are now to be formed from Table 2. By recalling the definition of L_{hk} in Eq. 14 on page 55, and by introducing the C^1 and C^2 columns for the weights of the G functions as used in Chapter V, we may rewrite the normal equations of page 59 in the form shown below. It will be observed that the terms on the diagonal are sums of squares formed from the columns of Table 2, and that the terms off the diagonal are the sums of cross-products formed from these columns. The numbers entered in the C^1 and C^2 columns are likewise the sums of squares and cross-products.

NORMAL EQUATIONS

Row	λ_1	λ_2	λ_3	λ_4	$= 1$	C^1	C^2	Sum
I	$\left[\dfrac{F_i^1 F_i^1}{w_i}\right]$	$\left[\dfrac{F_i^1 F_i^2}{w_i}\right]$	$\left[\dfrac{F_i^1 F_i^3}{w_i}\right]$	$\left[\dfrac{F_i^1 F_i^4}{w_i}\right]$	F_0^1	$\left[\dfrac{F_i^1 G_i^1}{w_i}\right]$	$\left[\dfrac{F_i^1 G_i^2}{w_i}\right]$	$\ldots$
2		$\left[\dfrac{F_i^2 F_i^2}{w_i}\right]$	$\left[\dfrac{F_i^2 F_i^3}{w_i}\right]$	$\left[\dfrac{F_i^2 F_i^4}{w_i}\right]$	F_0^2	$\left[\dfrac{F_i^2 G_i^1}{w_i}\right]$	$\left[\dfrac{F_i^2 G_i^2}{w_i}\right]$	$\ldots$
3			$\left[\dfrac{F_i^3 F_i^3}{w_i}\right]$	$\left[\dfrac{F_i^3 F_i^4}{w_i}\right]$	F_0^3	$\left[\dfrac{F_i^3 G_i^1}{w_i}\right]$	$\left[\dfrac{F_i^3 G_i^2}{w_i}\right]$	$\ldots (2)$
4	No entries below the diagonal because of symmetry			$\left[\dfrac{F_i^4 F_i^4}{w_i}\right]$	F_0^4	$\left[\dfrac{F_i^4 G_i^1}{w_i}\right]$	$\left[\dfrac{F_i^4 G_i^2}{w_i}\right]$	$\ldots$
5					0	$\left[\dfrac{G_i^1 G_i^1}{w_i}\right]$	$\left[\dfrac{G_i^2 G_i^2}{w_i}\right]$	$\ldots$

Unknowns spans columns λ_1–λ_4.

The sum column at the right checks the formation of the normal equations. Herein are entered (in pencil) the cumulation of the cross-multiplications formed with the sum column of Table 2; these should agree with the sums of the terms in the normal equations, the " 1 " column excluded; see Table 3 in Section 34, and the check formed immediately below. If no errors are found, the sums entered in pencil at the right of the normal equations are altered to include the " 1 " column, and the solution proceeds, being checked at the pivotal points (see the check marks in Rows II, III, and IV of the numerical solution in Sec. 34). The sums $[G_i^1 G_i^1 / w_i]$ and $[G_i^2 G_i^2 / w_i]$ must be checked otherwise, as by repetition.

The 0 in the bottom row of the normal equations is appended for the computation of the minimized sum of squares, S. The columns C^1 and C^2 assist in the computation of the weights of the functions G^1 and G^2.

The solution of the equations is to be carried out by the routine process already seen in simplified form on page 66, and to be illustrated more fully on pages 82–83, and symbolically on page 158. When the numerical values of the Lagrange multipliers (λ) have been worked out, the residuals $V_1, \cdots, V_n$ are to be calculated by Eq. 12 on page 54, and then used to find the " adjusted observations " $x_1, x_2, \cdots, x_n$ as follows:

$$
\left.
\begin{aligned}
x_1 &= X_1 - V_1 = X_1 - \frac{1}{w_1} \left(\lambda_1 F_1{}^1 + \lambda_2 F_1{}^2 + \lambda_3 F_1{}^3 + \lambda_4 F_1{}^4\right) \\[2mm]
x_2 &= X_2 - V_2 = X_2 - \frac{1}{w_2} \left(\lambda_1 F_2{}^1 + \lambda_2 F_2{}^2 + \lambda_3 F_2{}^3 + \lambda_4 F_2{}^4\right) \\[1mm]
&\ \ \vdots \\[1mm]
x_n &= X_n - V_n = X_n - \frac{1}{w_n} \left(\lambda_1 F_n{}^1 + \lambda_2 F_n{}^2 + \lambda_3 F_n{}^3 + \lambda_4 F_n{}^4\right)
\end{aligned}
\right\} \quad (3)
$$

It should be noted that the numerical values of the derivatives $F_1{}^1$, $F_2{}^1$, etc., required in the parentheses, are ready for use in Table 1, p. 72.

34. Numerical example: a surveying problem. A surveying party measures the sides and angles of the plane triangle PQR, with the following results:

On angle P: 51° 06′
(4 observations)   08
                     05
                     06
Average   51° 06′.25

On angle Q: 95° 05′
(2 observations)   04
Average   95° 04′.5

On angle R: 33° 49′
(2 observations)   50
Average   33° 49′.5

Side p: 1723.7 ft.
 " q: 2205.4 "
 " r: 1232.7 "

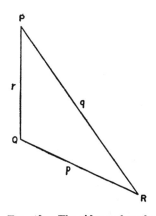

Fig. 12. The sides and angles of this plane triangle have been measured. The sum of the adjusted angles must be 180°; and the adjusted angles and sides must satisfy the sine law.

The transit man, from previous experience, has reason to believe that the standard error of single measurements on one angle is about one minute of arc, or 0.00029 radian. He takes the standard error of the chainmen to be one foot in 10,000 feet, and in proportion to the square root of the distance chained. The weights of the observations on the angles and sides are then in ratios as follows:

$$w_P : w_Q : w_R : w_p : w_q : w_r = \frac{4}{0.000\,29^2} : \frac{2}{0.000\,29^2} :$$

$$\frac{2}{0.000\,29^2} : \left(\frac{1}{\sqrt{\dfrac{1724}{10,000}}}\right)^2 : \left(\frac{1}{\sqrt{\dfrac{2205}{10,000}}}\right)^2 : \left(\frac{1}{\sqrt{\dfrac{1233}{10,000}}}\right)^2 \quad (4)$$

These ratios come from Eq. 13 on page 21, wherein the weight of a function f was defined to be inversely proportional to its variance. Since weights are relative and not absolute, the factor of proportionality (σ^2) in Eq. 13 on page 21 is arbitrary and can be chosen for convenience; accordingly we let

$$\sigma^2 = \tfrac{1}{2}\ 0.00029^2 = 4.23 \times 10^{-8} \tag{5}$$

whereupon the weights take these simple values:

$$w_P = 2, \qquad\qquad w_Q = 1, \qquad\qquad w_R = 1,$$
$$w_p = 24.6 \times 10^{-8}, \quad w_q = 19.2 \times 10^{-8}, \quad w_r = 34.3 \times 10^{-8} \tag{6}$$

It should be noted that the final adjusted values of the sides and angles, also their standard errors, are in no way dependent on the arbitrary choice made for σ^2; if σ^2 is doubled, all the weights are also doubled, and the standard errors of all functions are left unaltered.   Likewise χ^2 is unaltered.

The solution of the problem proceeds now according to the steps outlined at the beginning of this chapter (Sec. 33).

1st step.   The adjustment must be carried out to enforce the following three geometrical conditions:

$$\frac{\sin P}{p} = \frac{\sin Q}{q} = \frac{\sin R}{r} \tag{7}$$

$$P + Q + R = 180° + \epsilon \tag{8}$$

ϵ being the spherical excess, which, owing to the small size of the triangle, will here be taken as zero.   If it were other than zero, $F_0{}^3$ (Eq. 10) would be altered by the amount ϵ, and the adjusted values of the sides and angles and their standard errors would all be affected in an obvious manner.

For forcing the three conditions, let us set

$$\left. \begin{aligned} F^1(P, Q, R, p, q, r) &= \frac{\sin P}{p} - \frac{\sin Q}{q} \\[2mm] F^2(\text{``}\quad\text{``}\quad\text{``}\quad\text{``}\ \text{``}\ \text{``}) &= \frac{\sin P}{p} - \frac{\sin R}{r} \\[2mm] F^3(\text{``}\quad\text{``}\quad\text{``}\quad\text{``}\ \text{``}\ \text{``}) &= P + Q + R - 180° \end{aligned} \right\} \tag{9}$$

(The number of conditions is 3; i.e., the number ν occurring in Eqs. 3 on page 50 is 3.)

F^1, F^2, F^3 when evaluated do not give zeros, but give the small numbers $F_0{}^1$, $F_0{}^2$, $F_0{}^3$, which by direct substitution are found to be

$$
\left.
\begin{aligned}
F_0{}^1 &= \frac{\sin 51° \, 06'.25}{1723.7} - \frac{\sin 95° \, 04'.5}{2205.4} \\
&= -1.3271 \times 10^{-7} \\
F_0{}^2 &= \frac{\sin 51° \, 06'.25}{1723.7} - \frac{\sin 33° \, 49'.5}{1232.7} \\
&= -0.5416 \times 10^{-7} \\
F_0{}^3 &= 51° \, 06'.25 + 95° \, 04'.5 + 33° \, 49'.5 - 180° \\
&= 0° \, 0'.25 = 7.27 \times 10^{-5} \text{ radian}
\end{aligned}
\right\} \quad (10)
$$

If it had happened that the observations satisfied the conditions exactly, then $F_0{}^1$, $F_0{}^2$, and $F_0{}^3$ would have turned out to be zeros, and the adjusted values would have been identical with those observed. As it is, the observations satisfy the conditions nearly but not exactly, i.e., $F_0{}^1$, $F_0{}^2$, and $F_0{}^3$ are small but not zeros.

$F_0{}^3$ is the amount by which the sum of the angles exceeds 180°. In the simpler problem wherein the sides were not measured (*vide supra*, Sec. 31) it turned out that the least squares adjustment was simply an apportionment of this discrepancy among the three angles in inverse proportion to their weights. Now, however, the sides are involved; wherefore the adjustment, though possibly as reasonable as before, will not be so easy to arrive at. By looking ahead to page 84 we see that, in contrast with the residuals on page 61, the adjustments on the angles will not now be all in the same direction.

Now suppose that for some reason or other we should like to know the weights of

Angle P

The sum $P + Q + R$

The area of the triangle, which may be expressed as $\frac{1}{2}pr \sin Q$

Any number of others could be added (at increased labor) but three will suffice here. For those just named we take the three G functions

$$
G^1 = P, \qquad G^2 = P + Q + R, \qquad G^3 = \tfrac{1}{2}pr \sin Q \quad (11)
$$

2d step. The derivatives of the F functions are

$$
\left.
\begin{aligned}
&F_P{}^1 = \frac{\cos P}{p} && F_P{}^2 = \frac{\cos P}{p} && F_P{}^3 = 1 \\[2mm]
&F_Q{}^1 = -\frac{\cos Q}{q} && F_Q{}^2 = 0 && F_Q{}^3 = 1 \\[2mm]
&F_R{}^1 = 0 && F_R{}^2 = -\frac{\cos R}{r} && F_R{}^3 = 1 \\[2mm]
&F_p{}^1 = -\frac{\sin P}{p^2} && F_p{}^2 = -\frac{\sin P}{p^2} && F_p{}^3 = 0 \\[2mm]
&F_q{}^1 = \frac{\sin Q}{q^2} && F_q{}^2 = 0 && F_q{}^3 = 0 \\[2mm]
&F_r{}^1 = 0 && F_r{}^2 = \frac{\sin R}{r^2} && F_r{}^3 = 0
\end{aligned}
\right\}
\tag{12}
$$

The derivatives of the G functions are

$$
\left.
\begin{aligned}
&G_P{}^1 = 1 && G_P{}^2 = 1 && G_P{}^3 = 0 \\
&\text{The other} && G_Q{}^2 = 1 && G_Q{}^3 = \tfrac{1}{2}pr\cos Q \\
&\text{five derivatives} && G_R{}^2 = 1 && G_R{}^3 = 0 \\
&\text{are zero} && \text{The other} && G_p{}^3 = \tfrac{1}{2}r\sin Q \\
& && \text{three derivatives} && G_q{}^3 = 0 \\
& && \text{are zero} && G_r{}^3 = \tfrac{1}{2}p\sin Q
\end{aligned}
\right\}
\tag{13}
$$

3d step. The nearest numerical approximations that we can produce for these derivatives are found by substituting the observed angles and sides into the expressions just worked out, and these approximations will be more than close enough.

TABLE 1

THE DERIVATIVES (3D STEP)

i	w_i	$\sqrt{w_i}$	$10^6 F_i{}^1$	$10^6 F_i{}^2$	$F_i{}^3$	$G_i{}^1$	$G_i{}^2$	$G_i{}^3$
P	2	1.41	364	364	1	1	1	0
Q	1	1	40.1	0	1	0	1	−93916
R	1	1	0	−674	1	0	1	0
p	$24.6 \cdot 10^{-8}$	$4.96 \cdot 10^{-4}$	−0.262	−0.262	0	0	0	613.9
q	19.2 "	4.38 "	0.205	0	0	0	0	0
r	34.3 "	5.86 "	0	0.366	0	0	0	858.5

4th step. $\sqrt{w}$ is now used as a divisor to form Table 2 from Table 1.

TABLE 2

THE MATRIX FOR THE FORMATION OF THE NORMAL EQUATIONS (4TH STEP)

i	$\dfrac{10^3 F_i^1}{\sqrt{w_i}}$	$\dfrac{10^3 F_i^2}{\sqrt{w_i}}$	$\dfrac{F_i^3}{\sqrt{w_i}}$	$\dfrac{G_i^1}{\sqrt{w_i}}$	$\dfrac{G_i^2}{\sqrt{w_i}}$	$\dfrac{10^{-6} G_i^3}{\sqrt{w_i}}$	Sum s_i
P	0.257	0.257	0.707	0.707	0.707	0	2.635
Q	0.040	0	1	0	1	−0.094	1.946
R	0	−0.674	1	0	1	0	1.326
p	−0.528	−0.528	0	0	0	1.238	0.182
q	0.468	0	0	0	0	0	0.468
r	0	0.625	0	0	0	1.465	2.090
Sum	0.237	−0.320	2.707	0.707	2.707	2.609	8.647$\sqrt{}$

The powers of 10 in Table 2 are chosen with regard to convenience, and to bring the number of decimals to uniformity from column to column, to facilitate the cumulation of squares and cross-products in forming the normal equations (the next step). At this stage one may also cut off superfluous figures, reserving, as a rule, not more than three or four in the largest number occurring in any one column. This often means that some other entries in the same column appear as zeros, but this is as it should be.

5th step. The cumulations of squares and cross-products from the columns of Table 2 provide the coefficients required for the normal equations (Eqs. 2, p. 73). For instance,[1]

$$10^6 \left[\frac{F^1 F^1}{w} \right] = 0.257^2 + 0.040^2 + 0^2 + 0.528^2$$
$$+ 0.468^2 + 0^2 = 0.565 \quad (14)$$

as seen under λ_1 in the normal equations. Also

$$10^3 \left[\frac{F^2 F^3}{w} \right] = 0.257 \times 0.707 + 0 - 0.674 + 0 + 0 + 0$$
$$= -0.492 \quad (15)$$

---

[1] The subscript i will be omitted for convenience occasionally.

as seen under λ_3.   The student should verify the whole set appearing in Table 3.

TABLE 3

THE CUMULATION OF SQUARES AND CROSS-PRODUCTS FROM TABLE 2 FOR THE FORMATION OF THE NORMAL EQUATIONS

$$10^6 \left[\frac{F^1F^1}{w} \right] = 0.565, \quad 10^6 \left[\frac{F^1F^2}{w} \right] = 0.345, \quad 10^3 \left[\frac{F^1F^3}{w} \right] = 0.222$$

$$10^6 \left[\frac{F^2F^2}{w} \right] = 1.190, \quad 10^3 \left[\frac{F^2F^3}{w} \right] = -0.492$$

$$\left[\frac{F^3F^3}{w} \right] = 2.500$$

$$10^3 \left[\frac{F^1G^1}{w} \right] = 0.182, \quad 10^3 \left[\frac{F^1G^2}{w} \right] = 0.222, \quad 10^{-3} \left[\frac{F^1G^3}{w} \right] = -0.657$$

$$10^3 \left[\frac{F^2G^1}{w} \right] = 0.182, \quad 10^3 \left[\frac{F^2G^2}{w} \right] = -0.492, \quad 10^{-3} \left[\frac{F^2G^3}{w} \right] = 0.262$$

$$\left[\frac{F^3G^1}{w} \right] = 0.500, \quad \left[\frac{F^3G^2}{w} \right] = 2.500, \quad 10^{-6} \left[\frac{F^3G^3}{w} \right] = -0.094$$

$$\left[\frac{G^1G^1}{w} \right] = 0.500, \quad \left[\frac{G^2G^2}{w} \right] = 2.500, \quad 10^{-12} \left[\frac{G^3G^3}{w} \right] = 3.687$$

$$\left[\frac{F^1s}{w} \right] = 0.878*$$

$$\left[\frac{F^2s}{w} \right] = 0.994*$$

$$\left[\frac{F^3s}{w} \right] = 5.135*$$

* *Check* (Powers of 10 are disregarded in the sum checks):

$$0.565 + 0.345 + 0.222 + 0.182 + 0.222 - 0.657 = 0.879$$
$$0.345 + 1.190 - 0.492 + 0.182 - 0.492 + 0.262 = 0.995$$
$$0.222 - 0.492 + 2.500 + 0.500 + 2.500 - 0.094 = 5.136$$

The sums formed below the table to provide a check do not agree exactly with the numbers starred in the table, which are formed with the sums s_i of Table 2, but the agreement is within errors of rounding off, whereupon we conclude that the arithmetic in Table 3 is correct, save for the three $[GG/w]$ sums, which must be checked independently, as by repetition in reverse order. The cumulations shown in Table 3 are then entered into Rows I, 2, 3, 4 of the tabular scheme for the normal equations on the two following pages. The numbers entered in the " 1 " column of Rows I, 2, and 3 come from the values of $F_0{}^1$, $F_0{}^2$, and $F_0{}^3$ on page 77 after multiplication by appropriate powers of 10 to produce decimals of the same denomination as the other parts of the normal equations. (The factor 10^{-6} applies to the whole of the " 1 " column.)

The sums at the right of the normal equations are not the numbers 0.879, 0.995, and 5.136 previously seen in the check under Table 3 but are these numbers to which have been added the corresponding entries of the " 1 " column; the normal equations thus start off with a sum column that provides checks at the pivotal points of the solution (note the check marks in Rows II, III, and IV).

The solution proceeds according to the directions under " How obtained." The same system of solution has been seen in simple problems on pages 20, 33, and 66, and will be seen again on page 158 and in Chapter XI.

35. Conclusions from the solution of the normal equations.

1°: From Row IV,

$$S \quad \text{or} \quad \sum wV^2 = 0.042 \cdot 10^{-6}$$

It follows from Eq. 21 on page 28 that

$$\sigma^2(ext) = 0.042 \cdot 10^{-6} \div (6 - 3) = 1.4 \cdot 10^{-8}$$

Since this is only about one-third the prior σ^2 arbitrarily chosen on page 76, we conclude that so far there is no indication of blunders in the observations or recording.

2°: Rows 13, 12, and 11 in the solution on pages 82 and 83 give

$$\lambda_1 = -0.308, \quad \lambda_2 = 0.073, \quad \lambda_3 = 0.071 \cdot 10^{-3}$$

These used in Eq. 12, page 54, give

$$V_P = \tfrac{1}{2}(\lambda_1 F_P{}^1 + \lambda_2 F_P{}^2 + \lambda_3 F_P{}^3) = -0.0000075 \text{ radian}$$
$$= -0.03 \text{ min.}$$

COMBINED SOLUTION OF THE NORMAL EQUATIONS, THE COMPUTATION

		Unknowns			
Row		$10^{-6}\lambda_1$	$10^{-6}\lambda_2$	$10^{-3}\lambda_3$ =	1
I		0.565	0.345	0.222	-0.133×10^{-6}
2			1.190	-0.492	-0.054
3				2.500	0.073
4					0
	Factors				
5	$0.345/0.565 = 0.6106$		-0.211	-0.136	0.081
II			0.979	-0.628	0.027
6	$0.222/0.565 = 0.3929$			-0.087	0.052
7	$0.628/0.979 = 0.6415$			-0.403	0.017
III				2.010	0.142
8	$0.133/0.565 = 0.2354$				-0.031
9	$0.027/0.979 = 0.0276$				-0.001
10	$0.142/2.010 = 0.0706$				-0.010
IV					-0.042
13					$10^{-6}\lambda_1 = -0.308$ ⎫
12					$10^{-6}\lambda_2 = 0.073$ ⎬ $\times10^{-6}$
11					$10^{-3}\lambda_3 = 0.071$ ⎭
14	$0.182/0.565 = 0.3221$				
15	$0.071/0.979 = 0.0725$				
16	$0.474/2.010 = 0.2358$				
IV¹					
17	$0.222/0.565 = 0.3929$				
18	$0.628/0.979 = 0.6415$				
19	$2.010/2.010 = 1$				
IV²					
20	$0.657/0.565 = 1.1623$				
21	$0.663/0.979 = 0.6772$				
22	$0.589/2.010 = 0.2930$				
IV³					

(The powers of 10 written at the tops of the " 1," C^1, C^2,

OF ΣwV^2, AND THE WEIGHTS OF THREE FUNCTIONS

C^1	C^2	C^3	Sum	How obtained
0.182×10^{-3}	0.222×10^{-3}	-0.657×10^3	$0.746\sqrt{}$	
0.182	−0.492	0.262	$0.941\sqrt{}$	
0.500	2.500	−0.094	$5.209\sqrt{}$	
0.500	2.500	3.687	6.573	
−0.111	−0.136	0.401	−0.456	I(−0.6106)
0.071	−0.628	0.663	$0.485\sqrt{}$	(2)+(5)
−0.072	−0.087	0.258	−0.293	I(−0.3929)
0.046	−0.403	0.425	0.311	II(+0.6415)
0.474	2.010	0.589	$5.227\sqrt{}$	(3)+(6)+(7)
0.043	0.052	−0.155	0.176	I(+0.2354)
−0.002	0.017	−0.018	−0.013	II(−0.0276)
−0.033	−0.142	−0.042	−0.369	III(−0.0706)
0.508	2.427	3.472	$6.367\sqrt{}$	(4)+(8)+(9) +(10)
				Subst. from (11) & (12) into I
				Subst. from (11) into II
				III÷2.010
−0.059				I(−0.3221)
−0.005				II(−0.0725)
−0.112				III(−0.2358)
0.324				(4)+(14)+(15) +(16)
	−0.087			I(−0.3929)
	−0.403			II(+0.6415)
	−2.010			III(−1)
	0.000			(4)+(17)+(18) +(19)
		−0.764		I(+1.1623)
		−0.449		II(−0.6772)
		−0.173		III(−0.2930)
		2.302		(4)+(20)+(21) +(22)

and C^3 columns are understood to apply all the way down.)

$$V_Q = \lambda_1 F_Q{}^1 + \lambda_2 F_Q{}^2 + \lambda_3 F_Q{}^3 = 0.0000582 \text{ radian}$$
$$= 0.20 \text{ min.}$$

$$V_R = \lambda_1 F_R{}^1 + \lambda_2 F_R{}^2 + \lambda_3 F_R{}^3 = 0.0000214 \text{ radian}$$
$$= 0.07 \text{ min.}$$

$$V_p = \frac{10^8}{24.6} \left(\lambda_1 F_p{}^1 + \lambda_2 F_p{}^2 + \lambda_3 F_p{}^3 \right) = 0.25 \text{ ft.}$$

$$V_q = \frac{10^8}{19.2} \left(\lambda_1 F_q{}^1 + \lambda_2 F_q{}^2 + \lambda_3 F_q{}^3 \right) = -0.33 \text{ ft.}$$

$$V_r = \frac{10^8}{34.3} \left(\lambda_1 F_r{}^1 + \lambda_2 F_r{}^2 + \lambda_3 F_r{}^3 \right) = 0.08 \text{ ft.}$$

for the six residuals. It is important to note that the numerical values of the derivatives required here are already worked out in Table 1, page 78.

3°: By using these residuals with Eq. 6, page 52, we find that the adjusted value of

Angle P is $51° 06'.25 + 0'.03 = 51° 06'.28$
Angle Q is $95° 04'.5 - 0'.20 = 95° 04'.30$
Angle R is $33° 49'.5 - 0'.07 = 33° 49'.43$
Side p is $1723.7 - 0.25 = 1723.45$ ft.
Side q is $2205.4 + 0.33 = 2205.73$ "
Side r is $1232.7 - 0.08 = 1232.62$ "

Remark. Perfect closure (third condition on p. 76) may be secured by lowering angle R by the trifling amount $0'.01$; the value $33° 49'.42$ so obtained, along with the other adjusted angles and sides just written, will satisfy also the first and second conditions on page 76 to within 1 part in $\frac{1}{2}$ million, which is about all we should ask for. Whenever, as happened here, one or more of the conditions fails owing to cumulated inexactness of rounding off, the computer is at liberty to manipulate the terminal figure of one or more of the residuals, raising or lowering it a unit or so to force the conditions. If not inconvenient, he will ordinarily (as was just done here) select the quantities of least weight for any such manipulations. The amount involved will be small compared with the standard errors of the final results (cf. also p. 229).

4°: The weights and the standard errors of the three G functions (p. 77) are found as follows:

From Row IV[1] the weight of the adjusted angle P is $1/0.324 \cdot 10^{-6} \cdot 10^{+6} = 1/0.324$. In other words, 0.324 is the variance coefficient of angle P. Then with $\sigma^2 = 4.23 \cdot 10^{-8}$ (p. 76), it turns out that the standard error of the adjusted angle P is $(4.23 \cdot 10^{-8} \cdot 0.324)^{\frac{1}{2}} = 1.2 \cdot 10^{-4}$ radian = 0.40 min. So

$$\text{Angle } P = 51° \, 06'.3 \pm 0'.4$$

From Row IV[2] the weight of the adjusted sum of $P + Q + R$ is $1/0$ or ∞, as predicted. Hence the sum of the adjusted angles would be written

$$P + Q + R = 180° \text{ absolutely}$$

From Row IV[3] the weight of the area $\frac{1}{2}pq \sin R$ is $1/2.302 \times 10^{12}$. Its standard error is therefore $(4.23 \times 10^{-8} \times 2.30 \times 10^{12})^{\frac{1}{2}} = 312$ square feet; therefore the adjusted value of

$$\text{The area is } 1058028 \pm 312 \text{ sq. ft.}$$

The area would better be written $(105803 \pm 31) \times 10$ square feet, since not more than two figures of the standard error could be assumed known. In acres,

$$\text{The area} = 24.2890 \pm 0.0072 \text{ acres}$$

The area is found by using the adjusted values of p, q, and R and taking $\frac{1}{2}pq \sin R$. Of course one could as well use $\frac{1}{2}qr \sin P$ or $\frac{1}{2}pr \sin Q$ for the area; one is as good as another.

Exercise 1. Prove by Eq. 9, page 40, that after adjustment the weight of the area is a little more than double its weight before adjustment.

Hint: By using Eq. 9, page 40, we find that

$$\frac{1}{w_{\text{area}}} = \text{area}^2 \left\{ \frac{1}{p^2 w_p} + \frac{1}{q^2 w_q} + \frac{\cot^2 R}{w_R} \right\}$$

$$= 1.12 \times 10^{12} \{1.37 + 1.07 + 2.24\}$$

$$= 5.25 \times 10^{12} \text{ before adjustment}$$

Therefore

$$w_{\text{area}} = 0.19 \times 10^{-12} \text{ (before)}$$

We had

$$w_{\text{area}} = \text{weight of } G^3 = 0.43 \times 10^{-12} \text{ (after)}$$

The result stated follows at once.

Exercise 2. (From L. D. Weld's *Theory of Errors and Least Squares*, Macmillan, 1916.) Take the line AB, on which are located points C and D. The whole line and its segments are measured with the same rule under similar conditions, the results being

$$
\begin{aligned}
X_1 &= AC = 45.10 \text{ cm., mean of 2 observations}\\
X_2 &= AD = 77.96 \text{ "} \qquad \text{" " } 3 \qquad \text{"}\\
X_3 &= CD = 32.95 \text{ "} \qquad \text{" " } 2 \qquad \text{"}\\
X_4 &= CB = 98.36 \text{ "} \qquad \text{" " } 3 \qquad \text{"}\\
X_5 &= DB = 65.55 \text{ "} \qquad \text{" " } 2 \qquad \text{"}\\
X_6 &= AB = 143.55 \text{ "} \qquad \text{" " } 4 \qquad \text{"}
\end{aligned}
$$

FIG. 13. The line and its segments, corresponding to Exercise 2.

Problem. Find the least squares values of the lengths. Take $w_1 = 2$, $w_2 = 3$, $w_3 = 2$, $w_4 = 3$, $w_5 = 2$, $w_6 = 4$.

Conditions:

$$
\begin{aligned}
F^1 &= x_1 + x_3 + x_5 - x_6 = 0\\
F^2 &= x_1 - x_2 + x_3 \qquad\quad = 0\\
F^3 &= \qquad\quad x_3 - x_4 + x_5 = 0
\end{aligned}
$$

Show that the normal equations are as follows.

Row	λ_1	λ_2	λ_3	=	1	Sum
I	21	12	12		$60 \cdot 10^{-2}$	105
2		16	6		108	142
3			16		168	202
4					0	336

Solution:

$$\lambda_1 = -0.1145, \quad \lambda_2 = +0.0952, \quad \lambda_3 = +0.1552$$

Residuals:

$$V_1 = -0.0096 \text{ cm.}$$
$$V_2 = -0.0317 \text{ ``}$$
$$V_3 = +0.0680 \text{ ``}$$
$$V_4 = -0.0517 \text{ ``}$$
$$V_5 = +0.0203 \text{ ``}$$
$$V_6 = +0.0286 \text{ ``}$$

(by applying Eq. 12, p. 54)

Adjusted values:

$$AC = 45.110 \text{ cm.}$$
$$AD = 77.992 \text{ ``}$$
$$CD = 32.882 \text{ ``}$$
$$CB = 98.412 \text{ ``}$$
$$DB = 65.530 \text{ ``}$$
$$AB = 143.522 \text{ ``}$$

(AB actually turns out to be 143.521 cm., but the last decimal is raised one unit to satisfy the first condition. The other two conditions are satisfied perfectly by the adjusted segments.)

Exercise 3. (a) By Row IV in the solution of the normal equations of the preceding exercise, the minimized value of $\sum wV^2$ is 0.0246.

(b) Find $\sum' wV^2$ by direct computations, using the values V_1, V_2, etc., found in the solution. *Ans.* 0.0246.

Exercise 4. Find the standard errors of AB and AD, taking the standard error σ of a single measurement to be 0.05 cm.

Exercise 5. (a) Show that the estimate of σ made from $\sum wV^2$ is $\sigma(ext) = 0.09$.

(b) Show that, with $\sigma = 0.05$, $\chi^2 = $ about 10, and $P(\chi^2) = 0.02$, wherefore we might say that the discordance between the observed lengths of the segments is somewhat larger than one might expect from previous experience.

> *Note:* Since the individual measurements were not recorded, there is no possibility of estimating σ from the original observations; i.e., we have no $\sigma(int)$ to compare with the prior σ and $\sigma(ext)$.

Exercise 6. The three inside edges of a rectangular parallelepiped are measured with calipers and a linear scale; and the volume is measured in cubic units by filling it with mercury, which is afterward poured into a graduated cylinder. The results of a set of observations are as follows:

	Mean	n	Standard deviation
On edges parallel to the x direction,	X_1 (cm.)	n_1	s_1 (cm.)
On edges " " " y direction,	X_2 "	n_2	s_2 "
On edges " " " z direction,	X_3 "	n_3	s_3 "
On the volume,	X_4 (cc.)	n_4	s_4 (cc.)

If randomness has been demonstrated, one may pool the standard deviations of the measurements on the three sides to get an estimate of the standard error of a single observation on a linear measurement. If σ_1 denotes the standard error of a single linear measurement, then one would write

$$\sigma_1^2 \ (est'd) = \frac{n_1 s_1^2 + n_2 s_2^2 + n_3 s_3^2}{n_1 + n_2 + n_3 - 3} \quad \begin{array}{l}\text{(Cf. Eq. 67 in Deming}\\ \text{and Birge, cited on}\\ \text{p. 29.)}\end{array}$$

If $n_1 + n_2 + n_3$ is fairly large (20 or 30), this estimate will be reliable enough. For σ_4, the standard error of a direct determination of volume, one would likewise write

$$\sigma_4^2 \ (est'd) = \frac{n_4 s_4^2}{n_4 - 1}$$

If n_4 is as large as 20 or 30, this estimate will also be reliable enough. After obtaining estimates of σ_1 and σ_4 one would assign weights to the observations X_1, X_2, X_3, and X_4 as follows (see Eqs. 18, p. 26):

$$w_1 = \frac{n_1\sigma^2}{\sigma_1{}^2}$$

$$w_2 = \frac{n_2\sigma^2}{\sigma_1{}^2}$$

$$w_3 = \frac{n_3\sigma^2}{\sigma_1{}^2}$$

$$w_4 = \frac{n_4\sigma^2}{\sigma_4{}^2}$$

σ^2, as in Section 11, is an arbitrary factor of proportionality, the variance of observations of unit weight. If it is set equal to $\sigma_1{}^2$, we should have the convenient system of weights,

$$w_1, \ w_2, \ w_3, \ w_4 = n_1, \ n_2, \ n_3, \ \frac{n_4\sigma_1{}^2}{\sigma_4{}^2}$$

The weights having been settled on, we can proceed. The one and only condition on the adjusted values is that

$$x_4 = x_1x_2x_3$$

whence we put

$$F = x_4 - x_1x_2x_3$$

Suppose we need the standard error of the volume after adjustment; we set

$$G = x_4$$

(a) Show that the one and only normal equation is $L\lambda = F_0$, whence $\lambda = F_0/L$, where

$$L = X_4{}^2 \left\{ \frac{1}{X_1{}^2w_1} + \frac{1}{X_2{}^2w_2} + \frac{1}{X_3{}^2w_3} + \frac{1}{X_4{}^2w_4} \right\}$$

(b) In tabular form, the normal equation for finding λ, S, and the weight of the adjusted volume, is as follows:

Row	λ	=	1	C
I	L		F_0	$1/w_4$
2			0	
3			$-F_0F_0/L$	
II			$-F_0F_0/L$	
4				$-1/Lw_4{}^2$
II^1				$(1/w_4)(1 - 1/Lw_4)$

(*c*) The weight of the adjusted volume is $(1/w_4)(1 - 1/w_4L)$.

(*d*) (The standard error of the adjusted volume)$^2 = \sigma^2(1/w_4)$ $(1 - 1/w_4L)$.

> This variance is smaller than the standard error of the volume before adjustment by the fractional amount $1/Lw_4{}^2$.

(*e*) The minimized sum of the weighted squares of the residuals, S, is $F_0\lambda$.

(*f*) The estimate of σ^2 by external consistency (Sec. 13) is

$$\sigma^2(ext) = \frac{F_0\lambda}{4 - 1}$$

(*g*) What would you say if $\sigma^2(ext)$ were much larger than your assumed value of σ^2, i.e., $P(\chi)$ small?

> *Suggestions:* Edges not parallel; lack of perpendicularity; measurements not so good as initially supposed (i.e., σ_1 or σ_4 too small); just happened to be so.

(*h*) Show that after adjustment the standard error of the first edge is

$$\sigma\sqrt{\frac{1}{w_1}\frac{1 - X_4}{X_1L}}$$

36. Shorter method of computing the weights of a large number of functions.[2]

The theory on which the weights of the three G functions were calculated in Sections 34 and 35 rests on the fact that[3]

$$\frac{1}{(\text{wt. of } G)} =$$

$$\left[\frac{GG}{w}\right] - \left[\frac{F^1G}{w}\right]B' - \left[\frac{F^2G}{w}\right]B'' - \left[\frac{F^3G}{w}\right]B''' \quad (16)$$

[2] To be omitted on first reading; the suggestion is that the reader return to this after a study extending through Section 61.

[3] Gauss, *Theoria Combinationis* (cited in Sec. 13), Art. 29.

where B', B'', and B''' satisfy the equations

$$L_{11}B' + L_{12}B'' + L_{13}B''' = \left[\frac{F^1 G}{w}\right]$$

$$L_{21}B' + L_{22}B'' + L_{23}B''' = \left[\frac{F^2 G}{w}\right] \qquad (17)$$

$$L_{31}B' + L_{32}B'' + L_{33}B''' = \left[\frac{F^3 G}{w}\right]$$

In other words, the auxiliary constants B', B'', and B''' will satisfy the normal equations (Eqs. 2, p. 73) if the " C " column

$$\left[\frac{F^1 G}{w}\right]$$

$$\left[\frac{F^2 G}{w}\right]$$

$$\left[\frac{F^3 G}{w}\right]$$

replaces the " 1 " column.

One may, if he chooses, solve for the Lagrange multipliers, and any set of auxiliary constants B', B'', B''' as well, by first of all calculating the reciprocal matrix

$$\Delta^{-1} = \begin{vmatrix} c_{11} & c_{12} & c_{13} \\ c_{21} & c_{22} & c_{23} \\ c_{31} & c_{32} & c_{33} \end{vmatrix} \qquad \begin{array}{c} \text{(See Exs. 2, 4, and} \\ \text{5 of Sec. 61.)} \end{array} \qquad (18)$$

and then using it to calculate the Lagrange multipliers and the auxiliary multipliers in the manner following—

$$\lambda_1 = F_0{}^1 c_{11} + F_0{}^2 c_{12} + F_0{}^3 c_{13}$$

$$\lambda_2 = F_0{}^1 c_{21} + F_0{}^2 c_{22} + F_0{}^3 c_{23} \qquad (19)$$

$$\lambda_3 = F_0{}^1 c_{31} + F_0{}^2 c_{32} + F_0{}^3 c_{33}$$

$$B' = \left[\frac{F^1G}{w}\right] c_{11} + \left[\frac{F^2G}{w}\right] c_{12} + \left[\frac{F^3G}{w}\right] c_{13}$$

$$B'' = \left[\quad``\quad\right] c_{21} + \left[\quad``\quad\right] c_{22} + \left[\quad``\quad\right] c_{23} \qquad (20)$$

$$B''' = \left[\quad``\quad\right] c_{31} + \left[\quad``\quad\right] c_{32} + \left[\quad``\quad\right] c_{33}$$

The Lagrange multipliers (λ), after being calculated from Eqs. 19, are used in Eqs. 12, page 54, to compute the residuals V_1, $\cdots$, V_n, just as was done on page 81. The auxiliary constants B', B'', and B''' from Eqs. 20 are used in Eq. 16 to find the weight of the function G. It will be noticed that the coefficients multiplying the c coefficients in Eqs. 19 will already be available from the first step, outlined on page 70 and carried out numerically on page 77. The brackets in Eqs. 20 arise by cumulating squares and cross-products from Table 2 of the fourth step (pp. 72 and 79; summed numerically in Table 3 on p. 80). It is not difficult to extend Tables 2 and 3 to take account of a new G function any time it is desired to introduce one.

The work then proceeds rapidly, the reciprocal matrix Δ^{-1} being used over and over in Eqs. 20 for all the G functions. If one is working with a fairly good-sized number of G functions, this scheme will save considerable time over the direct computation illustrated in Section 34.

A distinct advantage of using the auxiliary multipliers is that the reciprocal matrix, once computed, is ready for use any time a new C column is produced, whereas, with the direct solution in Section 34 it is no little trouble to introduce a new C column after a solution has once been carried through.

The three G functions used in Section 34 will serve for an illustration. To calculate the reciprocal matrix Δ^{-1} we take the coefficients of the unknowns in the normal equations on pages 82 and 83, and put the unit matrix on the right of the equality sign, thus starting off with the equations

$$
\begin{aligned}
0.565 \cdot 10^{-6}x + 0.345 \cdot 10^{-6}y + 0.222 \cdot 10^{-3}z &= 1, 0, 0 \\
0.345 \cdot 10^{-6}x + 1.190 \cdot 10^{-6}y - 0.492 \cdot 10^{-3}z &= 0, 1, 0 \qquad (21)\\
0.222 \cdot 10^{-6}x - 0.492 \cdot 10^{-6}y + 2.500 \cdot 10^{-3}z &= 0, 0, 1
\end{aligned}
$$

The letters x, y, z designate the three unknowns that are to be solved for. Since there are three constant columns on the right, there will be three different solutions. The simplest way to obtain them would be to follow the regular routine for solving normal equations, as illustrated in Sections 34 and 61. However, one unfamiliar with that procedure may make three sepa-

rate solutions. First, one would use the constant column $\begin{matrix} 1 \\ 0 \\ 0 \end{matrix}$.

By any method of solution whatever he would obtain

$$x = 2.458 \times 10^6$$
$$y = -0.875 \times 10^6$$
$$z = -0.391 \times 10^3$$

Second, he would use the constant column $\begin{matrix} 0 \\ 1 \\ 0 \end{matrix}$ and find

$$x = -0.874 \times 10^6$$
$$y = 1.226 \times 10^6$$
$$z = 0.319 \times 10^3$$

Third, he would use the constant column $\begin{matrix} 0 \\ 0 \\ 1 \end{matrix}$ and find

$$x = -0.390 \times 10^6$$
$$y = 0.319 \times 10^6$$
$$z = 0.498 \times 10^3$$

The reciprocal matrix is simply a convenient way of filing these results systematically. It is written like this:

$$\Delta^{-1} = \begin{vmatrix} 2.458 \cdot 10^6 & -0.874 \cdot 10^6 & -0.390 \cdot 10^6 \\ -0.875 \cdot 10^6 & 1.226 \cdot 10^6 & 0.319 \cdot 10^6 \\ -0.391 \cdot 10^3 & 0.319 \cdot 10^3 & 0.498 \cdot 10^3 \end{vmatrix} \quad (22)$$

The occasional failure of symmetry in the third decimal place comes from not carrying more figures; but what we have is good enough. Supposing that the Lagrange multipliers have not been worked out, we should next compute them from Eqs. 19 as follows:

$$\left. \begin{aligned} \lambda_1 &= -0.133 \cdot 2.458 + 0.054 \cdot 0.875 - 0.073 \cdot 0.391 = -0.309 \\ \lambda_2 &= + \text{ ``} \quad 0.874 - \text{ ``} \quad 1.226 + \text{ ``} \quad 0.319 = \phantom{-}0.073 \\ 10^3 \lambda_3 &= + \text{ ``} \quad 0.390 - \text{ ``} \quad 0.319 + \text{ ``} \quad 0.498 = 0.071 \end{aligned} \right\} \quad (23)$$

These agree well enough with the values -0.308, 0.073, and 0.071 already found in Section 35 (conclusion $2°$, p. 81).

The chief aim at present is to compute the auxiliary constants B', B'', B''' for each of the three G functions of Section 34. Going back to Table 3 in Section 34 for the coefficients needed for Eqs. 20, we find that

For G^1

$$
\left.
\begin{aligned}
B' &= 10^3\{+0.182 \cdot 2.458 - 0.182 \cdot 0.875 - 0.500 \cdot 0.391\} \\
   &= 0.0933 \cdot 10^3 \\
B'' &= 10^3\{-0.182 \cdot 0.874 + 0.182 \cdot 1.226 + 0.500 \cdot 0.319\} \\
    &= 0.224 \cdot 10^3 \\
B''' &= \quad\; -0.182 \cdot 0.390 + 0.182 \cdot 0.319 + 0.500 \cdot 0.498 \\
     &= 0.236
\end{aligned}
\right\} \quad (24)
$$

These values used in Eq. 16 give

$$
\frac{1}{\text{wt.}} \text{ of } G^1 = 0.500 - 0.182 \cdot 0.0933 - 0.182 \cdot 0.224 - 0.500 \cdot 0.236
$$
$$
= 0.324 \tag{25}
$$

That is, the weight of $G^1 = 1/0.324$, in agreement with conclusion $4°$ in Section 35, page 85.

For G^2

$$
\left.
\begin{aligned}
B' &= 10^3\{+0.222 \cdot 2.458 + 0.492 \cdot 0.875 - 2.500 \cdot 0.391\} \\
   &= 0.00133 \cdot 10^3 \\
B'' &= 10^3\{-0.222 \cdot 0.874 - 0.492 \cdot 1.226 + 2.500 \cdot 0.319\} \\
    &= 0.00028 \cdot 10^3 \\
B''' &= \quad\; -0.222 \cdot 0.390 - 0.492 \cdot 0.319 + 2.500 \cdot 0.498 \\
     &= 1.0015
\end{aligned}
\right\} \quad (26)
$$

These used in Eq. 16 give

$$
\frac{1}{\text{wt.}} \text{ of } G^2 = 2.500 - 0.222 \cdot 0.00133 - 0.492 \cdot 0.00028 - 2.500 \cdot 1.0015
$$
$$
= -0.004 \tag{27}
$$

Since weights can not be negative, we may suppose that this negative result arises from not carrying enough figures. The lowest possible result, if all figures had been carried, would be 0. Since we know what the result ought to be, we shall call it 0, whereupon the weight of G^2 is infinity, as is already known (conclusion 4°, Sec. 35, p. 85).

For G^3

As an exercise, the student should calculate B', B'', and B''' for G^3 in like manner, obtaining

$$\left. \begin{array}{l} B' = -1.808 \cdot 10^9 \\ B'' = 0.865 \cdot 10^9 \\ B''' = 0.293 \cdot 10^6 \end{array} \right\} \tag{28}$$

whereupon

$$\frac{1}{\text{wt.}} \text{ of } G^3 = 10^{12}\{3.687 + 0.657 \cdot 1.808 + 0.262 \cdot 0.865 - 0.094 \cdot 0.293\}$$

$$= 2.300 \cdot 10^{12} \tag{29}$$

in agreement with conclusion 4° in Section 35 (p. 85).

> *Remark.* The number of auxiliary constants B', B'', B''', etc., in Eq. 16 is equal to the number ν of conditions, i.e., the number of F functions. This is also the number of Lagrange multipliers (λ), the number of equations in Eqs. 21, and the order of the reciprocal matrix. In contrast, the number of G functions whose weights are wanted may be any whatever, smaller or larger than the number of F functions.

CHAPTER VII

ADJUSTING SAMPLE FREQUENCIES TO EXPECTED MARGINAL TOTALS

37. Statement of the problem. In social and economic surveys that are carried out by sampling, it is sometimes desirable to adjust the sample frequencies, or to adjust certain sample ratios, to make them agree with certain corresponding totals or ratios that are known from other sources. This happens, e.g., in the work of the Census: there is a complete count of certain characteristics for the individuals in the population, but in consideration of efficiency in time and costs, data on some characteristics are collected on a sample basis in the first place, and the tabulations of these sample data need to be adjusted to the complete count. Moreover, many of the cross-tabulations or joint distributions of population characteristics that have been obtained on a complete count are limited to a sample when the data are processed in the Washington office, and these cross-tabulations likewise need to be adjusted. The sample, except in extremely fine classifications, is entirely adequate for purposes of action (the only purpose of taking any survey in the first place). The data of the sample are usually published as *estimates* of what would have been obtained by tabulating the characteristics for the entire population instead of only a sample thereof. This means that the sample is to be *adjusted* to certain totals that are known from other sources (as a complete count).

The situation may be as shown in Fig. 14 in parallel tables for the universe and for the sample. For the universe, the marginal totals $N_i.$ and $N_{.j}$ are known from the complete count, but not the individual cell frequencies N_{ij}; for the sample, however, tabulation gives both the sample marginal totals $n_i.$ and $n_{.j}$, and the sample cell frequencies n_{ij}. After adjustment, the marginal totals of

96

the (adjusted) sample and complete count will agree. The problem is to write in the cell frequencies of the universe, with the aid of the sample, preserving the marginal totals that are fixed by knowledge of the universe. It is the object of this chapter to show schemes for performing such adjustments.

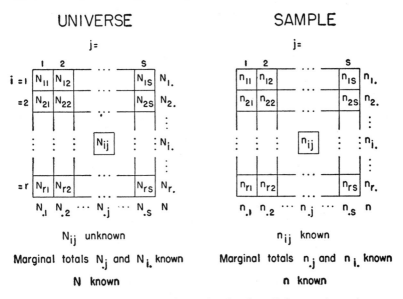

FIG. 14. Showing the system of notation for the cell frequencies and marginal totals of the universe and the sample in the two-dimensional problem.

38. Cell frequencies and sampling errors. A statistical table shows the frequencies of occurrence of the various members of subclasses within a population or universe, and is made up of cells, one for each subclass. A two-dimensional universe is formed by the crossing of two classifications, as depicted schematically in Fig. 14. An example is contained in Table 1, page 107. The title of the table ordinarily describes the universe. The box headings over the columns define various mutually exclusive classes according to one system of classification, and the stub does likewise for some other system of classification. A member of the universe will belong to one of the classes that are defined in the heading, and at the same time it will belong to one of the classes that are defined in the stub; it is said to be a member of the subclass that is defined by the combination or cross-classification of two particular classes described respectively in heading and stub. That is to say, a member of the universe must lie in one column or another, and at the same time it must lie in one row or another; in the table it lies in the space common to a particular column and a particular row. This space is called a *cell*. The number written in the cell is a *cell frequency* and it shows how many members of this particular subclass were recorded in the enumeration of the universe, by sample or complete count. For instance, in Table 1, in the cell designated by the combined ages 14 and 15 (shown in the heading), for the state of New Hampshire (shown in the stub), is recorded a sample frequency of 395. When the tabulation is prepared by crossing three classifications, the result is a three-dimensional table. A three-dimensional table is usually printed as a set of two-dimensional tables, rather than as a single table. These single two-dimensional tables all show the same heading and stub, and each one represents the members of one class of the third classification, as the heading will show. A three-dimensional universe is depicted schematically in Fig. 15. Similarly, one may have four-, five-, or *n*-dimensional tables. The sum obtained by adding the frequencies of an entire row or column is a *marginal total* or *rim total*, although it could well be called a class total.

When the data for the table arise from sampling, the frequencies (numbers) obtained are smaller than if the coverage had been complete. For instance, if the sample is a so-called 5 percent sample, the numbers in the table will be only about 5 percent of what they would have been had a complete count been taken. It is not possible to perform the sampling in such a way that the sample frequencies are *exactly* 5 percent of what would be obtained on a complete count. If the sampling were so carried out, it would be sufficient merely to multiply every cell frequency by 20, and every marginal total also by 20. (The number 20 is spoken of as the sampling ratio, the reciprocal of 5 percent.) But because of sampling errors, and possibly also because of certain biases that inevitably enter any survey, the sample frequencies will not be just 1/20th of the frequencies that would be shown by a complete count.   For the convenience of the user of a table, these sample frequencies are sometimes adjusted to some or all of the

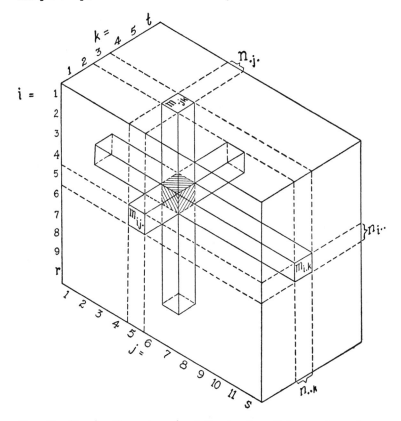

FIG. 15. Showing the system of notation for the cell frequencies and marginal totals in the three-dimensional sample.   The cell shown shaded is designated by the indices ijk.   The sample frequency falling in this cell is n_{ijk}.   The corresponding adjusted deflated frequency is m_{ijk}, and the adjusted inflated frequency is M_{ijk}.   Some of the tube and slice totals are indicated.

marginal totals that happen to be known from other sources, as by a complete count.   This is a convenience to the user, because after adjustment the identical marginal totals are found in tables having the same marginal specifications. Without adjustment, the frequencies might be alike enough for purposes of action, but perhaps not close enough for identification. The known marginal totals that are used in an adjustment are spoken of as *controls*, or *control totals*.

The adjustment is more than a convenience to the user; it diminishes the sampling variance to some extent; the more controls the smaller the sampling variance of the adjusted frequencies. (See the exercise at the end of Ch. V.) As a practical matter, however, this diminishing of the sampling variance should not be overemphasized, because biases and other difficulties may have a much greater effect than the sampling errors.

In the work of the Census not all sample tables are adjusted to all the known marginal totals. Even with the short cuts that will be described here, and which are more fully described elsewhere,[1,2] it may be more important to publish the table at once, after merely multiplying the sample results by the sampling ratio, rather than to wait for adjustments to be made. One of the main advantages of sampling is quick processing, and this is particularly important for government planning in times of economic and social stress, in which the delay of only the brief time required for adjustment may not be advisable.

39. Nature of the adjustment. It will perhaps be realized by now that the problems to be taken up in this chapter are similar to the geometric ones in the last two chapters — similar in that the conditions imposed on the adjusted values are rigorous, not involving adjustable parameters. The same procedure for enforcing the least squares criterion will be found to give us an answer in this problem, as it did in the geometric problems. Here, however, short cuts will be described, which will greatly diminish the amount of computational labor and expense.

---

[1] W. Edwards Deming and Frederick F. Stephan, "On a least squares adjustment of a sample frequency table when the expected marginal totals are known," *Annals of Mathematical Statistics*, vol. XI, No. 4, December 1940: pp. 427–444.

[2] Frederick F. Stephan, "An iterative method of adjusting sample frequency tables when expected marginal totals are known," *Annals of Mathematical Statistics*, vol. XIII, No. 2, June 1942: pp. 166–178.

40. A closer look at the problem. In estimating any cell frequency of the universe, such as N_{ij}, three possibilities present themselves: from the sample one may make an estimate from the sampling ratio of the ith row alone, another from the sampling ratio of the jth column alone, and still another from the over-all sampling ratio N/n. Specifically, the three estimates would be $n_{ij}N_i./n_i.$, $n_{ij}N._j/n._j$, and $n_{ij}N/n$. These being simple multiplications of the observed cell frequency n_{ij} by three sampling ratios, viz., the sampling ratio $N_i./n_i.$ in the ith row, $N._j/n._j$ in the jth column, and the over-all sampling ratio, N/n. Because of sampling errors, these three adjustments will not be identical except by accident, and though any of them by itself may be considered accurate enough, still, if the whole $r \times s$ table of universe cell frequencies were estimated by any one of these three adjustments, the marginal totals would not come out equal to the known values. This chapter presents three rapid methods of adjustment, which in effect combine all three of the estimates just mentioned, and at the same time enforce agreement with the marginal totals. These methods can be extended to varying degrees of cross-tabulation in three dimensions.

Any method of adjustment must provide as its end product a set of adjusted frequencies that will satisfy the controls provided by the known marginal totals. In any problem of adjustment where the controls are intricate (many conditions), and where the adjustments are carried out by the hundreds and thousands, as they are in the Census, it is necessary to have a method that is straightforward and self-checking; this is particularly important in three-way tabulations, where in one possible situation (Case VII in reference 1) the adjustment in one cell must be balanced by adjustments in at least seven others. It turns out, fortunately, that methods of the kind required in mass production can be devised (Secs. 45, 46, 48, and 49).

41. The least squares requirement. By the method of least squares one would enforce the controls (conditions), and at the same time minimize the sum

$$S = \sum \frac{1}{n_i} (m_i - n_i)^2 \tag{1}$$

n_i stands for the *observed* frequency in the ith cell, and m_i the adjusted sample frequency therein. n_i is found in the sample survey, and m_i arises in the adjustment.   Here the denominator n_i is taken as the reciprocal of the weight of the ith cell.   The bigger the frequency, the bigger the average sampling error (absolute error, not proportionate error), and accordingly the smaller the weight.   It might be argued that the weight should be taken inversely proportional to m_i rather than n_i, but, if the sampling is accurate enough for the purpose intended, it will make little difference which is used.   Strictly, in random sampling, the reciprocal of the weight of n_{ij} is $np_{ij}q_{ij}$, which is nearly equal to np_{ij}, where p and q have their usual connotations.   But since factors proportional to the weights may be substituted for them, it is sufficient to use n_{ij} as the reciprocal of the weight in cell ij, since the values of q_{ij} do not usually vary much over the table.   In stratified sampling, the weights are still closely inversely proportional to n_{ij}.

42. The two-dimensional problem.   Suppose that the data on two characteristics (e.g., age and highest grade of school completed) are obtained for each member of a universe of N individuals, but that tabulations of the complete data provide either

Case I.   Only one set of marginal totals, $N_1., N_2., \cdots, N_r.$;

or

Case II.   Both sets of marginal totals, viz., $N_1., N_2., \cdots, N_r.,$ and $N_{.1}, N_{.2}, \cdots, N_{.s}$ (See Fig. 14.)

The nature of the tabulations is presumed such that it is not feasible (too expensive) to count the numbers N_{ij} in the cells, as would be done if one character were crossed with the other in tabulation.   Suppose, however, that in a sample of n individuals selected in a random manner from the universe, the two characters are crossed with each other, so that not only all the $s + r$ marginal totals $n_{.1}, \cdots, n_r.$ of the sample are known, but also every one of the numbers $n_{ij} (i = 1, 2, \cdots, r; j = 1, 2, \cdots, s)$.   The problem is to estimate the unknown frequencies N_{ij} in the cells of the universe.   This will be done by first finding the calculated or adjusted sample frequencies m_{ij} and then inflating them by the sampling ratio N/n.

For the least squares solution we seek those values of m_{ij} that minimize[3]

$$S = \sum \frac{1}{n_{ij}} (m_{ij} - n_{ij})^2 \qquad (2)$$

wherein the m_{ij} are subjected to conditions of Case I or Case II.

Case I: One set of marginal totals known. Assume $N_{1.}, N_{2.}, \cdots,$ $N_{r.}$ to be known. Then we require the marginal adjustments

$$\sum_j m_{ij} = m_{i.} \qquad i = 1, 2, \cdots, r \qquad (3)$$

These r equations constitute r conditions on the adjusted m_{ij}, corresponding to Eqs. 3 of Chapter IV, page 50. Assuming that the adjusted values of the m_{ij} have been found, let each take on a small variation δm_{ij}; then the differentials of Eqs. 2 and 3 show that

$$\tfrac{1}{2}\, \delta S = \sum \frac{m_{ij} - n_{ij}}{n_{ij}} \delta m_{ij} = 0 \quad \text{(one equation)} \qquad (4)$$

$$\sum_j \delta m_{ij} = 0 \qquad i = 1, 2, \cdots, r \quad \text{(r equations)} \qquad (5)$$

Multiply now Eq. 5i by the arbitrary Lagrange multiplier $-\lambda_i$, and add Eqs. 4 and 5 to obtain

$$\sum \left\{ \frac{m_{ij} - n_{ij}}{n_{ij}} - \lambda_i \right\} \delta m_{ij} = 0 \quad \text{(one equation)} \qquad (6)$$

By the same argument that was advanced in Section 27, page 54, one may now set each brace equal to zero. The r Lagrange multipliers are then no longer arbitrary, but each must satisfy the resulting relation

$$m_{ij} = n_{ij}(1 + \lambda_i) \qquad (7)$$

[3] The sign $\sum$ will denote summation over all possible cells, unless otherwise noted. $\sum_i$ will denote summation over all values of i, and similarly for an inferior j or k. The dot in $n_{.j}$ will signify the result of summing the n_{ij} over all values of i in the jth column.

The adjusted frequencies m_{ij} can be computed at once as soon as the λ_i are found. To evaluate them one may rewrite the conditions (3) using the right-hand member of Eq. 7 for m_{ij}, obtaining

$$m_{i.} = n_{i.}(1 + \lambda_i) \tag{8}$$

Another way to arrive at this same relation is to sum each member of Eq. 7 in the ith row. However obtained, λ_i is now known, since $m_{i.}$ and $n_{i.}$ are known, and in fact Eq. 7 now reduces to

$$m_{ij} = n_{ij} \frac{m_{i.}}{n_{i.}} \tag{9}$$

The adjustment is thus a simple proportionate one by rows, the cells in any one row all being raised or lowered by the proportionate adjustment in the row total. Case I thus amounts to r independent one-dimensional proportionate adjustments, one for each row; and any one or all may be carried out, as desired. This result can be obtained by a simpler approach but is presented in this way for consistency with later cases.

The minimized sum of squares may be computed directly, or from the row totals by seeing that

$$S = \sum_i \frac{1}{n_{i.}} (m_{i.} - n_{i.})^2 \tag{10}$$

The term $(m_{i.} - n_{i.})^2/n_{i.}$ for the ith row may be considered separately, and used as χ^2 with $s - 1$ degrees of freedom, or all rows may be combined into the minimized S as given in Eq. 10, and used as χ^2 with $r(s - 1)$ degrees of freedom.

Case II: Both sets of marginal totals known. Here the adjusted cell frequencies must satisfy not only conditions (3) but also

$$\sum_i m_{ij} = m_{.j} \qquad j = 1, 2, \cdots, s - 1 \tag{11}$$

there being now a total of $r + s - 1$ conditions. In both cases,

$$m_{i.} = N_{i.} \frac{n}{N} \tag{12}$$

$$m_{.j} = N_{.j} \frac{n}{N} \tag{13}$$

In other words, $m_{i.}$ and $m_{.j}$ are the deflated marginal totals, i.e., $N_{i.}$ and $N_{.j}$ divided by the actual sampling ratio N/n. The $m_{i.}$ and $m_{.j}$ are not independent, because

$$N_{.1} + N_{.2} + \cdots + N_{.s} = N_1. + N_2. + \cdots + N_r. = N \quad (14)$$

It is for this reason that if i runs through all r values in Eq. 3, then j can run through only $s - 1$ in Eq. 11. A similar equation also exists for the marginal totals of the sample, namely,

$$n_{.1} + n_{.2} + \cdots + n_{.s} = n_1. + n_2. + \cdots + n_r. = n \quad (15)$$

Solution of the two-dimensional Case II. In addition to Eq. 5 we now have also

$$\sum_i \delta m_{ij} = 0 \qquad j = 1, 2, \cdots, s - 1 \quad (16)$$

which comes by differentiating Eqs. 11. By addition of Eqs. 4, 5, and 16, after multiplying Eq. 5i by $-\lambda_i$ and Eq. 16j by $-\mu_j$, we obtain

$$\sum \left\{ \frac{m_{ij} - n_{ij}}{n_{ij}} - \lambda_i - \mu_j \right\} \delta m_{ij} = 0 \quad (17)$$

Equating each brace to zero, as before, we find that

$$m_{ij} = n_{ij}(1 + \lambda_i + \mu_j) \quad (18)$$

wherein μ_s is to be counted 0. The adjustment is now no longer proportionate by rows, but involves every cell.

To evaluate the Lagrange multipliers in Eq. 18 we may sum the two members downward and across in Fig. 14 and obtain the $r + s - 1$ normal equations

$$\left. \begin{array}{l} n_i.\lambda_i + \sum_j n_{ij}\mu_j = m_i. - n_i. \quad i = 1, 2, \cdots, r \\ \sum_i n_{ij}\lambda_i + n_{.j}\mu_j = m_{.j} - n_{.j} \quad j = 1, 2, \cdots, s - 1 \end{array} \right\} \quad (19)$$

These can be reduced for numerical computation. The top row solved for λ_i gives

$$\lambda_i = \frac{1}{n_{i.}} \{ m_i. - \sum_j n_{ij}\mu_j \} - 1 \quad (20)$$

whereupon by substitution into the bottom row of Eqs. 19 we arrive at the $s - 1$ normal equations.

μ_1	μ_2	$\cdots$	μ_{s-1}	$=$	1
$n_{.1} - \sum_i \dfrac{n_{i1}n_{i1}}{n_{i.}}$	$-\sum_i \dfrac{n_{i1}n_{i2}}{n_{i.}}$	$\cdots$	$-\sum_i \dfrac{n_{i1}n_{i,s-1}}{n_{i.}}$	$m_{.1} - \sum_i \dfrac{n_{i1}m_{i.}}{n_{i.}}$	
	$n_{.2} - \sum_i \dfrac{n_{i2}n_{i2}}{n_{i.}}$	$\cdots$	$-\sum_i \dfrac{n_{i2}n_{i,s-1}}{n_{i.}}$	$m_{.2} - \sum_i \dfrac{n_{i2}m_{i.}}{n_{i.}}$	
		$\vdots$	$\vdots$	$\vdots$	(21)
			$n_{.s-1} - \sum_i \dfrac{n_{i,s-1}n_{i,s-1}}{n_{i.}}$	$m_{.s-1} - \sum_i \dfrac{n_{i,s-1}m_{i.}}{n_{i.}}$	
				0	

Because of symmetry in the coefficients, those below the diagonal are not shown, indeed, in the systematic computation already shown in Section 33 (p. 73), they are not used. The 0 in the bottom row is appended for the computation of the minimized S, if desired. The number of Lagrange multipliers to be solved for directly is $s - 1$, and the remaining ones come by substitution into Eq. 20, μ_s being counted 0.

A simple procedure for calculating the coefficients in the normal equations (21) is to set up a preparatory table by dividing each n_{ij} in the ith row by $\sqrt{n_{i.}}$; also to write down $m_{i.}/\sqrt{n_{i.}}$ for that row, for use on the right-hand side of the normal equations (compare Tables 1 and 2). In machine calculation the constant divisor $\sqrt{n_{i.}}$ would be left on the keyboard until the entire ith row is divided; or, if reciprocal multiplication is preferred, the multiplier $1/\sqrt{n_{i.}}$ would be left on the keyboard. From this preparatory table, the cumulation of squares and cross-products in the vertical gives the required summations for the coefficients. The sum check would be applied in the usual manner.

43. A numerical example of the two-dimensional Case II. The fact is that in practice one need not bother about forming and solving the normal equations because they will be displaced by a simplifying iterative procedure, to be explained in a later section. For illustration, however, we may do an example both ways, first using the normal equations and the adjustment (18), later on accomplishing the same results by the quicker method.

We may start with the unitalicized numbers in the 4×6 array of Table 1, assuming these to be the sampling frequencies n_{ij} to be adjusted. Actually, they were obtained by deflating 1/20th (for a supposed 5 percent sample) the New England age $\times$ state table on p. 1108 of vol. 2 of the *Fifteenth Census of the U. S.*, 1930, then varying the deflated values by chance with Tippett's numbers to

TABLE 1

A TABLE OF SAMPLE FREQUENCIES, A 5 PERCENT SAMPLE OF NATIVE WHITE
PERSONS OF NATIVE WHITE PARENTAGE ATTENDING SCHOOL, BY AGE BY STATE:
NEW ENGLAND, 1930

(*The adjusted frequency* m_{ij} *in each cell is shown italicized just below the corresponding sample frequency* n_{ij})

Age			7 to 13	14 & 15	16 & 17	18 to 20	
		$j =$	1	2	3	4	$n_i.$
		$\mu_j =$	0.0118	0.0149	0.0012	0	$m_i.$
State	i	λ_i					
Maine	1	−0.0146	3623	781	557	313	5274
			3613	*781*	*550*	*308*	*5252*
New Hampshire	2	−0.0003	1570	395	251	155	2371
			1588	*401*	*251*	*155*	*2395*
Vermont	3	0.0234	1553	419	264	116	2352
			1608	*435*	*270*	*119*	*2432*
Massachusetts	4	−0.0162	10538	2455	1706	1160	15859
			10492	*2452*	*1680*	*1141*	*15766*
Rhode Island	5	−0.0230	1681	353	171	154	2359
			1662	*350*	*167*	*150*	*2330*
Connecticut	6	−0.0034	3882	857	544	339	5622
			3915	*867*	*543*	*338*	*5662*
		$n._j$	22847	5260	3493	2237	33837
		$m._j$	*22877*	*5285*	*3462*	*2213*	*33837*

The adjusted frequencies m_{ij} (italicized) are rounded off, hence when summed may occasionally disagree a unit or so with the expected marginal totals (also italicized). The latter arise by deflation from the universe rather than by direct addition of the m_{ij}. λ_i and μ_j are found in the solution of Eqs. 20 and 21.

get fictitious sampling frequencies n_{ij}. The italicized entries in Table 1 represent the final (adjusted) frequencies m_{ij}, and it is these that we now set out to get. We start off with the sampling frequencies n_{ij} and the known marginal totals $m_{.1}$, $m_{.2}$, etc., where $m_{i.} = N_{i.}n/N$, $m_{.j} = N_{.j}n/N$, as in Eqs. 12 and 13. The Lagrange multipliers shown along the left-hand and top borders arise in the calculations now to be undertaken.

TABLE 2

EACH SAMPLE FREQUENCY IN TABLE 1 DIVIDED BY THE CORRESPONDING $\sqrt{n_i}$.

This operation would ordinarily be done a row at a time.

	$j =$				$m_{i.}/\sqrt{n_i}$	Sum
	1	2	3	4		
$i = 1$	49.89	10.75	7.67	4.31	72.32	144.94
2	32.24	8.11	5.15	3.18	49.19	97.87
3	32.02	8.64	5.44	2.39	50.15	98.64
4	83.68	19.49	13.55	9.21	125.19	251.12
5	34.61	7.27	3.52	3.17	47.97	96.54
6	51.77	11.43	7.26	4.52	75.51	150.49
Sum	284.21	65.69	42.59	26.78	420.33	839.60

Table 2 is the preparatory table, advised at the close of the last section. It is derived from Table 1 by dividing the ith row of sample frequencies by $\sqrt{n_{i.}}$. For example, the entry 8.64 in the cell $i = 3$, $j = 2$ comes by dividing 419 by $\sqrt{2352}$, 419 being the entry in the cell of the same indices in Table 1, and 2352 being the sum of the third row. The sums at the bottom and right-hand side are for checking the formation of the normal equations. The cumulations of squares and cross-products along the vertical give the summations required for the normal equations (Eqs. 21), which now appear numerically as Eqs. 22.

Row	μ_1	μ_2	μ_3	=	1	
I	7413	−3549	−2354		3197×10^{-2}	
2		4441	−544		2356	(22)
3			3129		−3222	
4					0	

Performing the solution by any favorite procedure one will obtain

$$\mu_1 = 0.01182 \qquad \mu_2 = 0.01490 \qquad \mu_3 = 0.00119 \qquad (23)$$

whereupon by substitution into Eq. 20 comes

$$\left. \begin{array}{ll} \lambda_1 = -0.0146 & \lambda_4 = -0.0162 \\ \lambda_2 = -0.0003 & \lambda_5 = -0.0230 \\ \lambda_3 = +0.0234 & \lambda_6 = -0.0034 \end{array} \right\} \qquad (24)$$

The next step is to compute the m_{ij} by Eq. 18.   Table 1 is now bordered with the Lagrange multipliers for a convenient arrangement of the factors required, and the calculation is completed.   It will be noted that, for example,

$$m_{32} = 419(1 + 0.0234 + 0.0149) = 435 \qquad (25)$$

The m_{ij} thus calculated are shown italicized in Table 1.   The marginal totals, found by adding the m_{ij} just calculated, do not agree exactly everywhere with the expected totals, because of rounding off to integers: the errors of closure, however, are slight, and it is a simple matter to raise or lower some of the larger cells by a unit or two to force exact satisfaction of the conditions, if this is desired.   (Compare with the triangle problem on p. 84.)

44. The three-dimensional problem.   Here the N cards of the universe are sorted and counted for one and perhaps a second and third characteristic, and possibly crossed by pairs in various combinations (Cases I–VII).   The sample of n, however, is crossed by all three characteristics, which is to say that the cell frequencies n_{ijk} are all known (refer to Fig. 15).   As before, the adjusted frequencies are required.

Case I: One set of slice totals known. Assume the slice totals $N_{1..}, N_{2..}, \cdots, N_{r..}$ to be known; the conditions are then

$$\sum_{jk} m_{ijk} = m_{i..} = N_{i..} \frac{n}{N}, \qquad i = 1, 2, \cdots, r \qquad (26)$$

being r in number.   The summation to be minimized here is

$$S = \sum \frac{(m_{ijk} - n_{ijk})^2}{n_{ijk}} \qquad (27)$$

being similar to that in Eq. 2, except that now there are three indices to be summed over instead of two.   Following a procedure similar to that used before, we differentiate Eqs. 26 and 27 and introduce the r Lagrange multipliers $\lambda_{i..}$ with Eq. 26.   The steps are identical with those of the two-dimensional Case I, and the result is at once

$$m_{ijk} = n_{ijk}(1 + \lambda_{i..}) = n_{ijk} \frac{m_{i..}}{n_{i..}} \qquad (28)$$

This adjustment, like that shown by Eq. 9, is a simple proportionate one, but this time by slices rather than by columns.   All cell frequencies having the same i index are raised or lowered in the same proportion.

Case II: Two sets of slice totals known.   Here, in addition to the slice totals of Case I we know also

$$N_{.1.}, N_{.2.}, \cdots, N_{.s.}$$

whence arise the $s - 1$ additional conditions

$$\sum_{ik} m_{ijk} = m_{.j.} = N_{.j.} \frac{n}{N}, \quad j = 1, 2, \cdots, s - 1 \qquad (29)$$

Using the Lagrange multipliers $\lambda_{.j.}$ here, and $\lambda_{i..}$ with Eq. 26 as before, we find that

$$m_{ijk} = n_{ijk}(1 + \lambda_{i..} + \lambda_{.j.}) \qquad (30)$$

in which $\lambda_{.s.}$ is to be counted zero.   This adjustment is proportionate by tubes, the ratio m_{ijk}/n_{ijk} being constant along the ijth tube and in fact equal to $m_{ij.}/n_{ij.}$, independent of k.   Unfortunately we do not here know the face totals $m_{ij.}$ and are unable to make use of the proportionality as we shall in Case IV.

To solve for the $r + s - 1$ Lagrange multipliers we sum the members of Eq. 30 over j and then over i and arrive at the normal equations

$$\left. \begin{aligned} n_{i..}\lambda_{i..} + \sum_j n_{ij.}\lambda_{.j.} &= m_{i..} - n_{i..}, \quad i = 1, 2, \cdots, r \\ \sum_i n_{ij.}\lambda_{i..} + n_{.j.}\lambda_{.j.} &= m_{.j.} - n_{.j.}, \quad j = 1, 2, \cdots, s - 1 \end{aligned} \right\} \quad (31)$$

These can be reduced to $s - 1$ equations in precisely the same way that Eqs. 19 were reduced, but, because of the great advantage of the iterative process to come further on, we shall not pursue the reduction here.

Case III: All three sets of slice totals known.   All slice totals

$$N_{.1.}, N_{.2.}, \cdots, N_{.s.}$$
$$N_{1..}, N_{2..}, \cdots, N_{r..}$$
$$N_{..1}, N_{..2}, \cdots, N_{..t}$$

now being known, in addition to conditions (26) and (29) we require here

$$\sum_{ij} m_{ijk} = m_{..k} = N_{..k} \frac{n}{N}, \quad k = 1, 2, \cdots, t - 1 \quad (32)$$

which makes a total of $r + (s - 1) + (t - 1)$ or $r + s + t - 2$ conditions.   The same kind of manipulation as used heretofore gives

$$m_{ijk} = n_{ijk}(1 + \lambda_{i..} + \lambda_{.j.} + \lambda_{..k}) \quad (33)$$

with $\lambda_{.s.}$ and $\lambda_{..t}$ to be counted zero.   The adjustment is no longer proportionate by slices or tubes, but involves every cell.   In practice, once the normal equations are solved and the Lagrange multipliers worked out, one proceeds very much as in the two-dimensional Case II: for each of the t slices, corresponding to the t values of k, there will be a two-dimensional adjustment, the 1 in Eq. 18 being replaced now by $1 + \lambda_{..k}$.

The normal equations for the Lagrange multipliers can be found by performing double summations on Eq. 33. The result is

$$
\left.
\begin{aligned}
& n_{i..}\lambda_{i..} + \sum_j n_{ij}\lambda_{.j.} + \sum_k n_{i.k}\lambda_{..k} = m_{i..} - n_{i..} \\
& \qquad\qquad\qquad\qquad i = 1, 2, \cdots, r \\
& \sum_i n_{ij}\lambda_{i..} + n_{.j.}\lambda_{.j.} + \sum_k n_{.jk}\lambda_{..k} = m_{.j.} - n_{.j.} \\
& \qquad\qquad\qquad\qquad j = 1, 2, \cdots, s - 1 \\
& \sum_i n_{i.k}\lambda_{i..} + \sum_j n_{.jk}\lambda_{.j.} + n_{..k}\lambda_{..k} = m_{..k} - n_{..k} \\
& \qquad\qquad\qquad\qquad k = 1, 2, \cdots, t - 1
\end{aligned}
\right\} \qquad (34)
$$

If these calculations were to be carried out, one would simplify the computation by solving the top row for $\lambda_{i..}$, getting

$$
\lambda_{i..} = \frac{1}{n_{i..}}\{m_{i..} - \sum_j n_{ij}\lambda_{.j.} - \sum_k n_{i.k}\lambda_{..k}\} - 1 \qquad (35)
$$

and then substituting this into the middle and last rows of Eqs. 34 to get a reduced set of $s + t - 2$ normal equations for the Lagrange multipliers $\lambda_{.j.}$ and $\lambda_{..k}$, the numerical values of which when set back into Eq. 35 give the $\lambda_{i..}$. In all the summations of Eqs. 34 and 35, $\lambda_{.s.}$ and $\lambda_{..t}$ would be counted zero. But here again, the iterative process to be explained later will displace the use of normal equations, so actually we are not interested in reducing them.

Case IV: One set of face totals known. It may be that the *rs* face totals

$$
N_{11.}, N_{12.}, \cdots, N_{ij.}, \cdots, N_{rs.}
$$

are known from crossing the i and j characters in the universe. The conditions are then

$$
\sum_k m_{ijk} = m_{ij.} = N_{ij.}\frac{n}{N}, \quad
\left.
\begin{aligned}
& i = 1, 2, \cdots, r \\
& j = 1, 2, \cdots, s
\end{aligned}
\right\} \qquad (36)
$$

The adjustment here turns out to be

$$
m_{ijk} = n_{ijk}(1 + \lambda_{ij.}) \qquad (37)
$$

but by summing both sides over the index k to evaluate $\lambda_{ij.}$ it is seen that

$$
m_{ij.} = n_{ij.}(1 + \lambda_{ij.}) \qquad (38)
$$

whence

$$m_{ijk} = n_{ijk} \frac{m_{ij.}}{n_{ij.}} \tag{39}$$

This adjustment is thus proportionate by tubes, like that in Eq. 30, though here the factor $m_{ij.}/n_{ij.}$ is known and Eq. 39 can be applied at once.

Case V: One set of face totals, and one set of slice totals known. Sometimes, in addition to the rs face totals of Case IV, the slice totals

$$N_{..1}, N_{..2}, \cdots, N_{..t}$$

will also be known, in which circumstances the conditions (36) are to be accompanied by

$$\sum_{ij} m_{ijk} = m_{..k} = N_{..k} \frac{n}{N}, \quad k = 1, 2, \cdots, t - 1 \tag{40}$$

The same procedure as previously applied yields now

$$m_{ijk} = n_{ijk}(1 + \lambda_{ij.} + \lambda_{..k}) \tag{41}$$

with $\lambda_{..t}$ to be counted zero. Summations performed over k, and then over i and j together, give the normal equations

$$\left. \begin{array}{l} n_{ij.}\lambda_{ij.} + \sum_{k} n_{ijk}\lambda_{..k} = m_{ij.} - n_{ij.} \\[2mm] \sum_{ij} n_{ijk}\lambda_{ij.} + n_{..k}\lambda_{..k} = m_{..k} - n_{..k} \end{array} \right\} \tag{42}$$

The number of equations is $rs + t - 1$, since $\lambda_{..t}$ does not exist. As before, a simplification can be effected by solving the top row for $\lambda_{ij.}$ and making a substitution into the lower one, but, because of the great advantage of the iterative process to be seen further on, we shall not carry out the reduction.

Before going on it might be noted that although this case is three-dimensional, it reduces to the two-dimensional Case II if one considers that $ij.$ is one index running through the values 11, 12, $\cdots$, 21, 22, $\cdots$, rs, and that $..k$ is a second index running through the values 1, 2, $\cdots$, t. This can be seen by the similarity between Eqs. 42 and 19.

Case VI: Two sets of face totals known. If in addition to the face totals of Case IV, the face totals

$$N_{.11}, N_{.12}, \cdots, N_{.st}$$

are also known from further crossing the j and k characters in the universe, we shall require

$$\sum_i m_{ijk} = m_{.jk} = N_{.jk}\frac{n}{N}, \quad \left. \begin{matrix} j = 1, 2, \cdots, s \\ k = 1, 2, \cdots, t - 1 \end{matrix} \right\} \quad (43)$$

in addition to the conditions (36). In place of Eq. 39 of Case IV we now find that

$$m_{ijk} = n_{ijk}(1 + \lambda_{ij.} + \lambda_{.jk}) \tag{44}$$

in which $\lambda_{.jt}$ is to be counted zero for all j. No simple relation such as Eq. 39 is possible here, because the adjustment is not proportionate by tubes; the Lagrange multipliers must be evaluated. This can be accomplished by summing the members of Eq. 44 over k and i in turn, resulting in the normal equations

$$\left. \begin{matrix} n_{ij.}\lambda_{ij.} + \sum_k n_{ijk}\lambda_{.jk} = m_{ij.} - n_{ij.} \\ \sum_i n_{ijk}\lambda_{ij.} + n_{.jk}\lambda_{.jk} = m_{.jk} - n_{.jk} \end{matrix} \right\} \quad (45)$$

Since $\lambda_{.jt}$ does not exist for any values of j, the number of equations is $rs + s(t - 1) = s(r + t - 1)$. They break up at once into s sets each of $r + t - 1$ equations, one set for every j value. In fact, the problem can be considered as s sets of the two-dimensional Case II. Any one value of j gives a slice, which can be looked upon as fulfilling the specifications of the two-dimensional Case II. Each set of normal equations can be reduced in the same manner that Eqs. 19 were reduced.

Case VII: All three sets of face totals known. All totals now being known, we require

$$\sum_k m_{ijk} = m_{ij.} = N_{ij.}\frac{n}{N}, \quad \left. \begin{matrix} i = 1, 2, \cdots, r \\ j = 1, 2, \cdots, s \end{matrix} \right\} \quad (36)$$

$$\sum_i m_{ijk} = m_{.jk} = N_{.jk}\frac{n}{N}, \quad \left. \begin{matrix} j = 1, 2, \cdots, s \\ k = 1, 2, \cdots, t - 1 \end{matrix} \right\} \quad (43)$$

$$\sum_j m_{ijk} = m_{i.k} = N_{i.k}\frac{n}{N}, \quad \left. \begin{matrix} i = 1, 2, \cdots, r - 1 \\ k = 1, 2, \cdots, t - 1 \end{matrix} \right\} \quad (46)$$

The adjusting relation is

$$m_{ijk} = n_{ijk}(1 + \lambda_{ij.} + \lambda_{.jk} + \lambda_{i.k}) \qquad (47)$$

in which $\lambda_{.jt}$ is to be counted zero for any j, $\lambda_{r.k}$ for any k, and $\lambda_{i.t}$ for any i. The normal equations for the Lagrange multipliers are

$$
\left.
\begin{aligned}
n_{ij.}\lambda_{ij.} + \sum_k n_{ijk}\lambda_{.jk} + \sum_k n_{ijk}\lambda_{i.k} &= m_{ij.} - n_{ij.} \\
\sum_i n_{ijk}\lambda_{ij.} + n_{.jk}\lambda_{.jk} + \sum_i n_{ijk}\lambda_{i.k} &= m_{.jk} - n_{.jk} \\
\sum_j n_{ijk}\lambda_{ij.} + \sum_j n_{ijk}\lambda_{.jk} + n_{i.k}\lambda_{i.k} &= m_{i.k} - n_{i.k}
\end{aligned}
\right\} \qquad (48)
$$

being $rs + rt + st - r - s - t + 1$ in number. They can be reduced in the same way that previous normal equations have been reduced; but here again, the iterative process will render the use of normal equations unnecessary, except for theoretical purposes, e.g., justification of the iterative process.

45. A simplified procedure — iterative proportions. The number of Lagrange multipliers in any problem is equal to the number of conditions imposed on the adjustment (Sec. 27). Here the conditions have appeared in sets, depending on which marginal totals are involved. By a comparison of Eqs. 9 and 28 on the one hand, with Eqs. 18, 30, 33, 41, 44, and 47 on the other, we see that wherever there was only one set of marginal totals involved we came out with a simple proportionate adjustment, but that in all other cases it was not so; the Lagrange multipliers involved were unfortunately related to one another through normal equations.

We need a simplification. It is a fact that as a first approximation the adjustments may all be considered proportionate, in either the horizontal or the vertical. We shall be able to write down an expression for the error in this approximation, and shall be able to reduce it sufficiently by a succession of proportionate adjustments.

Take the two-dimensional Case II for an example. In Eq. 20 one may recognize $(1/n_i.) \sum_j n_{ij}\mu_j$ as a weighted average of μ_j for the ith row. There will be a weighted average of μ_j for the first row, another for the second, etc., one for each value of i; consequently one may appropriately speak of the ith average of μ_j, writing it i-av μ_j. Substituting from Eq. 20 into 18 one then sees the adjustment (18) appear as

$$m_{ij} = n_{ij}\left(\frac{m_{i.}}{n_{i.}} + \mu_j - i\text{-av } \mu_j\right) \tag{49}$$

If, on the other hand, μ_j had been eliminated from Eqs. 19, instead of λ_i, the result would have been

$$m_{ij} = n_{ij}\left(\frac{m_{.j}}{n_{.j}} + \lambda_i - j\text{-av } \lambda_i\right) \tag{50}$$

From either Eq. 49 or 50 it is clear why the adjustment (18) is not proportionate by rows or columns, and why Case II does not break up into r or s sets of Case I: the reason is that μ_j in any cell is not necessarily equal to the average μ_j for that row, nor is λ_i in any cell necessarily equal to the average λ_i for that column. If nevertheless one were to make the simple proportionate adjustment

$$m_{ij}' = n_{ij}\frac{m_{i.}}{n_{i.}} \tag{51}$$

along the horizontal in the ith row, the horizontal conditions (3) will be enforced but not the vertical ones (11); i.e., it will be found that $m_{i.}' = m_{i.}$, but that usually not all $m_{.j}' = m_{.j}$. This is because Eq. 51 effects only a partial adjustment, each m_{ij}' being in error through the disparity between the μ_j proper to the jth column, and the average of all the μ_j for the ith row, as seen in Eq. 49. This error can then be diminished by turning the process around and subjecting these m_{ij}' to a proportionate adjustment in the vertical according to the equation

$$m_{ij}'' = m_{ij}'\frac{m_{.j}}{m_{.j}'} \tag{52}$$

which may be considered an application of Eq. 50 wherein the disparity between any λ_i and the average λ_i for the jth column has been neglected. It is the vertical conditions that will now be found satisfied, but perhaps not all of the horizontal ones, because some of the row totals may have been disturbed. The cycle initiated by Eq. 51 is thereupon repeated, and the process is continued until the table reproduces itself and becomes rigid with the satisfaction of all the conditions, both horizontal and vertical. The final results theoretically do not coincide with the least squares solution, but in practice they usually do, closely enough.

Usually two cycles suffice. In practice the work proceeds rapidly, requiring only about one-seventh as much time as setting up the normal equations and solving them. The Tables 3–5 show the various stages of the work when the method of iterative proportions is applied to the sample frequencies of Table 1. It will be noticed that the results of the third approximation (Table 5) are final, since if the process were continued, the table would only reproduce itself.

TABLE 3

THE METHOD OF ITERATIVE PROPORTIONS APPLIED TO THE DATA OF TABLE 1
(FIRST STAGE)

A proportionate adjustment by rows, by Eq. 51. Note that $m_{1.}' = m_{1.}$, *but that* $m_{.j}' \neq m_{.j}$.

	$j = 1$	2	3	4	$m_i.'$	$m_i.$
$i = 1$	3608	778	555	312	5253	5252
2	1586	399	254	157	2396	2395
3	1606	433	273	120	2432	2432
4	10476	2441	1696	1153	15766	15766
5	1660	349	169	152	2330	2330
6	3910	863	548	341	5662	5662
$m_{.j}'$	22846	5263	3495	2235	33839	
$m_{.j}$	22877	5285	3462	2213		33837

46. Iterative proportions in three dimensions. The same process can be extended to three or more dimensions with an even greater relative saving in time. To see how the method of iterative proportions applies in one of the three-dimensional cases, we may go back to the three-dimensional Case III. By the substitution afforded through Eq. 35 the adjusting Eq. 33 may be put

TABLE 4

A CONTINUATION OF THE PROCESS INITIATED IN TABLE 3
(SECOND STAGE)

The figures in Table 3 are now adjusted proportionately by columns according to Eq. 52. The vertical totals $m_{.j}''$ and $m_{.j}$ now are equal, but the agreement of the horizontal totals accomplished in Table 3 has been slightly disturbed.

	$j = 1$	2	3	4	$m_{i.}''$	$m_{i.}$
$i = 1$	3613	781	550	309	5253	5252
2	1588	401	252	155	2396	2395
3	1608	435	270	119	2432	2432
4	10490	2451	1680	1142	15763	15766
5	1662	350	167	151	2330	2330
6	3915	867	543	338	5663	5662
$m_{.j}''$	22876	5285	3462	2214	33837	
$m_{.j}$	22877	5285	3462	2213		33837

TABLE 5

THE CYCLE COMMENCED AGAIN
(THIRD STAGE)

The figures of Table 4 are subjected to a proportionate adjustment by rows, according to Eq. 51. And since these results turn out to be almost a reproduction of Table 4, but with both horizontal and vertical conditions satisfied, they are considered final. The agreement with the m_{ij} in Table 1 should be noted.

	$j = 1$	2	3	4	$m_{i.}'''$	$m_{i.}$
$i = 1$	3612	781	550	309	5252	5252
2	1587	401	252	155	2395	2395
3	1608	435	270	119	2432	2432
4	10492	2451	1680	1142	15765	15766
5	1662	350	167	151	2330	2330
6	3914	867	543	338	5662	5662
$m_{.j}'''$	22875	5285	3462	2214	33836	
$m_{.j}$	22877	5285	3462	2213		33837

into the form

$$m_{ijk} = n_{ijk} \left(\frac{m_{i..}}{n_{i..}} + \lambda_{.j.} + \lambda_{..k} - i\text{-av } \lambda_{.j.} - i\text{-av } \lambda_{..k} \right) \quad (53)$$

Equally well it could have been written

$$m_{ijk} = n_{ijk} \left(\frac{m_{.j.}}{n_{.j.}} + \lambda_{i..} + \lambda_{..k} - j\text{-av } \lambda_{i..} - j\text{-av } \lambda_{..k} \right) \quad (54)$$

or

$$m_{ijk} = n_{ijk} \left(\frac{m_{..k}}{n_{..k}} + \lambda_{i..} + \lambda_{.j.} - k\text{-av } \lambda_{i..} - k\text{-av } \lambda_{.j.} \right) \quad (55)$$

Any of these three equations shows why the adjustment (33) is not proportional by slices, and why this case does not break up into r or s or t sets of the three dimensional Case I. As a first approximation it does, as is now clear from these three equations, and by making successive proportionate adjustments we may thus arrive at the final values. To go about the work one could first calculate the values of

$$m_{ijk}' = n_{ijk} \frac{m_{i..}}{n_{i..}} \quad (56)$$

then

$$m_{ijk}'' = m_{ijk}' \frac{m_{.j.}}{m_{.j.}'} \quad (57)$$

followed by

$$m_{ijk}''' = m_{ijk}'' \frac{m_{..k}}{m_{..k}''} \quad (58)$$

These three successive adjustments would constitute a cycle, which would then be repeated in whole or in part until the table becomes rigid with the satisfaction of all three sets of conditions.

47. Simplification when only one cell requires adjustment. On occasions it happens in sampling that one is especially interested in one particular cell of the universe, and would like to have a result for it in advance before the other cells are adjusted. Sometimes it even happens that the others individually are of no particular concern. In such circumstances one merely places the cell of interest in one corner of the table by an appropriate interchange of rows and columns, and then compresses the rest of the table into the cells adjacent to it.   In the two-dimensional Case II one would thus work with a 2×2 table, one corner cell being the one of special interest, the other three being the result of compression.   The marginal totals of the row and column belonging to the cell of interest are unaffected.   For illustration we may suppose that from the sample shown in Table 1 we require only m_{61}.   We then start with the 2×2 Table 6, which is derived from Table 1 by compression.   Commencing with Table 6, one might first adjust by rows according to Eq. 51, then by columns by Eq. 52.   One cycle of iterative proportions is sufficient, as is seen in Table 7, and the value 3915 found for m_{61} is in good agreement with its value shown in Tables 1 and 5.   The scheme of compression provides a quick method of getting out an advance adjustment for a cell of special interest, and the result so obtained will ordinarily be in good agreement with what comes later when and if all the cells are adjusted.

In the three-dimensional Cases II, III, V, VI, and VII, one compresses the original table to a $2 \times 2 \times 2$ table, and then uses the method of iterative proportions.   (The other cases do not require consideration, since they are proportionate adjustments wherein one is already at liberty to adjust as few or as many cells as he likes without altering the equations or the routine.)   The

TABLE 6

DERIVED FROM TABLE 1 BY COMPRESSION, THE CELL $i = 6, j = 1$, REQUIRING ADJUSTMENT

	$j = 1$	$j = 2\text{-}4$	$n_{i.}$	$m_{i.}$
$i = 1\text{-}5$	18965	9250	28215	28175
$i = 6$	3882	1740	5622	5662
$n_{.j}$	22847	10990	33837	
$m_{.j}$	22877	10960		33837

same procedure can be extended to the adjustment of two cells, the only modification being that in two dimensions we shall compress to a 2 × 3 or a 3 × 3 table, depending on whether the two cells do or do not lie in the same row or column. In three dimensions we compress to a 2 × 2 × 3, or a 2 × 3 × 3, or a 3 × 3 × 3 table; the first if the two cells lie in the same i, j, or k tube, the second if they lie in the same slice but not in the same tube, the third if they are in separate slices.

TABLE 7

A ᴘʀᴏᴘᴏʀᴛɪᴏɴᴀᴛᴇ ᴀᴅᴊᴜꜱᴛᴍᴇɴᴛ ᴏꜰ ᴛᴀʙʟᴇ 6

Rows adjusted by Eq. 51

18938	9237	28157
3910	1752	5662
22848	10989	33837

Columns adjusted by Eq. 52

18962	9213	28175
3915	1747	5662
22877	10960	33837

Conclusion: $m_{61} = 3915$

48. The Stephan method. An iterative procedure devised by Stephan[2] has the advantage of being in theoretical agreement with the least squares solution. It is moreover self-checking and self-correcting, and requires the writing of only a few figures. Only one table is required, since the factors required in the computations are appended below and to the right, and all the figures needed can be written into this one table (see Table 8). The method will converge to the least squares solution even when some cells are vacant or contain huge sampling errors. This is possible because the method may be used under any desired system of weighting.

Directions follow for carrying out the computations of the Stephan method in two dimensions when the weight of any adjusted frequency is assumed to be inversely proportional to the corresponding sample frequency, as in the development of the normal equations (cf. Sec. 41). The numerical illustrations refer

[2] Frederick F. Stephan, " An iterative method of adjusting sample frequency tables when expected marginal totals are known," *Annals of Mathematical Statistics*, vol. XIII, No. 2, June 1942: pp. 166–178.

to Table 8 of this chapter, which is derived from the same sample frequencies as those in Table 1.

CYCLE 1

1. Compute the factors $p_i(1)$ equal to $m_i./2n_i.$. Enter each factor in the proper row, one below the other, in the column headed $p_i(1)$. (For instance, $p_2(1) = 2395/2 \times 2371 = 0.50506$, and is entered opposite the second row.)

2. Multiply each sample frequency n_{ij} in column j by the corresponding factor $p_i(1)$. These products are not needed individually; they are to be accumulated in the product register of the machine until the vertical total for the column is obtained. (In column 4, this vertical total is $313 \times 0.49791 + 155 \times 0.50506 + 116 \times 0.51701 + 1160 \times 0.49707 + 154 \times 0.49385 + 339 \times 0.50356 = 1117.46423$.) This total is not to be written down, but is to be transferred to the keyboard for the subtraction called for in the next step.

3. Subtract this accumulated total from the corresponding deflated universe column total $m._j$. Then divide this difference by the corresponding sample column total $n._j$ to get the factor $q_j(1)$. (For instance, $\{m._4 - \sum n_{i4} \times p_i(1)\}/n._4 = \{2213 - 1117.46423\}/2237 = 0.48973 = q_4(1)$. This is the only figure written down from steps 2 and 3.) Do steps 2 and 3 for every column.

CYCLE 2

4. Multiply each sample frequency in row i by its corresponding factor $q_j(1)$. These products are not needed individually; they are to be accumulated in the product register of the machine until the horizontal total for the row is obtained. (In row 2, this horizontal total is $1570 \times 0.50134 + 395 \times 0.50453 + 251 \times 0.49099 + 155 \times 0.48973 = 1185.53979$.) This total is not to be written down, but is to be transferred to the keyboard for the subtraction called for in the next step.

5. Subtract this accumulated total from the corresponding deflated universe row total $m_i.$. Then divide this difference by the corresponding sample row total $n_i.$ to get the factor $p_i(2)$. (For instance, $\{m_2. - \sum n_{2j} \times q_j(1)\}/n_2. = \{2395 - 1185.53979\}/2371 = 0.51011 = p_2(2)$.) Do steps 4 and 5 for every row.

6. Repeat step 2, using the factors $p_i(2)$. (In column 4, the vertical total is $313 \times 0.49580 + 155 \times 0.51011 + 116 \times 0.53384 + 1160 \times 0.49426 + 154 \times 0.48740 + 339 \times 0.50699 = 1116.44870$.)

7. Repeat step 3 to get the factors $q_j(2)$. (For instance, $\{m_{.4} - \sum n_{i4} \times p_i(2)\}/n_{.4} = \{2213 - 1116.44870\}/2237 = 0.49019 = q_4(2)$.)

CYCLE 3

The process can be continued, that is, steps 4 to 7 can be repeated again and again. In practice, cycle 3 is often the last one.

THE FINAL STEP; THE ADJUSTED TABLE

The process will be stopped when another cycle would merely result in a repetition of the same factors. When this stage is reached, the factor $p_i + q_j$ is formed and multiplied by the corresponding sample frequency n_{ij}, and the product is written in cell ij beneath the corresponding sample frequency n_{ij}. (For instance, for the cell $i = 3$, $j = 2$, the adjusted sample frequency is $419(0.53385 + 0.50431) = 435$, and this is written beneath the sample frequency 419.)

In the illustration, there was no need of going beyond the second cycle, since, as will be observed, the p and q factors obtained in the third cycle are practically identical with those obtained in the second. But of course, one could not perceive this without going through the third cycle.

It was mentioned earlier that the process is self-correcting. If a mistake is made somewhere in the computations, the process will converge faster or slower, depending on the magnitude and direction of the mistake. In consequence, fewer or more cycles will be required before the factors repeat themselves. The end result will nevertheless be the same as if no mistake had been made. The computer may therefore assume that when the factors repeat, his work is correct, and he is ready for the final step.

Since the Stephan method gives the least squares solution, the italicized figures in Table 8 (p. 124) are identical, except for rounding errors, with the results in Table 1 (p. 107), which were obtained by the use of normal equations. The least squares results in both Tables 1 and 8 are in close agreement with those yielded by the method of iterative proportions in Table 5 (p. 118), and with the results to be obtained by the Bruyère method (next section) in Table 10 (p. 126).

The choice between the different short-cuts (iterative proportions, Stephan, and Bruyère) may reasonably lie in personal preference, though the Stephan method has certain theoretical and practical advantages, as mentioned above, and in some situations these weigh heavily in its favor.

The Stephan method has been extended in the Census to three dimensions; for general instructions, see the reference to Stephan in footnote 2 on page 121.

TABLE 8

THE STEPHAN ADJUSTMENT APPLIED TO THE EXAMPLE SHOWN IN TABLE 1

$j = 1$	2	3	4	$n_i.$ $m_i.$	$p_i(1)$	$p_i(2)$	$p_i(3)$	
3623	781	557	313	5274	0.49791	0.49580	0.49580	
3613	*781*	*550*	*309*	*5252*				
1570	395	251	155	2371	.50506	.51011	.51011	
1588	*401*	*251*	*155*	*2395*				
1553	419	264	116	2352	.51701	.53384	.53385	
1608	*435*	*271*	*119*	*2432*				
10538	2455	1706	1160	15859	.49707	.49426	.49426	
10492	*2451*	*1681*	*1142*	*15766*				
1681	353	171	154	2359	.49385	.48740	.48739	
1662	*350*	*167*	*151*	*2330*				
3882	857	544	339	5622	.50356	.50699	.50699	
3914	*867*	*543*	*338*	*5662*				

	$j = 1$	2	3	4	
$n._j$	22847	5260	3493	2237	33837
$m._j$	*22877*	*5285*	*3462*	*2213*	*33837*
$q_j(1)$	0.50134	0.50453	0.49099	0.48973	
$q_j(2)$	.50137	.50431	.49084	.49019	
$q_j(3)$	.50137	.50431	.49084	.49019	

The adjusted frequencies m_{ij} (italicized) are rounded off, hence when summed may occasionally disagree a unit or so with the expected marginal totals (also italicized). The latter arise by deflation from the universe rather than by direct addition of the m_{ij}.

49. The Bruyère method. This method is closely related to the other two short-cuts, and may be described as a precipitous forcing at the end of the first half-cycle.   It was shown to me by Dr. Paul T. Bruyère, who had devised it some years earlier when he encountered the problem of adjusting sample frequencies in connexion with some surveys in medical research.   It does not give a least squares solution, but it is good enough, and has the advantage of being the most rapid of all methods here explained.

1. Same as the first step in the method of iterative proportions (Sec. 45): multiply the sample frequencies n_{ij} in Row i by the ratio $m_{i.}/n_{i.}$ as in Eq. 51. (This ratio will vary from row to row.)   Do this for every row.

For illustration, this proportionate adjustment will be carried out on Table 1 (p. 107), the result being Table 3 (p. 117).

2. Form the column total $m_{.j}'$.   Subtract it (usually mentally) from the known total $m_{.j}$, and enter it as a " vertical discrepancy " along the top of a new table (Table 9).   Do this for every column.   In the same way, form also the resulting horizontal discrepancies, $m_{i.} - m_{i.}'$.   (These would be zero except for errors in rounding off to integers.)

3. Make up a table of corrections (Table 9), based on the vertical discrepancies found in step 2.   Distribute any one of these discrepancies amongst the cells in that column, in proportion to the row totals, $m_{i.}$.   To do this, first calculate the ratios $m_{i.}/n$, where n is the total sample.   Enter these ratios along the left of Table 9: they constitute the multipliers for forming the final corrections, which are entered in the body of the table. The correction to be entered in row i and column j is the product of $m_{i.}/n$ by the discrepancy in column j.

4. These corrections must now be forced to equal the columnar discrepancies, exactly.   This forcing is to be carried out so that (a) the sum of the corrections in any row equals the corresponding " horizontal discrepancy," written in step 2 and entered in the right-hand column of Table 9, and so that (b) the sum of the corrections in any column equals the corresponding " vertical discrepancy," also written in step 2, and entered near the top of Table 9.   Parts (a) and (b) are entirely independent.   In Table 9 the forcing is indicated by putting parentheses around a figure obtained in step 3, and writing a new figure just to the left.   Usually the forcing is small (a unit or so in any cell), and needs to be done in only a few cells. Large cells should be altered in the forcing, rather than small ones.   (See page 84.)

TABLE 9

CORRECTIONS FOR FORCING THE MARGINAL TOTALS
(BRUYÈRE METHOD)

(*Steps 2, 3, and 4*)

	$\dfrac{m_i.}{n}$	$j = 1$ 31	2 22	3 −33	4 −22	Row sums	Horizontal discrepancies (written in step 2)
		Vertical discrepancies (written in step 2)					
$i = 1$	0.15521	5	3	−6 (−5)	−3	−1 (0)	−1
2	.07078	2	1 (2)	−3 (−2)	−1 (−2)	−1 (0)	−1
3	.07187	2	2	−2	−2	0	0
4	.46594	15 (14)	10	−15	−10	0 (−1)	0
5	.06886	2	2	−2	−2	0	0
6	.16733	5	4	−5 (−6)	−4	0 (−1)	0
Column sums		31 (30)	22 (23)	−33 (−32)	−22 (−23)		

TABLE 10

THE FINAL RESULTS OBTAINED BY THE BRUYÈRE METHOD

	$j = 1$	2	3	4	$m_i.''$	$m_i.$
$i = 1$	3613	781	549	309	5252	5252
2	1588	400	251	156	2395	2395
3	1608	435	271	118	2432	2432
4	10491	2451	1681	1143	15766	15766
5	1662	351	167	150	2330	2330
6	3915	867	543	337	5662	5662
$m_{.j}''$	22877	5285	3462	2213		
$m_{.j}$	22877	5285	3462	2213	33837	

5. Add each forced correction to the corresponding frequency in Table 3. The result is Table 10, which is the end product. Both row and column totals will agree with the controls, and the work is finished, except for multiplying all the frequencies in Table 10 by N/n, to make them correspond with the population values (not shown here).

50. Some remarks on the accuracy of an adjustment.   A least squares adjustment of sampling results must be regarded as a systematic procedure for obtaining satisfaction of the conditions imposed, and at the same time effecting an improvement of the data in the sense of obtaining results of smaller variance than the sample itself, under ideal conditions of sampling from a stable universe.   As a matter of fact, the variance of the residuals arising in the adjusted cells will decrease with the difference between the total number of cells and the number of control totals, according to the results of Exercise 3 at the end of Chapter V (p. 68).   It must not be supposed that any particular adjusted cell frequency is necessarily better than the original sample frequency in the sense of being closer to the complete count.   It may be, but also it may not be, and there is no statistical way of discovering which. All we know is that *on the average* the adjusted cell frequencies will be better.

But the decrease in variance is not all; adjustment to known control totals has at the same time the effect of eliminating biases in the nature of inherent differences between the sample and complete count.   This effect is often more important than the decrease in the variance of the sample frequencies.

It is desirable to get some idea of the errors of sampling by actual trial, such as by a comparison of certain sampling marginal totals with the corresponding universe totals, as can often be arranged by means of controls.   Also, the sample can be tested for regularity of patterns.   There is another aspect to the problem of error — even a 100 percent count is not by itself useful for formulating social and economic plans, except so far as we can assert on other grounds what secular changes are taking place.

PART D

CONDITIONS CONTAINING PARAMETERS

CHAPTER VIII

CURVE FITTING IN MORE COMPLICATED CIRCUM-STANCES

51. Some general remarks on the purpose of curve fitting. To extend the theme of Chapter I, we may say that the reason for fitting a curve to a set of data is to summarize the evidence provided by that experiment for making predictions with regard to future data. It is not the data fitted that are of primary interest: it is *the data of the next experiment* that one holds in awe. Will the curve fit, or will it not? And when we decide whether the curve fits, we do so on the basis of whether it fits *well enough to give useful results*. Are deductions (predictions) made from this curve borne out in practice closely enough so that it can be used *as a basis for action*? The method that gives the best predictions is the best method.

There have been many instances when deductions made from a fitted curve, or from a series of curves, have made it unnecessary to perform certain other experiments. As an instance, we may turn to Example 1 of Chapter XI, where a quartic is fitted to some compressibility data published by the Michels in Amsterdam. This quartic, when fitted to their compressibility data on carbon dioxide, and differentiated, integrated, and otherwise evaluated, gives data on the index of refraction, the Joule-Thomson coefficient, entropy, and other physical properties, that would be difficult and time consuming, if direct observation were required. When we say that the quartic, fitted to the compressibility data, gives values of the Joule-Thomson coefficient, we mean that for certain purposes, *the prediction is satisfactory* in place of the Joule-Thomson coefficient that would be observed directly. Certain checks, in terms of other experience and other deductions, which may be available in isolated portions of the ranges of pressure, volume, and temperature that are covered by the compressibility data, lend confidence to the results — confidence of the kind that can be translated into action, such as the design of compressors for refrigerators and other machinery.

In order to extend the region of prediction into other areas and other ranges (e.g., other cities, other economic levels, higher pressures, higher temperatures), not yet included in the experiments, it is necessary to have related experience, or meanwhile to regard extrapolations as pure conjectures. Such conjectures may be regarded as predictions, but without a high degree of belief, and not as a scientific basis for action.

It is important to keep in mind the ultimate purpose of curve fitting, particularly when one is actually fitting curves for purposes of action. Meanwhile, it is necessary that one learn to perform or understand some of the procedures by which curves can be fitted. To this end, we resume our study of the adjustment of observations, returning to the general solution worked out in Chapter IV.

It will be recalled that earlier in the book some simple problems in curve fitting were treated (Secs. 9 and 10, the single sample; Sec. 12, several samples; Sec. 15, a line through the origin). These problems were simple, not just because the functions were simple ones, but also because the errors in the variables entered in such manner that the parameters (adjustable constants) could be found directly by differentiating S. The solutions obtained for those circumstances were and still are satisfactory, but the research worker must be prepared for more complicated situations, such as both variables subject to error, or functions in which the parameters and the errors do not enter in so simple a manner.

A framework will be developed in this chapter for more complicated circumstances. The simple problems just mentioned will of course fit into this framework, as will occasionally be pointed out. Fortunately, the solution is already worked out in general terms; it is contained in the general normal equations on page 55. All we need to do now is to apply this solution to curve fitting, and see how it can be adapted to routine computational procedure.

There will be a function to be fitted. We might write it

$$F(x, y; \; a, b, c) = 0 \qquad (1)$$

to indicate that there is an equation involving x and y, and the (adjustable) parameters a, b, and c. In the examples already seen in Sections 9, 12, and 15, the equations were simple, namely, $x = a$, and $y = bx$.

The problems considered in the last three chapters (constituting Part C) did not contain parameters; the conditions were rigorous, being geometric, or forced by complete counts. No question arose concerning the adjustment of parameters, because there was none. We threw away with abandon certain rows and columns of the general solution that owed their origin to the parameters (p. 59). Now, however, we can not do this; the condition equations contain parameters, and we must deal with them. We shall see, though, that there will be simplifications of other kinds, and we shall develop a procedure not unlike that contained in Chapters V and VI.

52. Graphical considerations. It is desirable to have in mind the picture of curve fitting shown in Figs. 16 and 17, pages 132 and 133. There are observed points, calculated points, and true points. The calculated points, by definition, lie on the calculated curve, and the true points lie on the true curve. The equation of the calculated curve may be written in the form of Eq. 1, wherein x and y are the coordinates of any point on the curve, and a, b, c are the calculated (or adjusted) values of the parameters, which are to be found in the solution (see Eqs. 6, p. 52). The equation of the true curve is the same, except that it is drawn with the true parameters α, β, γ. It is assumed that if the errors of observation were negligible, the observed coordinates X and Y would satisfy the true curve. Actually, however, the observed points do not lie on either the calculated curve or the true curve; in fact, owing to errors of observation, the observed points usually do not lie on any curve at all of the form of Eq. 1, though they may approximate one closely.

As in Chapter IV, we shall need some approximate parameters a_0, b_0, c_0 to start off with. If they were used for drawing the curve, in place of a, b, c, there would be still another curve (not shown) in Figs. 16 and 17, which might be called the *approximate curve* if it needed a name.

The calculated coordinates, and the calculated parameters, satisfy Eq. 1 exactly. The observed coordinates, however, and the approximate parameters a_0, b_0, c_0, do not. When, for any point, the observed coordinates X and Y, and the approximate parameters, are substituted into the left-hand side of Eq. 1, the equation is usually not satisfied, which is to say that the left-hand side is usually not zero, but is instead some small quantity F_0, defined as

$$F_0 = F(X, Y; a_0, b_0, c_0) \quad \text{(Cf. Eq. 5, p. 52.)} \tag{2}$$

Of course, F_0 may by accident be zero at some point, and will be zero by design at any point through which the approximate curve is forced to pass, as when the method of selected points is used to determine satisfactory approximate values a_0, b_0, c_0 (cf. the reduced type at the end of Sec. 55). The quantities F_0 at point No. 1, No. 2, etc., will appear in the normal equations of Section 55.

> For simplicity and definiteness, the development will be written out for only two coordinates, x and y, at each point. The extension to three coordinates is obvious, in which event Eq. 1, instead of being the equation of a curve in the x, y plane, is written as the *surface* $F(x, y, z; a, b, c) = 0$ in the x, y, z space. See Example 3 on pp. 231 ff. for an illustration in three dimensions, and Exercise 26 of Section 71 for one in four dimensions. An increase in the number of dimensions does not necessarily increase the complexity of a problem.

A point is observed to be X, Y; that is, the x coordinate of some true point ξ, η is measured, perhaps several times, and the mean of these measurements is X with weight w_x. Likewise, the y coordinate of the same (true) point is measured, perhaps several times, and the mean of them is Y with weight w_y. By Eq. 16 on page 22, the weights of the observed coordinates X and Y at this point will be in the inverse ratio of the variances of protracted random series of measurements on the true coordinates ξ, η (Ch. I), and directly in the ratio of the numbers of observations taken. Otherwise expressed, if these variances are denoted by $Var\ x$ and $Var\ y$, and the numbers of observations by N_x and N_y, then the ratio of the weights will be

$$w_x : w_y = \frac{N_x}{N_y} \frac{Var\ y}{Var\ x} \tag{3}$$

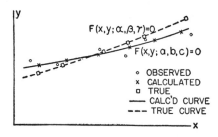

FIG. 16. A typical situation in curve fitting. It is assumed that the "true points," wherever they are, lie on the "true curve" $F(x, y;\ \alpha,\ \beta,\ \gamma) = 0$, α, β, γ being the true and unknown values of the parameters. The "calculated points" all lie on the "calculated curve" $F(x,\ y;\ a,\ b,\ c) = 0$, a, b, c being the calculated values of the parameters. This figure and the next one first appeared in an article entitled "On the chi-test and curve fitting," *J. Amer. Stat. Assoc.*, vol. 29, 1934: pp. 372–382.

Of course, this ratio may vary from point to point, depending on the variation of the factors on the right (cf. Example 2, pp. 218–230).

53. The conditions. For each point observed, there is a calculated point, and this calculated point is forced to lie on the calculated curve (preceding section). The residuals must be just the distances required to put the calculated point on the calculated curve; see Figs. 16 and 17. Now since the calculated point must lie on the calculated curve, its coordinates must satisfy Eq. 1 (p. 130), which is to say that

$$F(x, y;\ a, b, c)$$

must vanish at every one of the calculated points, as indeed it must at all points along the calculated curve. Thus, for every point there is one condition imposed on the adjusted coordinates. Altogether, there are as many conditions as there are points. For n points there are n conditions.

Next, we look at the general normal equations (p. 55), also at the conditions that were imposed (Eqs. 3, p. 50), and we seek a

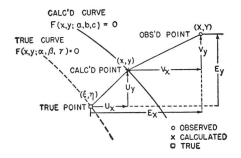

FIG. 17. Relations between the "true," "observed," and "calculated" points. The x and y coordinates of a point are observed; these observations when plotted give the "observed points." The point that was measured is the "true point," which is unknown and lies on the unknown "true curve" $F(x, y; \alpha, \beta, \gamma) = 0$, α, β, γ being the true but unknown values of the parameters. The "calculated curve" is found by adjusting a series of observed points; its equation will have the same form as the true curve, but the parameters therein will be the "calculated parameters" a, b, c. Corresponding to each observed point there will be a "calculated point," whose coordinates are found by subtracting the "residuals" V_x and V_y from the observed coordinates X and Y. E_x and E_y denote the "errors in the observed points"; E_x, E_y, and U_x and U_y are unknown, but V_x and V_y are calculated along with the parameters a, b, c by the method of least squares. As the figure happens to be drawn, each of the six quantities $E_x, E_y, U_x, U_y, V_x, V_y$ is positive. Their signs are indicated by the directions of the arrows.

way of writing these conditions so as to force the calculated points to lie on the calculated curve. This can be done by writing the condition functions in the form

$$F^h = F(x_h, y_h; a, b, c) \qquad h = 1, 2, \cdots, n \qquad (4)$$

wherein the function F on the right is the function found in Eq. 1, which is to be fitted, and x_h, y_h are the final calculated or adjusted coordinates at point h. These coordinates, along with the calculated parameters a, b, and c, are to have such values that the function F on the right vanishes at every calculated point.

54. The L coefficients. Immediately upon writing the condition functions in this way, we perceive that the coordinates of point h will enter the condition function $F(x_h, y_h; a, b, c)$ for that point, but not the condition function $F(x_g, y_g; a, b, c)$ for some other point g. As a consequence,[1]

$$\left. \begin{array}{l} \dfrac{\partial}{\partial x_g} F(x_h, y_h; \ a, b, c) = 0 \\[2mm] \dfrac{\partial}{\partial y_g} F(x_h, y_h; \ a, b, c) = 0 \end{array} \right\} \quad \text{if } g \neq h \qquad (5)$$

It then follows from Eq. 14, page 55 (wherein L was defined for the general solution), that

$$L_{gh} = 0 \quad \text{when} \quad g \neq h \qquad (6)$$

This means that the L coefficients in the general normal equations (p. 55) standing off the diagonal are zero.[1] Moreover, the L coefficients standing *on* the diagonal contain only two terms each, because all the other derivatives are zero. For these two, we may write

$$\left. \begin{array}{l} F_x = \dfrac{\partial}{\partial x_h} F(x_h, y_h; \ a, b, c) \\[4mm] F_y = \dfrac{\partial}{\partial y_h} F(x_h, y_h; \ a, b, c) \end{array} \right\} \qquad (7)$$

and

whereupon

$$L = \frac{F_x F_x}{w_x} + \frac{F_y F_y}{w_y} \qquad (8)$$

The suffix h has been omitted, it being simpler to leave it understood that the derivatives and the weights, and hence the L coefficients, may vary from point to point.

---

[1] A problem in which the coordinates of one point do enter the condition function for an adjacent point was published by the author in the *Phil. Mag.*, vol. 17, 1934: pp. 804–829. The problem dealt with the oscillations of the pointer on a chemical balance.

Remark 1. The first term on the right of Eq. 8 drops out at any point where X is free of error, for then the denominator w_x is ∞; and similarly the second term drops out if Y is free of error. If both X and Y are subject to error, the two terms may be of comparable magnitude, and both accordingly retained. (Cf. Remark 3 in Exercise 4 of Sec. 65, p. 181.)

Remark 2. From the way in which the L coefficients enter the normal equations, and affect the standard errors of the parameters (Sec. 62), it will be seen that one object in the design of an experiment should be to produce small values of L. The two terms on the right of Eq. 8 give an indication of where time and funds may wisely be apportioned. If one term is already small (possibly a quarter) compared with the other, then it might not be worth the necessary expenditure to reduce that term, already small, to half its value. Better it would be to spend even more time and funds to halve the larger term. Similarly, if the L coefficient at one point is already small compared with the L coefficients at some of the other points, then instead of using time and funds to reduce the small one further, it might be wiser first to reduce the L coefficients at those points where they are largest.

Remark 3. By Eq. 9, page 40, we see that the L coefficient at a particular point is none other than the reciprocal of the weight of F evaluated with the corresponding *observed* coordinates X, Y. This value of F would be written $F(X, Y; a, b, c)$. It is the quantity designated as F_0' in Exercises 3, 4, and 5 of Section 58, pages 145–146. Since L is the reciprocal of a weight, $1/W$ will frequently be written in place of L as we go along. (Cf. Remark 3, p. 181.)

55. The normal equations for curve fitting.

The general normal equations (p. 55) now take the form shown below. These can

λ_1	λ_2	λ_3	$\cdots$	λ_n	A	B	C	$=$	1
L_1	0	0	$\cdots$	0	$F_a{}^1$	$F_b{}^1$	$F_c{}^1$		$F_0{}^1$
0	L_2	0	$\cdots$	0	$F_a{}^2$	$F_b{}^2$	$F_c{}^2$		$F_0{}^2$
0	0	L_3	$\cdots$	0	$F_a{}^3$	$F_b{}^3$	$F_c{}^3$		$F_0{}^3$
$\cdot$	$\cdot$	$\cdot$	$\cdot$	$\cdot$	$\cdot$	$\cdot$	$\cdot$		$\cdot$
$\cdot$	$\cdot$	$\cdot$	$\cdot$	$\cdot$	$\cdot$	$\cdot$	$\cdot$		$\cdot$
$\cdot$	$\cdot$	$\cdot$	$\cdot$	$\cdot$	$\cdot$	$\cdot$	$\cdot$		$\cdot$
0	0	0	$\cdots$	L_n	$F_a{}^n$	$F_b{}^n$	$F_c{}^n$		$F_0{}^n$
$F_a{}^1$	$F_a{}^2$	$F_a{}^3$	$\cdots$	$F_a{}^n$	0	0	0		0
$F_b{}^1$	$F_b{}^2$	$F_b{}^3$	$\cdots$	$F_b{}^n$	0	0	0		0
$F_c{}^1$	$F_c{}^2$	$F_c{}^3$	$\cdots$	$F_c{}^n$	0	0	0		0

(9)

quickly be reduced to a smaller set, in number equal to the number of adjustable parameters. First, eliminate $\lambda_1, \lambda_2, \cdots, \lambda_n$ by solving for them in the upper n equations, getting

$$
\left.\begin{aligned}
\lambda_1 &= \frac{1}{L_1}\,(F_0{}^1 - F_a{}^1 A - F_b{}^1 B - F_c{}^1 C) \\[6pt]
\lambda_2 &= \frac{1}{L_2}\,(F_0{}^2 - F_a{}^2 A - F_b{}^2 B - F_c{}^2 C) \\
&\;\;\cdot \qquad \cdot \\
&\;\;\cdot \qquad \cdot \\
&\;\;\cdot \qquad \cdot \\
\lambda_n &= \frac{1}{L_n}\,(F_0{}^n - F_a{}^n A - F_b{}^n B - F_c{}^n C)
\end{aligned}\right\} \quad
\begin{array}{l}\text{(A } \lambda \text{ for} \\ \text{each point)}\end{array} \quad (10)
$$

Then substitute these values of $\lambda_1, \lambda_2, \cdots, \lambda_n$ into the lower three rows of Eqs. 9. The result is Eqs. 11. As in Chapter V (see p. 59), the coefficients below the diagonal have been omitted.

A	B	C	$=$	1
$\left[\dfrac{F_a F_a}{L}\right]$	$\left[\dfrac{F_a F_b}{L}\right]$	$\left[\dfrac{F_a F_c}{L}\right]$		$\left[\dfrac{F_a F_0}{L}\right]$
	$\left[\dfrac{F_b F_b}{L}\right]$	$\left[\dfrac{F_b F_c}{L}\right]$		$\left[\dfrac{F_b F_0}{L}\right]$
		$\left[\dfrac{F_c F_c}{L}\right]$		$\left[\dfrac{F_c F_0}{L}\right]$

(The normal equations for curve fitting) (11)

These are the *normal equations for curve fitting.* They contain only the parameter-residuals A, B, C as unknowns. The arrangement of the coefficients is symmetrical, and their quadratic form positive definite, like the general normal equations whence they came (Sec. 28). Once the parameter-residuals A, B, and C are obtained from the solution of the normal equations, the adjusted values a, b, c of the parameters are found immediately by subtraction. More explicitly,

$$
\left.\begin{aligned}
a &= a_0 - A \\
b &= b_0 - B \\
c &= c_0 - C
\end{aligned}\right\} \quad \text{(Eqs. 6, p. 52)}
$$

The calculated curve is Eq. 1 into which the adjusted values of a, b, and c have been inserted.

Several details remain: to adjust the observations (Secs. 56 and 58); to work out a systematic procedure for forming the normal equations and solving them (Secs. 60 and 61); to discover in this systematic procedure a quick way of calculating the minimized sum of squares, S (p. 57 and the exercise following); to calculate the variance and product variance coefficients of a, b, c (found in the reciprocal matrix, Secs. 61 and 62).

It is important to observe that the final values of a, b, and c will be independent of the approximations a_0, b_0, c_0. That is to say, two computers, starting off with slightly different approximations (but with the same observations), will find their parameter-residuals A, B, and C to be just enough different so that their final calculated values of a, b, and c, and hence their final calculated curves, are practically identical.

Under some circumstances, and for some purposes, however, the approximations a_0, b_0, c_0 must not be too rough. In other problems it makes no difference what these approximations are, except that always the rougher they are, the more figures are required in the normal equations, hence the greater the computational effort required. These remarks are repeated more specifically in Exercises 4, 5, and 10 in Chapter X (pp. 179, 183, and 187).

In regard to the matter of arriving at the approximations a_0, b_0, c_0, it should be made clear at the outset that in practice this is usually not difficult. Often one will have good enough approximations simply from previous experience. There are graphical methods, by which one draws in a curve free-hand, after making a judicious choice of scales, such as changing $y = ae^{bx}$ into the logarithmic form $\ln y = \ln a + bx$, to make it straight. There is the " method of averages," called by Norman Campbell[2] the " method of zero sum," by which one finds what values of a, b, and c will force the calculated curve to

---

[2] Norman Campbell, *Phil. Mag.*, vol. 39, 1920: pp. 177–194. See also Whittaker and Robinson's *Calculus of Observations*, Art. 131, p. 258. According to them, the method of averages (i) was much used in the latter half of the 18th century; (ii) was first published by Tobias Mayer in 1748 and 1760. A recent paper by Wald contains some interesting and valuable theoretical work on the method of averages. It turns out that when the x and y observations have weights in constant ratio, the method of averages is unbiased, and in statistical efficiency compares well with the method of least squares, at a considerable saving in labor (in agreement with Campbell). The reference to Wald's work is the *Annals of Math. Statistics*, vol. 11, 1940: pp. 284–300.

average out correctly over groups of points (three groups if there are three parameters). Then there is Cauchy's method,[3] which has much to recommend it.

Lastly, there is the so-called method of selected points, concerning which brief mention was made at the end of Section 25, page 52. By this method one simply selects three points — usually two end points and a middle point, if there are three parameters — and solves three simultaneous equations to find what values of a, b, and c force the calculated curve to pass through these points. The values so found serve as a_0, b_0, c_0. If there are two parameters, two points are selected, and so on. This calculation is often fairly simple to carry out, and it possesses the advantage of giving the computer zero values for three of his F_0 functions, thus slightly cutting down his computational effort.

The method of selected points is much used and easily justified on grounds of simplicity, yet it is about the worst conceivable method of curve fitting. If the computer is not careful to select representative points, he throws away practically all the information contained in the rest of the points. Yet this much can be said, if there were no errors in any of the points, it would yield the correct results for a, b, and c.

For free-hand methods of curve fitting, and for general advice in the interpretation of statistical calculations, Ezekiel's *Methods of Correlation Analysis* (John Wiley, 2d ed., 1941) is heartily recommended.

56. Adjusting the observations, or finding the calculated points.

Going back to Eqs. 12 on page 54, we see that the x and y residuals will depend on the Lagrange multipliers in the following manner —

$$V_x = \frac{1}{w_x} \lambda_h F_x \quad (x \text{ residual at point } h) \tag{12x}$$

$$V_y = \frac{1}{w_y} \lambda_h F_y \quad (y \text{ residual at point } h) \tag{12y}$$

Once the residuals V_x and V_y have been computed, the adjusted (calculated) coordinates at point h can be found from the equations

$$x_h = X_h - V_x \tag{13x}$$
$$y_h = Y_h - V_y \tag{13y}$$

(Cf. Eqs. 6, p. 52.)

[3] Cauchy, *Comptes rendus*, vol. 25, 1847: p. 650.

The numerical value of the Lagrange multiplier λ_h can be found from Eq. 10 (p. 136). F_x and F_y are numerical values of the derivatives of F at point h. After differentiation, F_x and F_y are functions of x, y, and a, b, c. We can not evaluate these derivatives numerically at the calculated point h until we find the residuals and the calculated coordinates, but that is just what we are trying to do now. In practice, fortunately, for use in Eqs. 10 and 12 it is sufficient to evaluate the derivatives at the *observed* point, using the approximate parameters, though the final calculated parameters can be used if desired.

Eqs. 13 give the coordinates of the calculated point corresponding to the observed point X_h, Y_h. Finding the calculated points is the process of *adjusting the observations*; when x_h and y_h have been calculated, the observations X_h, Y_h are said to be *adjusted*. The calculated point x_h, y_h is the *least squares estimate* of the position of the unknown true point ξ_h, η_h. Obviously, it will depend not only upon X_h, Y_h, and their weights, but also more or less upon all the other points and their weights. In randomness, the variances of the calculated coordinates are less than the variances of the observed coordinates.

Just how is this dependence tied up with the other points? Through the normal equations (Eqs. 9, p. 135), or their equivalent, Eqs. 10 and 11. Eqs. 11 supply the parameter-residuals A, B, and C, which are to be used in Eqs. 10 to find λ_1, λ_2, $\cdots$, λ_n. These in turn are used in Eqs. 12 to compute the x and y residuals at each point, by which the observations are adjusted, as indicated in Eqs. 13.

We now have a method of adjusting the observations and of estimating the parameters a, b, c, when both the x and y coordinates are subject to error, but it must be remembered that the solution depends on certain simplifying assumptions; namely, that the squares and higher powers of the residuals can be neglected in the Taylor series of Chapter IV.

Remark 1. A familiar method of adjusting the observations, valid when all the x coordinates are free of error, is to substitute the coordinate free of error into the formula $F(x, y;\ a, b, c) = 0$ (Eq. 1), and solve for the other coordinate. Thus in the parabola,

$$y = a + bx + cx^2 \tag{14}$$

if x is free of error, it is easy to calculate y for a given x, once a, b, and c are determined. But if x is subject to error, one must either solve a quadratic for x in terms of a known y, or — what is usually easier — adjust the x coordinate by using Eqs. 12 and 13, after evaluating the Lagrange multipliers in Eqs. 10.

When the function F of Eq. 1 is not solved for y explicitly, it may be easier to adjust the y coordinates by means of Eqs. 10, 12, and 13, rather than to substitute directly into Eq. 1 and solve for y in terms of x. Similar remarks apply for adjusting the coordinates when x alone is subject to error.

When both coordinates are subject to error, one must apply Eqs. 10, 12, and 13, if he would adjust the observations. (For a numerical illustration, see the example treated in Section 78, pages 227 ff. As an exercise, the student could at this time work out the numerical values of the remaining nine calculated points in that example.)

Remark 2. Gauss and others gave methods for adjusting the observations in problems of geodesy and astronomy (Chs. V, VI, and VII, constituting Part C). Unfortunately, they did not give much attention to problems in which the conditions contain parameters (curve fitting), especially when more than one coordinate is subject to error.

It has sometimes been said that least squares is reasonable enough in surveying and astronomy, but that it is illogical and equivocal in curve fitting. Actually, the principle of least squares is always the same (p.14). The distinction between the problems lies in the conditions that the adjusted quantities are subjected to. A neglected but worthy paper by Kummell[4] in 1879, had it not been overlooked, could have set matters straight. Later papers by Stewart[5] (1920) and Uhler[6] (1923) also emphasized the unity of the different kinds of problems.

Remark 3. The term "adjustment of observations," as it has often been applied heretofore to curve fitting, has meant a calculation of the parameters a, b, c from a set of data. Now we see that the parameters enter only as unknowns in the conditions that are forced upon the adjusted quantities. Least squares is primarily a method of adjusting the observations, and the parameters enter only incidentally. As a matter of fact, least squares is the only method of curve fitting by which

[4] Charles H. Kummell, *The Analyst* (Des Moines), vol. 6, 1879: pp. 97–105.
[5] R. Meldrum Stewart, *Phil. Mag.*, vol. 40, 1920: pp. 217–227.
[6] Horace S. Uhler, *J. Optical Soc.*, vol. 7, 1923: pp. 1043–66.

one can profess to adjust his observations. But, of course, the determination of useful values of the parameters and their standard errors is often the prime purpose of an investigation.

Remark 4. The method of least squares is the only analytic device for curve fitting that takes account of the weights of the observations. If both x and y are subject to error, it is necessary that both coordinates be given their proper weighting at every point. In graphical methods of curve fitting, the eye can be trained, to some extent, to take account of weights.

Remark 5. In the next chapter we shall see that it is possible to compute

$$S = \sum (w_x V_x^2 + w_y V_y^2) \tag{15}$$

without calculating the individual x and y residuals, nor squaring, weighting, and adding them. However, it is often found worth while to draw the calculated curve, and to lay off the x and y residuals, to be able to note whether any of them is especially large. In this manner, it is sometimes possible to discover sources of spurious observations that would be hidden in a comprehensive test like the chi-test.

57. The distribution of χ^2. The least squares value of

$$\chi^2 = \frac{1}{\sigma^2} \sum (w_x V_x^2 + w_y V_y^2) \tag{16}$$

for a fitted curve (provided it is the right curve, and the observations are random) has the probability distribution[7]

$$P(\chi^2)d\chi^2 = \frac{1}{\Gamma(\frac{1}{2}k)2^{\frac{1}{2}k}} (\chi^2)^{\frac{k-2}{2}} e^{-\frac{1}{2}\chi^2} d\chi^2 \tag{17}$$

wherein

$$k = \text{number of points} - \text{number of adjustable parameters} \tag{18}$$

k is commonly called the " degrees of freedom." It was recognized by Gauss, though he gave it no particular name (cf. footnote 6 in Ch. II). The effect of including both x and y residuals in χ^2 is merely to add the second term in the summation in Eq. 16. The form of the distribution is unaffected.

[7] See an article by the author in the *J. Amer. Stat. Assoc.*, vol. 29, 1934: pp. 372–382. A necessary lemma thereto is given in the *Phil. Mag.*, vol. 19, 1935: pp. 389–402.

Historical note. The distribution of χ^2 for problems in curve fitting where y alone is subject to error was first published by P. Pizzetti in an article entitled " I fondamenti matematici per la critica dei risultati sperimentali," *Atti della Regia Università di Genova*, vol. xi, 1892: pp. 113–333. Helmert's distribution of s for the simplest problem in curve fitting (Sec. 9), arrived at also many years later by Student in 1908, can easily be converted into the distribution of χ^2. Helmert gave this distribution in Schlömilch's *Zeitschrift für Math. und Physik*, vol. 21, 1876: pp. 300–3, and it is interesting to note that Pizzetti referred to Helmert's work. Helmert's derivation is reproduced in Emanuel Czuber's *Beobachtungsfehler* (Teubner, 1891), pp. 147–150. Pizzetti's result was generalized by the author for errors in both the x and y coordinates, in the paper referred to in footnote 7. The assumption of normally distributed observations was presumed.

There is no such thing as a distribution of χ^2 unless the fitting is done by least squares; in other words, only the *minimized* χ^2 has a distribution.

58. Some geometry concerning the adjustment of observations.
Now let us consider some of the details connected with the calculated points, or the adjusted observations. Let Q be the line segment joining the observed and calculated points. By Eqs. 12 we can find the slope of this line segment; it is

$$\text{Slope of } Q = \frac{\text{the } y \text{ residual}}{\text{the } x \text{ residual}} = \frac{V_y}{V_x} = \frac{w_x}{w_y} \frac{F_y}{F_x} = \frac{w_x}{w_y} \frac{\dfrac{\partial F}{\partial y}}{\dfrac{\partial F}{\partial x}} = -\frac{w_x}{w_y} \frac{dx}{dy}$$

$$(19)$$

The last step here involves the very important relation learned in elementary calculus, that if $F(x, y) = c$, then $\dfrac{dy}{dx} = -\dfrac{\dfrac{\partial F}{\partial x}}{\dfrac{\partial F}{\partial y}} = -\dfrac{F_x}{F_y}.$

Eq. 19 says that

$$\text{The slope of } Q = -\frac{w_x}{w_y} \frac{1}{\text{the slope of the curve}} \qquad (20)$$

Hence if $w_x = w_y$ at point h, the two slopes are negative reciprocals of one another, and, if the x and y scales are equal, *the line segment* Q *will be perpendicular to the curve* (but see Exercise 1 at the end of this section).

If at any point, $w_x : w_y = \infty$ or is very large, which is to say that X is relatively infallible, then the line segment Q is vertical and the adjustment is all in the y coordinate. An exception may occur in the neighborhood of any portion of the curve that is vertical or nearly so; there the derivatives F_x and F_y usually affect the normal equations and Eq. 20 in such a way that the curve is brought close to the observed point, and the line segment Q is drawn away from the vertical.

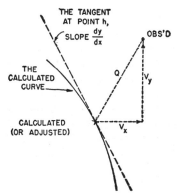

FIG. 18.   A portion of Fig. 17 redrawn for further consideration.

If at any point, $w_y : w_x = \infty$ or is very large, which is to say that Y is relatively infallible, then the line segment Q is horizontal and the adjustment is all in the x coordinate. An exception may occur in the neighborhood of any portion of the curve that is horizontal or nearly so; there the derivatives F_x and F_y usually affect the normal equations and Eq. 20 in such a way that the curve is brought close to the observed point, and the line segment Q is drawn away from the horizontal.

If at any point, $w_x : w_y$ is finite, i.e., both X and Y are subject to error, the line segment Q will be neither horizontal nor vertical, but inclined, and there is adjustment in both the x and y coordinates. Exceptions occur. In the neighborhood of any vertical portion of the curve, the line segment Q may be pulled to a nearly horizontal position, and, in the neighborhood of any horizontal portion of the curve, the line segment Q may be pulled to a nearly vertical position.

Exercises

Exercise 1. Suppose that the x and y scales are equal on the graph of a certain curve, and that, at one of the points, the weights of X and Y are equal, wherefore the line segment Q in Fig. 18 (p. 144) is perpendicular to the curve at that point. Then suppose that the graph is redrawn, and that the units in which Y is measured are changed, as from feet to inches, while the units of X remain unchanged.

(a) Prove that the line segment Q is no longer perpendicular to the fitted curve. (*Hint:* The ratio $w_y : w_x$ was unity before the change in scale, but it is not so afterward. If all the y coordinates are multiplied by C, because of the change in units, then the weights of all y observations are decreased by the factor $1/C^2$, and the new value of $w_x : w_y$ is C^2 times the old one. Moreover, the new slope of the curve is C times as great as before. By Eq. 20, the slope of the line segment Q is also C times as great as before, and it follows that Q is no longer perpendicular to the curve.)

(b) Show that the change in the units of measuring Y affects the normal equations only in such a way that the y coordinates of the calculated curve and the adjusted points are all multiplied by C. (Thus any change in units is automatically taken care of by the normal equations. This is in contrast with the arbitrariness of curve fitting by eye, by which very different results may arise merely from a change in units.)

Exercise 2. When there are three coordinates, the surface

$$F(x, y, z;\ a, b, c) = 0$$

is to be fitted to the n observed points. L then contains three terms — the two already written in Eq. 8 plus $F_z F_z / w_z$. Show that if x, y, z are observed with equal weight at any point, the line segment Q joining the observed and calculated points is normal to the fitted surface.[8] In such a problem, the calculated points lie on the calculated (fitted) surface. See Section 81 for an example in three dimensions, and Exercise 26 of Section 71 for one in four dimensions.

Exercise 3. Show that the minimized sum of squares, S, can be written as $\sum W F_0'^2$, wherein F_0' is the left-hand side of Eq. 1 (p. 130) evaluated with the observed coordinates X, Y, and the calculated parameters a, b, c; and W is the weight of F_0' (cf. Remark 3 at the end of Sec. 54).

From the way F_0' and W are defined, it turns out that

$$F_0' = F(X, Y; a, b, c)$$
$$= F_0 - F_a A - F_b B - F_c C \quad \text{(Neglecting residuals of higher order)}$$
$$= F_x V_x + F_y V_y \quad \text{(See Eq. 7, p. 53.)} \tag{21}$$

and

$$W = \frac{1}{L} \text{ at point } h \tag{8}$$

The solution to the problem then lies in writing, as usual,

$$S = \sum (w_x V_x^2 + w_y V_y^2)$$

and noting that from Eqs. 10 (p. 136)

$$\lambda = W F_0' \text{ at point } h \tag{22}$$

whence Eqs. 12 give

$$\left. \begin{array}{l} V_x = \dfrac{1}{w_x} W F_0' F_x \\[2mm] V_y = \dfrac{1}{w_y} W F_0' F_y \end{array} \right\} \tag{23}$$

for the x and y residuals at point h. Substitution into $w_x V_x^2 + w_y V_y^2$ gives the required result in terms of F_0' (due to Kummell, 1879). This result is useful in Exercise 3 of Section 61, page 163.

Exercise 4. Prove that W in the preceding exercise is actually the weight of F_0', i.e., of $F(X, Y; a, b, c)$. (*Hint:* Apply Eq. 9,

---

[8] This result was proved by the author in the *Phil. Mag.*, vol. 11, 1931: pp. 146–156.

p. 40.)   Hence the new expression $\sum WF_0'^2$ for S can be regarded as a sum of the weighted squares of residuals, F_0' now being defined as a new kind of residual.

Exercise 5.   If the x coordinate is free of error, $WF_0'^2$ is equal to $w_y V_y^2$, and, if Y is free of error, $WF_0'^2$ is equal to $w_x V_x^2$.

Exercise 6.   Prove that for any observed point in the neighborhood of which the slope of the fitted curve is positive, the residuals V_x and V_y will have opposite signs; but, if the slope is negative, then V_x and V_y will have the same sign.   In other words, when the fitted curve lies below the observed point, then the calculated point lies below and to the right of the observed point if the slope of the fitted curve is positive, but below and to the left if the slope is negative; and when the fitted curve lies above the observed point, then the calculated point lies above and to the left if the slope is positive, above and to the right if the slope is negative (see Fig. 19).

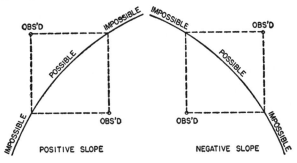

Fig. 19.   Showing the possible and impossible positions of the calculated point.

Exercise 7.   Show that in fitting

$$y = a + bx + cx^2 \tag{24}$$

with y alone subject to error, Eqs. 10 reduce to

$$\lambda = w_y\{Y - (a_0 + b_0x + c_0x^2) + (A + Bx + Cx^2)\} \tag{25}$$

$$= w_y(Y - y) \tag{26}$$

whence Eqs. 12 and 13 on page 138 reduce to

$$y = Y - \frac{\lambda}{w_y}$$
$$= Y - \{Y - (a_0 + b_0 x + c_0 x^2) + (A + Bx + Cx^2)\} \quad (27)$$

or

$$y = a + bx + cx^2$$

In this circumstance, therefore, y may be calculated at any point merely by substituting the x coordinate into the equation with the adjusted values of a, b, c.

CHAPTER IX

SYSTEMATIC COMPUTATION FOR FITTING CURVES BY LEAST SQUARES

59. Preliminary note on the tabular solution. In the systematic solution of the normal equations for geometric conditions, given on pages 82 and 83, we saw an easy way of computing the minimized sum of squares, S. In Section 61, we shall see that the same routine for solving the normal equations in curve fitting will also yield S. We shall, moreover, see how our initial approximation to the sum of squares is diminished as one parameter after another is adjusted.

In order to gain some preliminary familiarity with these characteristics of the routine, we shall return to the simple illustration considered in Section 10, where we had the n observations and

OBSERVATIONS AND WEIGHTS (COLUMNS 1 AND 2)

COMPUTATIONS FOR FINDING x AND s (COLUMNS 3 AND 4)

(1)	(2)	(3)	(4)
Observation	Weight	Weighted deviation from a_0	Weighted square of the deviation from a_0
x_1	w_1	$w_1(x_1 - a_0)$	$w_1(x_1 - a_0)^2$
x_2	w_2	$w_2(x_2 - a_0)$	$w_2(x_2 - a_0)^2$
x_3	w_3	$w_3(x_3 - a_0)$	$w_3(x_3 - a_0)^2$
.	.	.	.
.	.	.	.
.	.	.	.
x_n	w_n	$w_n(x_n - a_0)$	$w_n(x_n - a_0)^2$

$$\text{Wtd. av.} = \frac{\sum w(x - a_0)}{\sum w} \equiv P \qquad \text{Wtd. av.} = \frac{\sum w(x - a_0)^2}{\sum w} \equiv Q$$

weights listed in columns 1 and 2 of the table on page 148.   The weights could be merely the relative frequencies of occurrence.

The problem now is the same as it was in Section 10, namely, to find what value of the parameter a in the equation

$$x = a \qquad\qquad (1)$$

renders the (weighted) sum of squares, S, a minimum.   Now, however, we shall start off differently, because we wish to pattern the solution after the framework to be explained in Section 61 for more complicated problems.   We shall use an approximation a_0 for a, and shall correct it later by finding the residual A, which, when subtracted from a_0, gives the final value of a (turn back to Eqs. 6 on p. 52).

Corresponding to Eqs. 11 in Section 55 (the normal equations for curve fitting), there will here be one and only one normal equation, with one unknown.   We proceed to calculate the one and only L coefficient therein; also the right-hand member.

For the present problem we set

$$F = x - a \qquad\qquad \text{(Eq. 1 of Ch. VIII)}$$

whereupon

$$F_0 = x_h - a_0 \qquad\qquad \text{(For observation No. } h)$$

The derivatives are

$$F_x = 1, \quad F_a = -1 \quad \text{(Turn to Eq. 5 of Ch. VIII.)}$$

whence

$$L = \frac{F_x F_x}{w_x} = \frac{1}{w} \qquad \text{(Eq. 8 of Ch. VIII)}$$

The right-hand member of the one and only normal equation will be

$$\left[\frac{F_a F_0}{L} \right] = - \sum w(x - a_0)$$

The sum of squares formed with a_0 will be

$$\sum w(x - a_0)^2$$

which, be it noted, can be written as $[F_0F_0/L]$, a symbol that in more complicated problems denotes the sum of squares formed with the approximate values (a_0, b_0, c_0) of the parameters. In Section 61 and beyond, this symbol is abbreviated to $[oo]$.

We now make substitutions into Eqs. 11 on page 136. Row I constitutes the one and only normal equation. For reasons that may become clear later, we introduce Row 2, containing in the " 1 " column the sum of squares formed with the approximation a_0. Rows 3 and II are formed by the manipulations described in the column " How obtained."

Row	A	$=$	1	
I	$\sum w$		$-\sum w(x - a_0)$	
2			$\sum w(x - a_0)^2$	How obtained
3			$-\{\sum w(x - a_0)\}^2/\sum w$	Multiply I by $+\sum w(x - a_0)/\sum w$
II			$\sum w(x - a_0)^2 - \{\sum w(x - a_0)\}^2/\sum w$	Add 2 and 3

Solving Row I for A, we get

$$A = -\frac{\sum w(x - a_0)}{\sum w} \tag{2}$$

whereupon

$$a = a_0 - A \qquad \text{(Cf. Eqs. 6, p. 52.)}$$
$$= a_0 + \frac{\sum w(x - a_0)}{\sum w}$$
$$= a_0 + \frac{\sum wx}{\sum w} - a_0$$
$$= \frac{\sum wx}{\sum w} = \bar{x} \qquad \text{(By definition of } \bar{x}) \tag{3}$$

The least squares value for a is thus $\bar{x}$, the weighted mean of the observations, as was obtained by the direct solution in Section 10a.

The extreme left entry in Row II is none other than S, the minimized sum of squares.   This is so because

(The extreme left entry

$$\text{in Row II}) = \sum w(x - a_0)^2 - \frac{\{\sum w(x - a_0)\}^2}{\sum w}$$

$$= \sum wx^2 - \frac{(\sum wx)^2}{\sum w}$$

$$= \sum wx^2 - \bar{x}^2 \sum w \qquad (4)$$

which is the value of S shown by Eq. 11 in Section 10a, page 19.

> This tabular solution will be extended later in this chapter to the calculation of parameter residuals (called A, B, C) and the minimized sum of squares, S, in more complicated problems in curve fitting.

At this point, it is interesting to perceive that the tabular solution just described is equivalent to a certain rapid method, often used in statistics, for computing the mean $\bar{x}$ and the standard deviation s of a set of n observations such as those shown in column 1 above.   The method will be described in steps.

> i. Select an arbitrary datum, perhaps a rounded-off guess at $\bar{x}$, which takes the place of the approximation a_0 in the tabular solution just described.

> ii. Write down in column 3 the deviations of the observations from a_0, and weight them.

> iii. Form the squares of these deviations, weight them, and enter the weighted squares in column 4.

> iv. Take the weighted averages of columns 3 and 4.   Call these averages P and Q.   They are the correction factors to be used in finding $\bar{x}$ and s^2, according to Eqs. 5 and 6, ahead.

The weighted mean and standard deviation of the n observations are then calculated by writing

$$\bar{x} = a_0 + P \qquad (5)$$

$$s^2 = Q - P^2 \qquad (6)$$

Now the correction factor P may be considered either as the average residual reckoned from the arbitrary datum a_0, or as the distance between $\bar{x}$ and a_0. Q is the average squared residual, when the residuals are reckoned from a_0, and s^2 is the average squared residual, when the residuals are reckoned from a. In words, Eqs. 5 and 6 state that

$$\bar{x} = \text{(the arbitrary datum } a_0\text{)} + \text{(the average residual reckoned from } a_0\text{)} \qquad (7)$$

$$s^2 = \text{the average squared residual reckoned from } a$$

$$= \text{(the average squared residual reckoned from } a_0\text{)}$$
$$- \text{(the distance between } a \text{ and } a_0\text{)}^2 \qquad (8)$$

It can be seen from Eq. 4 that the extreme left entry in Row II (p. 150) divided by $\sum w$ is

$$Q - P^2$$

which is none other than s^2. Therefore the (minimized) sum of squares S is just $(\sum w)s^2$. Hence the tabular scheme shown above for calculating A and S is equivalent to the steps outlined for the rapid method for getting $\bar{x}$ and s^2.

It is important to note that the entry $\sum w(x - a_0)^2$ in Row 2 in the "1" column arises by summing squares of deviations reckoned from a_0, and the quantity in Row 3 just below it is precisely the amount by which $\sum w(x - a_0)^2$ must be diminished to get the minimum sum of squares, called S. Likewise, the quantity Q arises by summing squares of deviations reckoned from a_0, and P^2 is the amount by which this sum of squares must be diminished to get s^2 (see Eq. 6).

> In this example, both in the tabular solution and the "rapid method" for computing $\bar{x}$ and s^2, the number a_0 need not be close to a. It can have any value whatever, but in practice it will usually be a rounded-off guess at the mean (which is the final value of a).

60. Systematic procedure for forming the normal equations for the parameters. There will be a formula to be fitted. It might be

$$y = a + bx + cx^2 \qquad (9)$$

or it might be

$$y = ae^{bx} \qquad (10)$$

or it might be something else.   Whatever it is, we can transpose one member and write it in the form

$$F(x, y; \ a, b, c) = 0 \quad \text{(Same as Eq. 1, p. 130)} \quad (11)$$

Thus, for Eq. 9 above, F would be $y - (a + bx + cx^2)$, and for Eq. 10, F would be $y - ae^{bx}$.

The reader may recall the use of the symbol F_0 in the preceding chapter (Sec. 52). F_0 stood for the value of the function F at some particular *observed* point X, Y (not a calculated point), and evaluated furthermore with the *approximate* parameters a_0, b_0, c_0.   For instance, if the form of the function F were fixed by Eq. 9, the numerical value of F_0 at the (observed) point X, Y would be $Y - (a_0 + b_0X + c_0X^2)$.   For Eq. 10, F_0 would be $Y - a_0e^{b_0X}$.

In fitting a function by least squares, the first thing to do is to fix the form of the function F by transposing all terms of the formula to one side of the equation, to get it in the form of Eq. 11. The steps then to be followed are outlined below.   It is interesting to compare these steps with those of Section 33, wherein there were no parameters.

1st step.   (a) Work out somehow satisfactory approximations a_0, b_0, c_0 for the parameters (cf. the reduced type in Secs. 25 and 55); (b) calculate numerical values of F_0 at every point.

> In some problems, depending on the formula and the weighting, it is permissible to take $a_0 = b_0 = c_0 = 0$ when calculating F_0 (but not L), in which event the residuals A, B, C turn out to be the adjusted values $-a$, $-b$, $-c$ themselves (cf. Exercises 4, 5, and 10 in Secs. 65-6).   But this is not usually advisable even when permissible.   As a matter of saving time, a good rule is to commence the adjustment with as good approximations a_0, b_0, c_0 as can be found with a reasonable amount of trouble, and thus to cut down the number of figures required in the formation and solution of the normal equations.

2d step.   This step requires some differential calculus.   It consists of writing down the various derivatives of F, namely

$$F_a, \ F_b, \ F_c, \ F_x, \text{ and } F_y$$

The first three may be needed in forming the normal equations, the last two for calculating

$$L = \frac{F_x F_x}{w_x} + \frac{F_y F_y}{w_y} \quad \text{(Same as Eq. 8, p. 134)}$$

and the summation required at the n points. L may vary from point to point, and some or all of the derivatives F_a, F_b, and F_c almost surely will. So will F_0.

3d step. Work out the numerical values of F_a, F_b, F_c, and L, at every point. The following tabulation is suggested.

TABLE 1

PRELIMINARY TO THE MATRIX (3D STEP)

h	F_x	w_x	F_y	w_y	L	$\sqrt{L}$	F_a	F_b	F_c	F_0
1	...	...	...	...	...	...	...	...	...	...
2	...	...	...	...	...	...	...	...	...	...
3	...	...	...	...	...	...	...	...	...	...
.										.
.										.
.										.
n	...	...	...	...	...	...	...	...	...	...

Of course auxiliary columns may be required, depending on the problem and the whims of the computer. Or, perhaps some columns listed will not be needed, e.g., if w_x were ∞ all the way down (x free from error) then F_x and w_x would be omitted, since y alone would contribute to L, which would be merely $F_y F_y / w_y$. Likewise, if y were free from error all the way down, then the F_y and w_y columns would not be needed, for then L would be simply $F_x F_x / w_x$.

4th step. Divide each entry under F_a, F_b, F_c, and F_0 by the corresponding $\sqrt{L}$. The sums at the right or bottom (one but not both) of Table 2 can be formed by cumulating these quotients in the horizontal or vertical, the individual quotients being entered in the table. (This cumulation requires a machine with a double multiplying dial, one to be locked for cumulating quotients, while

the other clears when desired.   See a remark following Table 2 in
Sec. 33, p. 72.)

TABLE 2

THE MATRIX FOR THE FORMATION OF THE NORMAL EQUATIONS[1]   (4TH STEP)

h	$\dfrac{F_a}{\sqrt{L}}$	$\dfrac{F_b}{\sqrt{L}}$	$\dfrac{F_c}{\sqrt{L}}$	$\dfrac{F_0}{\sqrt{L}}$	Sum
1	...	...	...	...	...
2	...	...	...	...	...
3	...	...	...	...	...
.					.
.					.
.					.
n	...	...	...	...	...
Sum	...	...	...	...	... $\sqrt{}$

The sums at the right and along the bottom are used for checking
the formations of the normal equations exactly as was done with
Table 2 in Section 33.   First of all, the sum across the bottom
should equal the sum down the right-hand side, as indicated by
the check mark.   In running down the columns, cumulating squares
and cross-products (the fifth step, p. 156), the final total in the multiplier register will equal the sum at the bottom of the multiplier
column provided no changes in sign occur in the multiplicand
column.   In a machine with a double multiplier register, one part
of which can be locked for cumulation while the other clears,
individual multipliers can be checked at will in one dial, while
the sum of the multipliers cumulates in the other one for checking
at the bottom.

A maximum of three or four significant figures in any column
will suffice.   This means that if there is great variation in the
sizes of the numbers in any column, some entries in Table 2 may
have only two, or one, or not even *any* figures; see, for instance,
pages 213 and 224; also page 79.

The denominations of the different columns should be made
uniform by writing powers of 10 at the top of each row, to apply
to the whole column (see the solved examples at the end; also the
one in Sec. 34).   No attention need be given to the powers of 10
until the end, when the solution of the normal equations is decoded.

[1] Concerning the use of the term matrix here, see the note appended to
Table 2 in Ch. VI, p. 72.

5th step. Form the normal equations from Table 2 by the familiar process of adding squares and cross-products of columns. Thus, no matter how complicated the weighting, and no matter what be the form of the fitted curve, the whole procedure is uniform, and we are brought to a uniform and familiar process for the formation of the normal equations.

As already suggested at the commencement of this section, the student should compare this matrix with the previous Table 2 of Section 33 (p. 72), which arose in the consideration of conditions *not* containing parameters. The headings in the tables are different there, of course; but to the computer, the routine procedure of forming the normal equations from Table 2 is the same here as it was there. Also, the routine of solution is the same (compare Secs. 34 and 61). The exercises in Chapter X will provide practice in the necessary steps for setting up the normal equations for several types of functions.

Remark. By the procedure here explained for the formation of Table 2, whence the normal equations are to be set up, the solution of the normal equations (i.e., the values of A, B, C, etc.) is *unequivocal.* That is, it does not matter in what form the equation to be fitted is written. If one had, for example, $y = ae^{bx}$, he could put the same equation in the form $\ln y = \ln a + bx$, using in the former case $F = y - ae^{bx}$ and in the latter case, $f = \ln y - \ln a - bx$. Further illustrations will occur in the exercises of Chapter X. When the normal equations are made up according to the steps outlined above, the results will be *the same from any form of the fitted equation,* to within higher powers of the residuals.

As another example, the straight line can be written as $y = a + bx$ or as $x = -a/b + y/b$, and F may be $y - a - bx$ or $x + a/b - y/b$. Either way, the results will be the same to within higher powers of the residuals. Summed up, the results — *the final calculated parameters, and the adjusted observations, are independent of the form in which the equation is written.* Very large residuals, i.e., very rough data, will invalidate this statement to some extent, but if the data are as rough as that, they may not be worth fitting anyhow. See some other remarks in Section 26, also in Exercises 18 and 23 of Chapter X.

61. Systematic solution of the normal equations. The reciprocal matrix. Systematic computation of S. As has just been noted, the sums of squares and cross-products occurring in the normal equations for curve fitting (p. 136) are formed directly from

Table 2 of the preceding section. Thus, the summation $[F_aF_a/L]$
on page 136 is the sum of squares under the column of Table 2
headed $F_a/\sqrt{L}$; the summation $[F_aF_b/L]$ is the cumulation of
cross-products under the columns of Table 2 headed $F_a/\sqrt{L}$ and
$F_b/\sqrt{L}$; $[F_aF_0/L]$ is the cumulation of cross-products under the
columns headed $F_a/\sqrt{L}$ and $F_0/\sqrt{L}$; etc.

We shall suppose that the normal equations have been formed
in this manner. The numerical values of the squares and cross-
products called for on page 156 will be entered as numbers in Rows
1, 2, 3, 4, page 158. On this page, the abbreviated symbols

$$[aa] \quad \text{for} \quad \left[\frac{F_aF_a}{L}\right]$$

$$[ab] \quad \text{for} \quad \left[\frac{F_aF_b}{L}\right]$$

$$[oo] \quad \text{for} \quad \left[\frac{F_0F_0}{L}\right]$$

etc., have been introduced for convenience. The unit matrix in
the columns C_1, C_2, C_3 is entered for the calculation of the reciprocal matrix, and the sums at the right are formed for checking. The
Gauss symbols $[bb.1]$, $[cc.2]$, etc., seen in Rows II and III, will
facilitate reference to certain entries later on, as in the exercises
beginning on page 161.

The solution proceeds according to the operations of multiplication and addition indicated by the directions under the column
headed " How obtained." The procedure here outlined is similar
to Doolittle's[2] solution, which in turn goes back to Gauss.[3] The
check marks show the " sum check " at the pivotal points. The
normal equations on pages 82 and 83 were solved this way. Further numerical examples occur in Chapter XI. Note that A is
eliminated in Row II; A and B are both eliminated in Row III.
The values of the parameter-residuals appear in Rows 11, 12, and
13, in the " 1 " column.

[2] M. H. Doolittle, *Coast and Geodetic Survey Report for 1878* (Washington),
App. 8, pp. 115–118.

[3] Gauss, *Supplementum Theoriae Combinationis* (Göttingen, 1826; *Werke*,
vol. 4), Art. 13.

Row 11 comes by dividing III through by [cc.2] to get C.
Row 12 comes by substituting from 11 into II to get B.
Row 13 comes by substituting from 11 and 12 into I to get A.
This is the "back solution."

THE NORMAL EQUATIONS AND THEIR SOLUTION

Row	A	B	C	=	1	C_1	C_2	C_3	Sum
	Unknowns								
I	[aa]	[ab]	[ac]		[ao]	1	0	0	$\cdots$ √
2		[bb]	[bc]		[bo]	0	1	0	$\cdots$ √
3			[cc]		[co]	0	0	1	$\cdots$ √
4	How obtained				[oo]	0	0	0	$\cdots$ √
5 I × − [ab]/[aa]		$-\dfrac{[ab]^2}{[aa]}$	$-\dfrac{[ac][ab]}{[aa]}$		$-\dfrac{[ao][ab]}{[aa]}$	$-\dfrac{[ab]}{[aa]}$	0	0	$\cdots$
II 2 + 5		[bb.1]	[bc.1]		[bo.1]	$-\dfrac{[ab]}{[aa]}$	1	0	$\cdots$ √
6 I × −[ac]/[aa]			$-[ac]\dfrac{[ac]}{[aa]}$		$\cdots$	$\cdots$	$\cdots$	$\cdots$	$\cdots$
7 II × −[bc.1]/[bb.1]			$-[bc.1]\dfrac{[bc.1]}{[bb.1]}$		$\cdots$	$\cdots$	$\cdots$	0	$\cdots$
III 3 + 6 + 7			[cc.2]		[co.2]	$\cdots$	$\cdots$	1	$\cdots$ √
8 I × −[ao]/[aa]					$-\dfrac{[ao]^2}{[aa]}$	$-\dfrac{[ao]}{[aa]}$	0	0	$\cdots$
9 II × −[bo.1]/[bb.1]					$-\dfrac{[bo.1]^2}{[bb.1]}$	$\cdots$	$-\dfrac{[bo.1]}{[bb.1]}$	0	$\cdots$
10 III × −[co.2]/[cc.2]					$-\dfrac{[co.2]^2}{[cc.2]}$	$\cdots$	$\cdots$	$-\dfrac{[co.2]}{[cc.2]}$	$\cdots$
IV 4 + 8 + 9 + 10					S	$\cdots$	$\cdots$	$\cdots$	$\cdots$ √
13 I solved for A					A	c_{11}	c_{12}	c_{13}	
12 II solved for B					B	c_{21}	c_{22}	c_{23}	
11 III solved for C					C	c_{31}	c_{32}	c_{33}	$\cdots$ √

Note. The ellipsis $(\cdots)$ in the tabular array denotes a space wherein a number would ordinarily be entered in numerical calculation, but in which it is not worth while to show the entry in symbols.

The reciprocal matrix is set off in Rows 11, 12, and 13, in the columns headed C_1, C_2, C_3. The entries c_{11}, c_{21}, c_{31}, in the C_1 column are the values that would be obtained for A, B, C if the right-hand members of the normal equations were $\begin{smallmatrix}1\\0\\0\end{smallmatrix}$, as found in the C_1 column. Likewise, the entries c_{12}, c_{22}, c_{32} in the C_2 column are the values of A, B, C that would be obtained for A, B, C if the right-hand members of the normal equations were $\begin{smallmatrix}0\\1\\0\end{smallmatrix}$, as found in the C_2 column. Similar remarks hold for the entries c_{13}, c_{23}, c_{33} in the C_3 column. The values of the elements of the reciprocal matrix, in terms of the coefficients comprising the normal equations, are given in Exercise 2a, following this section.

> *Remark 1.* Many variations of the procedure shown on page 158 have been published. Each possesses merits peculiar to the machines available, preference of the operator, and other circumstances. The computer should be expected to develop variations that are advantageous to the peculiar requirements and conditions under which he works, and to his likes and dislikes.

> *Remark 2.* Methods of solution quite different from that described above have been contrived, but not yet adapted to mass production. Some of them are devices for calculating the reciprocal matrix to be used as a multiplier, for example, T. Smith's,[4] and a very promising scheme of matrix squaring devised by Hotelling and Girshick on the basis of a theorem regarding the characteristic equation of a determinant.[5] In another direction there is Kelley and Salisbury's[6] ingenious acceleration of an iterative process usually known as Seidel's (1874), though described earlier by Gauss and Jacobi,[7] the same being

[4] T. Smith, " The calculation of determinants and their minors," *Phil. Mag.*, vol. 3, 1927: pp. 1007–9.

[5] This was published by M. D. Bingham, *J. Amer. Stat. Assoc.*, vol. 36, 1941: pp. 530–534.

[6] Truman L. Kelley and Frank S. Salisbury, *J. Amer. Stat. Assoc.*, vol. 21, 1926: pp. 281–292.

[7] Whittaker and Robinson, *Calculus of Observations* (Blackie & Son, 1924), Art. 130.

particularly effective when good initial approximations are available. Then there is a fascinating pivotal process invented by Aitken[8] in 1932, after T. Smith's method; he has now, however, superseded this solution by the introduction of a number of important unpublished refinements. It is also interesting to note that electrical circuit machines, capable of solving something like 10 linear equations, practically instantaneously after plugging the coefficients, are in operation and undergoing further development at several centers.

Remark 3. The reciprocal matrix contains the variance and product variance coefficients for the parameters a, b, c. Its use in this connexion will be illustrated in Section 62.

Remark 4. The reciprocal matrix has also another use, namely, as a multiplier for finding the unknowns in the normal equations, in the same manner in which it was used in Eqs. 23, 24, and 26, on pages 93 and 94. The theory of the reciprocal matrix as a multiplier originated with Gauss.[9] The essentials of this theory are contained in the exercises following.

The " reciprocal solution," gotten by using the reciprocal matrix as a multiplier, is a very sensitive indicator of instability. It is just for this reason that the reciprocal solution is likely to break down in the case of near indeterminacy[10] — a fact that detracts rather drastically from its usefulness in the solution of normal equations in curve fitting, where near indeterminacy is surprisingly common. Near indeterminacy exists when Δ, the determinant of the coefficients, is very small. The freezing of the solution — the near vanishing of one of the extreme left coefficients (such as the entry $[cc.\ 2]$ in Row III) — is indicative of near indeterminacy, which is usually but not always accompanied by instability.

With regard to the source of near indeterminacy and the remedy, Palmer[11] gives this excellent advice. " . . . it occasionally happens that one of the equations is so nearly a multiple or

---

[8] A. C. Aitken, " On the evaluation of determinants, the formation of their adjugates," *Proc. Edinburgh Math. Soc.*, vol. 3, 1932: pp. 207–219.

[9] Gauss, *Supplementum Theoriae Combinationis Erroribus Minimis Obnoxiae* (Göttingen, 1826; *Werke*, vol. 4), Art. 8.

[10] See a paper by the author in *Science*, May 7, 1937; also Henry Schultz, *The Theory and Measurement of Demand* (Chicago, 1938), pp. 761–3. Appendix C can be highly recommended for techniques of curve fitting.

[11] A. de Forest Palmer, *The Theory of Measurements* (McGraw-Hill, 1912), p. 77. This book, by the way, is one of the best on experimental science and scientific inference.

submultiple of another that an exact solution becomes difficult if not impossible. In such cases the number of observation equations may be increased by making additional measurements on quantities that can be represented by known functions of the desired unknowns. The conditions under which these measurements are made can generally be so chosen that the new set of normal equations, derived from all of the observation equations now available, will be so distinctly independent that the solution can be carried out without difficulty to the required degree of precision."

Remark 5. An important consideration in the solution of equations is the maximum error in the values found for the unknowns — *maximum* error, not just the average or standard error — arising from errors in the coefficients. Tuckerman[12] shows a simple procedure by which this maximum error can be determined.

Exercises

Exercise 1. (a) The determinant of the coefficients of the normal equations on page 158 can be evaluated as

$$\Delta \equiv \begin{vmatrix} [aa] & [ab] & [ac] \\ [ab] & [bb] & [bc] \\ [ac] & [bc] & [cc] \end{vmatrix} = [aa]\,[bb.1]\,[cc.2] \qquad (12)$$

which is to say that the determinant Δ is the product of the extreme left numbers in the Roman-numbered Rows I, II, III. This result is important, because it shows that in near indeterminacy, i.e., when Δ is small, one of these factors on the right will be small. The so-called phenomenon of freezing (the vanishing of $[bb.1]$ or $[cc.2]$) is thus associated with a small determinant, which usually but not always gives rise to instability. (See the reference to Tuckerman below.)

Hint: Chio's pivotal expansion will be found admirably suited to the demonstration of Eq. 12. The work might pro-

[12]L. B. Tuckerman, *Annals of Math. Statistics*, vol. 12, 1941: pp. 307–316.

ceed as follows, the pivot element being unity in the upper left corner.

$$\Delta \equiv \begin{vmatrix} [aa] & [ab] & [ac] \\ [ab] & [bb] & [bc] \\ [ac] & [bc] & [cc] \end{vmatrix} = [aa] \begin{vmatrix} 1 & \dfrac{[ab]}{[aa]} & \dfrac{[ac]}{[aa]} \\ [ab] & [bb] & [bc] \\ [ac] & [bc] & [cc] \end{vmatrix}$$

$$= [aa] \begin{vmatrix} [bb] - [ab]\dfrac{[ab]}{[aa]} & [bc] - [ac]\dfrac{[ab]}{[aa]} \\ [bc] - [ac]\dfrac{[ab]}{[aa]} & [cc] - [ac]\dfrac{[ac]}{[aa]} \end{vmatrix}$$

$$= [aa] \begin{vmatrix} [bb.1] & [bc.1] \\ [bc.1] & [cc] - [ac]\dfrac{[ac]}{[aa]} \end{vmatrix}$$

$$= [aa][bb.1] \begin{vmatrix} 1 & \dfrac{[bc.1]}{[bb.1]} \\ [bc.1] & [cc] - [ac]\dfrac{[ac]}{[aa]} \end{vmatrix}$$

$$= [aa][bb.1][cc.2]$$

(b) Show that none of the extreme left entries in Rows I, II, and III can be negative. (*Hint:* Make use of Sec. 29. Or, use the Schwarz-Christoffel inequality.)

Exercise 2. The matrix reciprocal to Δ can be denoted by

$$\Delta^{-1} \equiv \begin{vmatrix} c_{11} & c_{12} & c_{13} \\ c_{21} & c_{22} & c_{23} \\ c_{31} & c_{32} & c_{33} \end{vmatrix} \tag{13}$$

(a) Show that the solution of the normal equations with the constant columns C_1, C_2, and C_3 leads to the values

$$c_{11} = \frac{\text{cof. of } [aa]}{\Delta}, \quad c_{12} = \frac{\text{cof. of } [ab]}{\Delta}, \quad c_{13} = \frac{\text{cof. of } [ac]}{\Delta},$$

$$c_{21} = \frac{\text{cof. of } [ab]}{\Delta}, \quad c_{22} = \frac{\text{cof. of } [bb]}{\Delta}, \quad c_{23} = \frac{\text{cof. of } [bc]}{\Delta},$$

$$c_{31} = \frac{\text{cof. of } [ac]}{\Delta}, \quad c_{32} = \frac{\text{cof. of } [bc]}{\Delta}, \quad c_{33} = \frac{\text{cof. of } [cc]}{\Delta}$$

The abbreviation cof. denotes cofactor.

Since Δ falls in the denominator of each element, a small value of Δ, near indeterminacy, results in high standard errors of the parameters; see Exercises 2a and 12b of Chapter X.

(b) Like the determinant Δ of the coefficients, the reciprocal matrix Δ^{-1} is symmetrical, i.e., $c_{12} = c_{21}$, $c_{13} = c_{31}$, $c_{23} = c_{32}$.

(c) The matrices Δ and Δ^{-1} are also alike in another respect — the terms on the main diagonal will always be positive.

(d) Show that $c_{33} = 1/[cc.2] =$ the reciprocal of the coefficient of the third unknown in Row III.

Exercise 3. (a) Combine Eq. 17 on page 57, and Eqs. 10 on page 136 to get

$$S = [oo] - [ao]A - [bo]B - [co]C \tag{14}$$

Show also that

$$S = \frac{\begin{vmatrix} [aa] & [ab] & [ac] & [ao] \\ [ab] & [bb] & [bc] & [bo] \\ [ac] & [bc] & [cc] & [co] \\ [ao] & [bo] & [co] & [oo] \end{vmatrix}}{\begin{vmatrix} [aa] & [ab] & [ac] \\ [ab] & [bb] & [bc] \\ [ac] & [bc] & [cc] \end{vmatrix}} \tag{15}$$

Hint: Expand the numerator and get

$$S = -[ao]\frac{\begin{vmatrix} [ab] & [ac] & [ao] \\ [bb] & [bc] & [bo] \\ [bc] & [cc] & [co] \end{vmatrix}}{\Delta} + [bo]\frac{\begin{vmatrix} [aa] & [ac] & [ao] \\ [ab] & [bc] & [bo] \\ [ac] & [cc] & [co] \end{vmatrix}}{\Delta}$$

$$-[co]\frac{\begin{vmatrix} [aa] & [ab] & [ao] \\ [ab] & [bb] & [bo] \\ [ac] & [bc] & [co] \end{vmatrix}}{\Delta} + [oo]\frac{\Delta}{\Delta}$$

which reduces to Eq. 14 when it is observed that the coefficient of $-[ao]$ is none other than A, the coefficient of $[bo]$ is $-B$, and the coefficient of $-[co]$ is C.

(*b*) Prove that the extreme left entry in Row IV of the solution exhibited on page 158 is actually S. Thus, the minimized sum of squares of the residuals comes automatically in the routine of the solution.

(*c*) Show also, by noting how Rows 8, 9, and 10 are formed, that

$$S = [oo] - [aa]A''^2 - [bb.1]B'^2 - [cc.2]C^2 \qquad (16)$$

where $A'' = [ao]/[aa] =$ the value of A that would be obtained if b and c were fixed (not adjustable) at the values b_0 and c_0, and wherein also $B' = [bo.1]/[bb.1] =$ the value of B that would be obtained if c were fixed at the value c_0, but a and b both adjustable.

Remark 1. This result sheds a singular elegance on the form of the solution exhibited on page 158. The term $[oo]$ seen in Row 4 is the sum of the weighted squares of the residuals calculated under the assumption that $a = a_0$, $b = b_0$, $c = c_0$ (see Exercise 3 of Sec. 58, p. 145). The three negative terms in the "1" column of Rows 8, 9, and 10 on page 158 are precisely the amounts subtracted from $[oo]$ by the terms on the right of Eq. 16, and in the same order. That is to say, by the routine solution outlined on page 158 there will appear (1°) in Row 8 the reduction in weighted squares that is brought about by allowing a to be adjustable while b and c are fixed at b_0 and c_0; (2°) in Row 9 the further reduction that is accomplished by allowing b to be adjustable while c is held at c_0; and (3°) in Row 10 the final reduction that comes from allowing c to be adjustable, the net result being the minimized sum of weighted squares, S, in Row IV.

After a solution has been carried out upon the parameters a, b, c, the question often arises, what would have been the result for S if the parameter c had not been adjusted, but had been fixed at (say) γ_0? Now if this γ_0 is not too far from the final value of c, one need only add $[cc.2](c - \gamma_0)^2$ to S in order to see what *would* have been obtained for S had c been fixed at γ_0 (see Examples 1 and 2 of Chapter XI). The value of σ^2 (*ext*) would then be $S + [cc.2](c - \gamma_0)^2$ divided by $n - 2$, not $n-3$ ($n =$ the number of points).

Under certain conditions, the restriction that γ_0 and c be not far apart can be removed; the polynomial $y = a + bx + cx^2$

with x free of error is an example. It all depends on whether the parameter c enters the L factors of Tables 1 and 2 in Section 60. If it does not, then no matter how wide the disparity between c and γ_0, the term $[cc.2](c - \gamma_0)^2$ still represents the increment in S that would be brought about by adjusting a and b to the condition $c = \gamma_0$.

In like manner, and under similar restrictions, a term $(b - \beta_0)^2/c_{22}$ will represent the increment in S that would be brought about by adjusting a and c to the condition $b = \beta_0$ (see Exercise 2d).

Similarly, the two terms $[bb.1]$ $(b - \beta_0)^2$ and $[cc.2]$ $(c - \gamma_0)^2$ added to the S found in Row IV will give what would have been obtained for S if only a had been adjusted, b and c fixed at β_0 and γ_0. In this circumstance, $\sigma^2(ext)$ would be computed with $n - 1$ degrees of freedom.

It is important, as a practical matter, to note that the coefficients $[bb.1]$ and $[cc.2]$, needed for these increments, are *already at hand*, *numerically*, in Rows II and III in the finished solution, page 158.

Remark 2. In both parts (a) and (c), S is shown as three terms subtracted from $[oo]$. Evidently

$$[ao]A + [bo]B + [co]C = [aa]A''^2 + [bb.1]B'^2 + [cc.2]C^2$$

(d) From Eq. 16 it follows that if c be changed by the amount δc, while a and b remain fixed, the change δS in the sum of squares obeys the relation

$$\frac{\delta S}{\sigma^2} = \left(\frac{\delta c}{\text{S. E. of } c}\right)^2 \tag{17}$$

Exercise 4. Prove that the solution for A, B, and C found from the " 1 " column will also be given by the equations

$$\left. \begin{array}{l} A = [ao]c_{11} + [bo]c_{12} + [co]c_{13} \\ B = [ao]c_{21} + [bo]c_{22} + [co]c_{23} \\ C = [ao]c_{31} + [bo]c_{32} + [co]c_{33} \end{array} \right\} \tag{18}$$

This method of finding the unknowns A, B, and C is called the *reciprocal solution* because the reciprocal matrix is used as a multiplier along with the constant (" 1 ") column $[ao]$, $[bo]$, $[co]$. The reciprocal solution is particularly useful when the same coefficients, hence the same reciprocal matrix, are repeated over and over from one problem to another, but with a new constant column for each problem, and hence with a new set of values for A, B, and C each time. See, however, the reference to difficulties that may be encountered in near indeterminacy, mentioned earlier in this section, also in Example 1 of Chapter XI. Theoretically, the direct and reciprocal solutions should agree, and they will if the computer carries enough decimals.

In matrix notation, the results of this exercise can be expressed as

$$\Delta v = H$$

where Δ is the matrix of the coefficients of the unknowns.

H is the matrix of the " 1 " column, namely,
$$\begin{matrix} [ao] \\ [bo] \\ [co] \end{matrix}$$

and

v is the matrix of the three unknowns, namely,
$$\begin{matrix} A \\ B \\ C \end{matrix}$$

The solution of the above equation is

$$v = \Delta^{-1} H$$

To evaluate Δ^{-1} we set

$$\Delta c = 1 \quad \text{(the unit matrix)}$$

and find

$$c = \Delta^{-1}$$

Having now the matrix Δ^{-1}, we use it as a multiplier with H to find the matrix v from the relation above, getting $v = cH$. This is the matrix expression for the results stated in the preceding exercise. For illustrations of the reciprocal solution see Section 36 and Examples 1 and 2 of Chapter XI.

Exercise 5. Prove that the values of the determinants Δ and Δ^{-1} are reciprocals. (Δ and Δ^{-1} defined on page 162.)

Exercise 6. (a) If $x = r \cos \theta$, $y = r \sin \theta$, the two Jacobians as matrices, namely,

$$\begin{vmatrix} \dfrac{dx}{dr} & \dfrac{dy}{dr} \\[2mm] \dfrac{dx}{d\theta} & \dfrac{dy}{d\theta} \end{vmatrix} \quad \text{and} \quad \begin{vmatrix} \dfrac{\partial r}{\partial x} & \dfrac{\partial \theta}{\partial x} \\[2mm] \dfrac{\partial r}{\partial y} & \dfrac{\partial \theta}{\partial y} \end{vmatrix}$$

are reciprocals of one another; i.e., their product gives the unit matrix

$$\begin{vmatrix} 1 & 0 \\ 0 & 1 \end{vmatrix}$$

(b) Show that a similar relation exists in three dimensions.

In the derivatives taken with the symbol d, θ is constant while x, y, and r vary, and again r is constant while x, y, and θ vary. In the derivatives taken with the symbol ∂, x is constant while r, θ, and y vary, and again y is constant while r, θ, and x vary.

62. The weights of the parameters; their standard errors. The standard error of a function of the parameters.   The standard error of a curve.   It is a fact[13] that the reciprocals of the weights of the parameters are found on the diagonal of Δ^{-1} (see Exercise 2 of the preceding section), i.e.,

$$w_a = \frac{1}{c_{11}}, \quad w_b = \frac{1}{c_{22}}, \quad w_c = \frac{1}{c_{33}} \tag{19}$$

where

$c_{11} = $ var. coeff. of a, $c_{22} = $ var. coeff. of b, $c_{33} = $ var. coeff. of c

Then, since weights are reciprocals of variance coefficients (p. 21),

$$\sigma_a^2 = c_{11}\sigma^2, \quad \sigma_b^2 = c_{22}\sigma^2, \quad \sigma_c^2 = c_{33}\sigma^2 \tag{20}$$

or

$$\left. \begin{array}{l} (\text{S. E. of } a)^2 = c_{11}\sigma^2 \\ (\text{ ``  `` } b)^2 = c_{22}\sigma^2 \\ (\text{ ``  `` } c)^2 = c_{33}\sigma^2 \end{array} \right\} \tag{21}$$

Let f be a function of the parameters.   Then

$$\begin{aligned} \sigma_f^2 &= (f_a\sigma_a)^2 + 2(f_af_b r_{ab}\sigma_a\sigma_b + f_af_c r_{ac}\sigma_a\sigma_c) \\ &\quad + (f_b\sigma_b)^2 + 2f_bf_c r_{bc}\sigma_b\sigma_c + (f_c\sigma_c)^2 \quad \text{(By Eq. 7, p. 40)} \\ &= \sigma^2\{c_{11}f_a^2 + 2c_{12}f_af_b + 2c_{13}f_af_c + c_{22}f_b^2 \\ &\qquad\qquad\qquad\qquad\qquad + 2c_{23}f_bf_c + c_{33}f_c^2\} \end{aligned} \tag{22}$$

[13] The theory of all this goes back to Gauss, *Theoria Combinationis*, Art. 21. An excellent reference is Whittaker and Robinson's *Calculus of Observations*, Arts. 121–123.

As in Section 13 we write for the unbiased estimate of σ^2 by external consistency,

$$\sigma^2(ext) = \frac{S}{k}, \quad \text{where} \quad k = n - p$$

n being the number of points and p the number of adjustable parameters. When σ is not known from any better source, this estimate may have to suffice, and $\sigma^2(ext)$ would replace σ^2 in Eqs. 21 and 22, giving respectively

$$\left. \begin{array}{l} (\text{Est'd S. E. of } a)^2 = c_{11}\,\sigma^2(ext) \\ (\quad " \quad " \quad " \quad b)^2 = c_{22}\,\sigma^2(ext) \\ (\quad " \quad " \quad " \quad c)^2 = c_{33}\,\sigma^2(ext) \end{array} \right\} \tag{23}$$

and

$$(\text{Est'd S. E. of } f)^2 = \sigma^2(ext)\{c_{11}f_a{}^2 + 2c_{12}f_af_b + 2c_{13}f_af_c \\ + c_{22}f_b{}^2 + 2c_{23}f_bf_c + c_{33}f_c{}^2\} \tag{24}$$

The student is urged to study Chapter V of R. A. Fisher's *Statistical Methods for Research Workers*, wherein examples of the manipulation of the reciprocal matrix will be found.

63. The error bands associated with a curve. Rejection of observations. When we write

$$y = f(x;\ a, b, c) \tag{25}$$

and ask for the standard error of y, we are merely asking for the standard error of a function of a, b, and c, but not of x; consequently, we can apply Eqs. 22 or 24 at once. x enters merely as a constant.

The distinction between Eqs. 22 and 24 is that, in the former, σ is supposed to be known or approximated closely enough, under conditions of randomness, as from previous experience, or from internal consistency (Sec. 13), or from any other source that does not depend on the way the particular points in question fit the curve. In Eq. 24, on the other hand, σ is estimated from the fit of the points, as was explained in Section 13. Eq. 22, when applied at abscissa x along the fitted curve, gives the standard error of the curve for that particular abscissa.   If this calculation is made for several abscissas, one may plot points along the standard error band.   Error bands are plotted to show one or more standard errors above and below the fitted curve.   In Fig. 22 (p. 228) the band shown is ±1.96 standard errors.   This width of band would, on the average, leave 5 percent of the points outside the band if the coordinates were distributed normally about their true values with standard errors $\sigma/\sqrt{w_x}$ for x and $\sigma/\sqrt{w_y}$ for y.   Sometimes the " probable error " band is drawn,[14] or a multiple thereof.

When σ is estimated from the fit of the points and used in Eq. 24, one obtains a confidence band for the curve.   A confidence band is different in principle from an error band only in using $\sigma(ext)$ in place of a presumably better known value of σ.   This, however, is often an important difference, because, although σ itself is supposed to be constant, the external estimate of σ will vary from one experiment to another, even in randomness, unless $n - p$ is as large as 20 or preferably 30.   The width of the band may be adjusted to give various degrees of " confidence."   This is done by using an integral of Student's distribution, which is easy to do by looking up the corresponding value of t in Fisher's tables[15] for $n - p$ degrees of freedom.   Thus, to compute a 95 percent confidence band, one would look up t_{95} in Fisher's table, and then compute $|Y - y|$ for several values of x, using the equation

$$t_{95} = \frac{|Y - y|}{\text{Est'd S. E. of } y} \qquad (26)$$

[14] A probable error, for normally distributed observations, is 0.67 times the standard error.   For other distributions, some other factor is required, but calculations are ordinarily made with the factor 0.67 for which $\frac{2}{3}$ is a close enough approximation.   Birge uses the probable error band along with his curves.   The following papers of his are recommended for their scientific insight, and for simple derivations of the standard error formulas: (a) *Physical Review*, vol. 40, 1932: pp. 207–261;   (b) *Amer. Physics Teacher*, vol. 7, 1939: pp. 351–357.

[15] V. A. Nekrassoff's very handy nomograph may be used.   It was published in *Metron*, vol. 8, No. 3, 1930, and is reproduced in W. A. Shewhart's *Economic Control of Quality* (Van Nostrand, 1931), p. 490; see also Deming and Birge *Statistical Theory of Errors* (The Graduate School, Department of Agriculture, Washington, 1938), p. 136.

The distance $|Y - y|$ laid off above and below the curve defines points on the confidence band, and the result will have the appearance of Fig. 20. (The capital Y used here is not to be confused with the same letter used in Fig. 17 and elsewhere for an observed coordinate.)

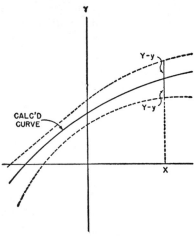

Fig. 20. A fitted curve and the corresponding confidence band. An error band is laid off in like manner as a multiple of the standard error of the function, and has a similar appearance.

Remark 1. A convenient reference showing the application of Eq. 24 to curve fitting is a paper by Henry Schultz, *J. Amer. Stat. Assoc.*, vol. 25, 1930: pp. 139–185. Schultz shows curves and confidence bands of width twice the standard error of the curve for several kinds of curves. It should be mentioned, as Schultz does, that all these things were well known to Gauss and others in his time, but that they did not take the trouble to write out the formulas explicitly and draw the graphs for all the things that interest us today.

Remark 2. It must be remembered that, even in a state of randomness, a new set of points (i.e., a new experiment) will give a new curve and a new set of parameters; hence, curve and error band, will be shifted to a new position by a new experiment. Moreover, since the external estimate of σ will fluctuate from one set of data to another, then not only will the curve and confidence band be shifted to a new position by a new set of data, but the width of the band itself will also be different.   This is one of the reasons why a single experiment, without consideration of other knowledge, is not a basis for action, particularly if the consequences of the wrong action are hazardous (cf. Ch. I).

Confidence intervals for any other function of a, b, and c are made up in like manner, and similar remarks apply.

The purpose in drawing an error band or confidence band is to invoke statistical aid in detecting spurious conditions in the data, or, more precisely, in the experimental conditions that gave rise to the data.   A point that lies outside an error band of width two or three standard errors should be investigated; but it is to be discarded, and the curve refitted, only if investigation discloses anomalous experimental conditions at that point.   Whether one uses a band of width two standard errors or three standard errors is a matter that can be decided only by personal preference and experience in a particular line of work.   The wider the band, the fewer the points outside it, and on this criterion the less likely one is to look for experimental difficulties.   On the other hand, if the band is too narrow, one will look for experimental difficulties too often — that is, he will be looking for trouble too often when there is no trouble.[16]   Many papers and chapters have been written on the statistical rejection of observations, but the best practice seems to be contained in the statements just given.   In summary, *a point is never to be excluded on statistical grounds alone.*[17]

[16] These thoughts follow the reasoning expounded by Shewhart in 1924 when he introduced the control chart.   The student of modern statistical theory will recognize in them the arguments inherent in errors of the first and second kinds.

[17] R. A. Fisher, " On the mathematical foundations of theoretical statistics," *Phil. Trans. Royal Soc.*, vol. 222A, 1922: p. 322 in particular.

PART E

EXERCISES AND NOTES

CHAPTER X

EXERCISES ON FITTING VARIOUS FUNCTIONS

64. Purpose of the chapter. The exercises and notes in this chapter will serve two purposes: *first*, to provide practice in forming the normal equations for various functions commonly met in practice; *second*, to provide a compendium of results, handy for reference. Once these exercises are mastered, other functions that arise in practice should present little or no difficulty.

A special note should be made concerning the fitting of polynomials such as

$$y = a + bx, \quad y = a + bx + cx^2, \quad \text{etc.}$$

When x is free of error and uniformly spaced, certain short-cuts, eminently worth while learning if the problem is to occur frequently, are provided by the use of orthogonal functions. Since good references are accessible, the subject need not be treated here. The methods shown in the following exercises will work under very general conditions. But if a polynomial is to be fitted again and again when x is free of error and equally spaced, the reader is advised to learn the method of orthogonal functions. The theory is complicated, but the application is not. The following list of references will suffice for clear descriptions of several different procedures:

1. R. A. Fisher, *Statistical Methods for Research Workers* (Oliver & Boyd); sections 28, 28.1, and 29.2 in the 6th and later editions. Fisher's procedure and his description thereof have justifiably found great favor.

2. R. A. Fisher and Frank Yates, *Statistical Tables for Biological, Agricultural, and Medical Research* (Oliver & Boyd, 1938). An extension of these tables has recently been pub-

lished by R. L. Anderson and E. E. Houseman, " Tables of orthogonal polynomial values extended to $n = 104$ " (Ames, *Research Bulletin* 297, 1942).

3. Raymond T. Birge and John D. Shea, " A rapid method of calculating the least squares solution of a polynomial of any degree " (*University of California Publications in Mathematics*, vol. 2, No. 5, 1927; now unfortunately out of print). This procedure is rapid and possesses great merit. Up to a certain stage it seems to be equivalent to Harold T. Davis' method, but beyond that stage the remaining work is simpler than Davis', and requires fewer decimals.

4. A. C. Aitken, *Proc. Royal Soc.* (Edinburgh), vol. 53, 1932–1933: pp. 54–78.

5. Max Sasuly, *Trend Analysis of Statistics* (The Brookings Institution, Washington, 1934).

65. The line[1]

In the exercises that follow, the symbols $[x]$, $[xx]$, $[xy]$, $[xF_0]$, and the like, refer to summations formed with the *observed* coordinates. Moreover, $\bar{x}$ and $\bar{y}$ refer to the mean values of the observed coordinates. The distinction made in Chapters IV, VII, and IX — capital letters for observed coordinates, and small letters for the adjusted coordinates — can now be dropped. In this chapter and the next, it will be convenient to use capital letters to denote logarithms (Y for log y; etc.). When there seems to be special need of distinguishing observed from calculated coordinates, the subscript *obs* or *calc* will be affixed. In the numerical evaluation of the derivatives, and of W or L (Tables 1 and 2 of Sec. 60), if x and y are called for, their observed values are to be inserted, along with the approximate determinations a_0, b_0, c_0 for the parameters.

Exercise 1.   (a) Given the line

$$y = a + bx$$

to be fitted to n points, x free of error, all y coordinates of equal weight (unity).   Here we take

$$F = y - (a + bx)$$

[1] The line $y = bx$, forced to pass through the origin (i.e., with $a = 0$), was discussed to some extent in Section 15.

The derivatives are

$$F_a = -1, \quad F_b = -x$$

$$F_x = -b \quad \text{(not needed here)}, \quad F_y = 1$$

$$L = 1 \quad \text{(Why? See Eq. 8, p. 134.)}$$

With the approximate values a_0 and b_0 we compute

$$F_o = y_{obs} - (a_0 + b_0 x)$$

at every point. Since $L = 1$ at every point, Tables 1 and 2 of Section 60 coalesce, and the normal equations are seen to be these:

Row	A	B	=	1	C_1	C_2	Sum	
I	n	$[x]$	$-[F_0]$	1	0	$\cdots$		(Set 1, Exer-
2		$[xx]$	$-[xF_0]$	0	1	$\cdots$		cise 1)
3			$[F_0F_0]$	0	0	$\cdots$		

(b) The solution for A and B, found by the routine of Section 61 or any other method of solution, is

$$A = -\frac{[F_0]}{n} - \bar{x}B$$

$$B = \frac{-[xF_0] + \bar{x}[F_0]}{n\mu_2}$$

where

$$n\mu_2 = [xx] - n\bar{x}^2$$

$n\mu_2$ is the second moment of the x coordinates about an axis parallel to Oy and passing through the centroid $\bar{x}, \bar{y}$.

(c) The adjusted values of a and b turn out to be

$$a = a_0 - A = \bar{y} - b\bar{x}$$

$$b = b_0 - B = \sum \frac{(x - \bar{x})(y - \bar{y})}{n\mu_2} = \frac{[xy] - n\bar{x}\bar{y}}{n\mu_2}$$

The fitted line therefore passes through the centroid $\bar{x}, \bar{y}$. But note that when there is error in both x and y coordinates at some or all of the observed points, the weights being such that w_x/w_y is not constant throughout, the line does *not* pass through the centroid (see Remark 2 in Exercise 4).

(*d*) The solution just found for a and b is the same as would have been found from the normal equations shown below as Set 2, in which the unknowns are the full values of a and b. In this problem it is therefore permissible to take a_0 and b_0 both as zero, whereupon F_0 is simply y_{obs}.

Row	a	b	=	1	C_1	C_2	Sum	
I	n	$[x]$		$[y]$	1	0	. . .	(Set 2,
2		$[xx]$		$[xy]$	0	1	. . .	Exercise 1)
3				$[yy]$	0	0	. . .	

Note that a calculation of F_0 is required at every point in forming the normal equations of Set 1, but not for the formation of Set 2, because in the latter, F_0 is the same as y_{obs}. However, in Set 1 it is only the residuals A and B that are to be solved for, the main part of the adjustment having already been allowed for in fixing the approximate values a_0 and b_0. It is different in Set 2; there the unknowns are the full values of a and b, requiring the computer to carry more figures. These additional figures usually more than offset the time required for computing F_0. It therefore is usually advisable to find good approximations and use Set 1. The better the approximations, the fewer figures required. Birge and Shea make use of this principle in their method of fitting polynomials (mentioned in the preceding section).

(*e*) When the solution of either Set 1 or 2 is carried out according to the scheme of calculation exhibited on page 158, the extreme left entry in Row III will be the minimized sum of squares S, or $\sum (y_{obs} - y_{calc})^2$. The sum of squares removed from $[F_0F_0]$ in Set 1, and from $[yy]$ in Set 2, by the successive adjustments of a and b, appear in the extreme left entries of Rows 5 and 6. Show that

$$S = [yy] - n\bar{y}^2 - n\mu_2 b^2$$

the last term being the sum of squares removed by allowing the line to have slope b instead of slope 0 — in other words, the *sum of squares removed by regression*. The two terms $n\bar{y}^2$ and $n\mu_2 b^2$ appear in Rows 5 and 6 of the solution of Set 2.

(*f*) If V denotes $y_{obs} - y_{calc}$ at any point, the solution for a and b renders $\sum V = 0$. (But note that neither $\sum V$ nor $\sum wV$ is necessarily zero in least squares solutions; it only happens to be so here. In fact, in Sec. 15a we saw a simple example wherein neither $\sum V$ nor $\sum wV$ was zero. See Remark 4 in Exercise 4; see also Exercise 5.)

Exercise 2. (*a*) The reciprocal matrix for the normal equations in the preceding exercise appears in the C_1 and C_2 columns of Rows 7 and 8 (these numbers refer to the solution of the equations solved according to the form on p. 158). It turns out to be

$$\Delta^{-1} = \begin{vmatrix} \dfrac{1}{n} + \dfrac{\bar{x}^2}{n\mu_2} & -\dfrac{\bar{x}}{n\mu_2} \\[3ex] -\dfrac{\bar{x}}{n\mu_2} & \dfrac{1}{n\mu_2} \end{vmatrix}$$

(*b*) From the upper left and lower right elements of this array we may say that

$$\text{The weight of } a = \frac{n}{1 + \bar{x}^2/\mu_2}$$

$$\text{The weight of } b = n\mu_2$$

Thus, if the experimental conditions were random, our confidence in b would increase as the " spread " of the points increases. Is this reasonable? Why does the weight of a depend on $\bar{x}$?

(*c*)   (S. E. of $a)^2 = \sigma^2(1/n + \bar{x}^2/n\mu_2)$
              (S. E. of $b)^2 = \sigma^2/n\mu_2$

Note that the weights and standard errors of a and b do not involve the y coordinates of the points. Compare with part d of the next exercise. Note also that the denominator of the last fraction is equal to Δ, since

$$n^2\mu_2 = \begin{vmatrix} n & [x] \\ [x] & [xx] \end{vmatrix} = \Delta$$

hence near indeterminacy (a small value of Δ) is closely associated with large standard errors of a and b, and a rapid " fanning out " of the standard error of y_{calc} each side of $\bar{x}$, $\bar{y}$ (see the next part; also Exercise 2a of Sec. 61).

(d) From Eq. 8, page 40, and the reciprocal matrix of part (a) of this exercise, prove that the

$$(\text{S. E. of } y_{calc})^2 = \frac{\sigma^2}{n}\left\{1 + \frac{(x - \bar{x})^2}{\mu_2}\right\}$$

Thus the standard error of y_{calc} is least at the center of gravity ($\bar{x}$, $\bar{y}$) of the points, and fans out each side of it.   (See Sec. 63 and the reference to Henry Schultz; also Figs. 20 and 22.)

(e) The standard error of the calculated line of Exercise 1 at the center of gravity is $\sigma/\sqrt{n}$, as it would be for n observations made on a single unknown.   (Do this in two ways: 1° put $x = \bar{x}$ in part d; 2° put $\bar{x} = 0$ in part c for the standard error of a.)

Exercise 3.   (a) Carry out the solution of the normal equations of Exercise 1a in symbols, following the outline given in Section 61, and show that the minimized value of S or of $\sum (y_{obs} - y_{calc})^2$ comes in the " 1 " column of Row III (which will be the extreme left entry in III).   The same is true if the approximations a_0 and b_0 are used, as is advised in Exercise 1d.

(b) Show that the minimized sum of squares in this problem can be written

$$\sum res^2 = n(1 - r^2)s_y^2$$

where

$$r = \sum \frac{(x - \bar{x})(y - \bar{y})}{n s_x s_y} = \text{the correlation coefficient}$$

and

$$ns_y^2 = [yy] - n\bar{y}^2$$
$$ns_x^2 = [xx] - n\bar{x}^2$$

(s_x^2 is here used in place of μ_2 for consistency with s_y.)

(c) The estimate of σ made from the fit of the line is

$$\sigma^2(ext) = \frac{n(1 - r^2)s_y^2}{n - 2} \quad \text{(See Sec. 13)}$$

(*d*) The

$$(\text{Est'd S. E. of } a)^2 = \frac{1 - r^2}{n - 2} s_y{}^2 \left(1 + \frac{\bar{x}^2}{s_x{}^2}\right)$$

$$(\text{Est'd S. E. of } b)^2 = \frac{1 - r^2}{n - 2} \frac{s_y{}^2}{s_x{}^2}$$

Note that the estimated standard errors of a and b involve the y coordinates; compare with part (*c*) of the preceding exercise.

(*e*) The

$$(\text{Est'd S. E. of } y_{calc})^2 = \frac{1 - r^2}{n - 2} s_y{}^2 \left\{1 + \frac{(x - \bar{x})^2}{s_x{}^2}\right\}$$

Exercise 4. (*a*) If both x and y coordinates are subject to error with varying precisions at some or all of the n points, one must perform the calculations called for in Tables 1 and 2 of Section 60. For the line

$$y = a + bx$$

one may take

$$F \equiv y - a - bx$$

Some good approximate values a_0 and b_0 having been found, one can then calculate the numerical value of

$$F_0 = y_{obs} - (a_0 + b_0 x_{obs})$$

at each of the n points. The derivatives of F are

$$F_x = -b, \quad F_y = 1, \quad F_a = -1, \quad F_b = -x$$

whereupon

$$L = \frac{b^2}{w_x} + \frac{1}{w_y}$$

L varies from point to point with w_x or w_y.

The headings for Table 1 of Section 60 would be these:

h, or Point No.	w_x	w_y	L	$\sqrt{L}$	$F_b = -x$	F_0

(It is not necessary to tabulate F_x, F_y, and F_a since they remain constant from point to point.)

The headings for Table 2 of Section 60 would be as shown below.

h, or Point No.	$F_a/\sqrt{L} = -1/\sqrt{L}$	$F_b/\sqrt{L} = -x/\sqrt{L}$	$F_0/\sqrt{L}$	Sum

It has already been remarked (Remark 3, Sec. 54) that there is some theoretical advantage in writing W in place of $1/L$, though it is a fact that with machines having automatic division and two dials for quotients — one for the individual quotients needed for Table 2, and another for cumulating the quotients across the rows for the " Sum " column of Table 2 — there may be a practical advantage in tabulating $\sqrt{L}$ rather than $\sqrt{W}$ in Table 1, and using divisions by $\sqrt{L}$, rather than multiplications by $\sqrt{W}$, to form Table 2.

Writing now

$$\frac{1}{W} = \frac{b^2}{w_x} + \frac{1}{w_y} \quad \text{for } L$$

we see that $W = w_y$ if x is free of error or if $b = 0$ (see the next exercise), and $W = w_x/b^2$ if y is free of error, but that *both terms are required* if x and y are both subject to varying errors, and if the line is inclined so that b is not small (see Exercise 8b).

In terms of W the headings of Table 2 might be these:

h, or Point No.	$\sqrt{W}$	$-x\sqrt{W}$	$\sqrt{W} \cdot F_0$	Sum

(b) The normal equations are formed in the usual way by summing squares and cross-products from Table 2. They can be symbolized as shown in Set 1.

Row	A	B	$=$	1	C_1	C_2	Sum	
I	$[W]$	$[Wx]$	$-[WF_0]$	1	0	...		
2		$[Wxx]$	$-[WxF_0]$	0	1	...		(Set 1,
3			$[WF_0F_0]$	0	0	...		Exercise 4)

The systematic solution of the normal equations (shown on p. 158) gives A and B from the " 1 " column, and the reciprocal matrix Δ^{-1} as usual from the C_1 and C_2 columns. The adjusted values of a and b will be

$$a = a_0 - A$$
$$b = b_0 - B$$

The systematic solution gives the minimized value of $\sum (w_x V_x^2 + w_y V_y^2)$ in Row III, column " 1." That portion of the sum of the weighted squares subtracted from $[WF_0F_0]$ by shifting the first parameter from a_0 to a appears in Row 5, and the portion further removed by shifting the second parameter from b_0 to b appears in Row 6 (see Exercise 3 of Sec. 61; also Exercise 1 of this section).

Note that a_0 and b_0 *may* be taken as 0 (with the necessary increase in the number of decimals required in the normal equations), so far as F_0 is concerned, in which event F_0 becomes simply

$$F_0 = y_{obs}$$

The normal equations are then symbolized like those following,

Row	a	b	$=$	1	C_1	C_2	Sum	
I	$[W]$	$[Wx]$	$+[Wy]$	1	0	$\ldots$	(Set 2,
2		$[Wxx]$	$+[Wxy]$	0	1	$\ldots$	Exercise 4)
3			$[Wyy]$	0	0	$\ldots$	

and the solution gives a and b directly. Why are more decimals required in these equations than in the preceding ones giving the (supposedly small) residuals A and B?

But note carefully that an approximate value of b *must* be used in the calculation of W at each point where x is subject to error. b_0 may be called 0 in the calculation of F_0 (as noted above) but *not* in the calculation of W. If this admonition is disregarded, the effect of the weighting of x is lost. In fact, if it turns out that the approximate value of b used for calculating W was too far removed from the final b, it may be desirable to make a *second adjustment* to secure improved weightings W, which can be obtained by using the value of b from the first adjustment; but this is seldom found necessary in practice.[2]

[2] As Gauss put it, in a somewhat different problem: " Quodsi dein calculo absoluto contra exspectationem valores incognitarum p', q', r', s', etc., tanti emergerent, ut parum tutum videatur, quadrata productaque neglexisse, eiusdem operationis repetitio (acceptis loco ipsarum π, χ, ρ, σ, etc., valoribus correctis ipsarum p, q, r, s, etc.) remedium promtum afferet." *Theoria Motus Corporum Coelestium* (Hamburg, 1809), Art. 180.

Remark 1. Of course, it may happen in some particular problem that b actually is very small, and that 0 is therefore a good approximation for b. In such circumstances the line is practically horizontal, the weighting of x does not matter much, and the computer may as well simplify matters and set $W = w_y$, ignoring the weighting of x — not because x is free of error (i.e., not because w_x is infinite), but because b is zero or nearly so. The student should ponder over the situation where b is actually known to be 0; do the values of x count at all in the solution? Does this not take us back to the simplest problem in curve fitting, seen in Section 10? The solution obtained there can be translated to the needs of the present circumstances by interchanging x and y, and rewriting Eq. 10 on page 19 to get

$$a = \frac{\sum wy}{\sum w},$$

then rewriting Eqs. 12 and 12′ on page 21 to get

$$w_a = \sum w$$

and the

$$(\text{S. E. of } a)^2 = \frac{\sigma}{\sum w}$$

In all these equations, w now denotes the weight of y, not x.

Remark 2. When x and y are both subject to error at some or all of the observed points, the line does not pass through the center of gravity

$$\bar{x} = \frac{[xw_x]}{[w_x]}, \quad \bar{y} = \frac{[yw_y]}{[w_y]}$$

But the line will in any case pass through a *quasi center* defined as

$$x' = \frac{[xW]}{[W]}, \quad y' = \frac{[yW]}{[W]}$$

Remark 3. With $1/W$ written in place of L, Eq. 8, page 134, gives

$$\frac{1}{W} = \frac{F_xF_x}{w_x} + \frac{F_yF_y}{w_y} \quad (\text{Cf. Remark 3, p. 135.})$$

As has already been seen, the first term drops out if x is free of error, and the second term drops out if y is free of error. To make the change from a solution in which x is free of error to one wherein both coordinates are subject to error, we merely add the other term in $1/W$ and recalculate W at every point, the procedure being otherwise the same. There is a close analogy with celestial mechanics; when one wishes to compute the orbit of a body of mass m about another of mass M, he may at first make the simplifying assumption that M is infinite (i.e., immovable), and solve the equations, later replacing m by μ where

$$\frac{1}{\mu} = \frac{1}{m} + \frac{1}{M}$$

This replacement yields the absolute motion of the two bodies, neither being of infinite mass (i.e., neither one immovable).

Remark 4. When x and y are both subject to error at some or all of the points, we can not always assert that

$$\sum V_x = 0, \quad \text{or} \quad \sum V_y = 0, \quad \text{or} \quad \sum (w_x V_x + w_y V_y) = 0$$

though these may sometimes happen, as in Exercises 1 and 5, q.v. We have already seen a simple example in Section 15, where these summations were not zero. There is, however, a property of least squares by which one can always assert that after the adjustment,[3]

$$\sum (w_x U_x V_x + w_y U_y V_y) = 0$$

(For definitions of U_x, etc., see Figs. 16 and 17 on pp. 132 and 133.)

Remark 5. It is interesting to note that in the routine solution of Set 2, the minimized S appears in the extreme left entry of Row III, but that, in contrast with Set 1, unless the final value of b is actually or very near 0, the entry in Row 6 directly above S will *not* show the increment in S that would result from fixing b at either the value 0 or b_0. The reason is that a good value of b *must* be used in W at each point where x is subject to error: if we want to know what the solution would have been with $b = 0$, we must actually make a solution with b set equal to 0 in the computation of W, in which circumstance W reduces to w_y, as already noted.

Exercise 5. Given

$$y = a + bx$$

to be fitted to n points, x free of error, the y coordinates each having weight w_y, varying from point to point. This is similar to

---

[3] Published by the author in the *Phil. Mag.*, vol. 19, 1935: pp. 389–402.

Exercise 1 except that now the y coordinates have unequal precisions. Here we take

$$F = y - a - bx$$

as in the preceding exercise, the derivatives being also the same. But since x is free of error, w_x is infinite, and it follows that W (defined as $1/L$) is none other than w_y. All we have to do is replace W in the preceding exercise by w_y, and the results will apply here. The headings of Table 1 of Section 60 will be these:

h, or Point No.	w_y	$\sqrt{w_y}$	$F_b = -x$	F_0

For Table 2 they will be these:

h, or Point No.	$\sqrt{w_y}$	$F_b/\sqrt{L} = -x\sqrt{w_y}$	$\sqrt{w_y} \cdot F_0$	Sum

The normal equations are written in the same symbols as those of the preceding exercise, but with w_y in place of W. Row III in the systematic solution of the normal equations (p. 158) gives the minimized value of $\sum w_y(y_{obs} - y_{calc})^2$. In Rows 5 and 6 are found the portions of the weighted squares removed by A and B, as in Exercise 1e (p. 175).

Note that, as in the preceding exercise, it is permissible to take a_0 and b_0 as zeros, if the number of decimals in the normal equations is increased accordingly. In this event,

$$F_0 = y_{obs}$$

and the normal equations may be written

Row	a	b	$=$ 1	C_1	C_2	Sum
I	$[w]$	$[wx]$	$[wy]$	1	0	...
2		$[wxx]$	$[wxy]$	0	1	...
3			$[wyy]$	0	0	...

giving a and b directly. Row III in the systematic solution will give the minimized value of $\sum w_y(y_{obs} - y_{calc})^2$ in the " 1 " column, and Rows 5 and 6 will show the sum of squares removed successively by a and b, as in Exercise 1e. Since w_x is infinite, the question of an approximate value of b for use in the calculation of W does not come up.

> *Remark.* For the conditions stated (x free of error) the sum of the weighted y residuals is zero, i.e.,

$$\sum wV = 0$$

See Remark 4 of Exercise 4, page 182.

Exercise 6.   (a) Given the line

$$y = a + bx$$

to be fitted to n points, both x and y coordinates subject to error but in such a way that w_x/w_y is constant and not infinite nor zero, the line passes through the center of gravity $\bar{x} = [w_x x]/[w_x]$, $\bar{y} = [w_y y]/[w_y]$, with slope

$$b = \frac{c[wv^2] - [wu^2] + \sqrt{\{c[wv^2] - [wu^2]\}^2 + 4c[wuv]^2}}{2c[wuv]}$$

> This is equivalent to a result obtained by Kummell in 1876, Karl Pearson in 1901, and Gini in 1921. Here u and v are the x and y coordinates of a point, measured from the center of gravity $\bar{x}, \bar{y}$; i.e., $u_i = x_i - \bar{x}$, and $v_i = y_i - \bar{y}$. c is written for w_y/w_x, and w in place of w_x, for convenience.

(b) If the plus sign be changed to minus in front of the radical, the result is the slope of the *worst* fitting line, that which *maximizes* the value of $\sum (w_x V_x{}^2 + w_y V_y{}^2)$.

(c) Prove that under these conditions of weighting, the best and worst fitting lines are perpendicular to each other.

Exercise 7.   (a) Given

$$y = a + bx$$

to be fitted to n points when y is free of error and all x coordinates are of equal weight (unity), we may write

$$x = p + qy$$

and find the following normal equations for p and q.   These are

Row	p	q	=	1	C_1	C_2	Sum
I	n	$[y]$	$[x]$	1	0	...
2		$[yy]$	$[yx]$	0	1	...
3			$[xx]$	0	0	...

like Set 2 of Exercise 1 with x and y interchanged.

Row III in the solution of the normal equations gives $\sum res^2$ where now the deviations are measured *parallel to the* x *axis*.

(b) The reciprocal matrix Δ^{-1} found in the C_1 and C_2 columns of Rows 7 and 8 of the solution will be

$$\Delta^{-1} = \begin{vmatrix} \dfrac{1}{n} + \dfrac{\bar{y}^2}{ns_y{}^2} & -\dfrac{\bar{y}}{ns_y{}^2} \\[3ex] -\dfrac{\bar{y}}{ns_y{}^2} & \dfrac{1}{ns_y{}^2} \end{vmatrix}$$

where $s_y{}^2$ has the same significance as in Exercise 3.

(c) (The S. E. of x_{calc})$^2 = \dfrac{\sigma^2}{n}\left\{1 + \dfrac{(y - \bar{y})^2}{s_y{}^2}\right\}$

(d) The normal equations of Exercise 7a give $\sum V_x = 0$. (See the remarks in Exercises 1f, 4, and 5.)

Exercise 8. (a) Prove that with y free of error, and all x coordinates of equal precision, the normal equations for a and b (or for A and B) in Exercise 4 will give the same line as the normal equations in Exercise 7a (i.e., will give $p = -a/b$ and $q = 1/b$), *except* for the effect of the neglect of the squares of the x residuals. The solution of Exercise 7a is the more accurate in not throwing away any higher powers of residuals. This may occasionally be important. (See also Exercises 18 and 23.)

(b) Show that if x has the same weight (i.e., the same precision) over all n points, and y likewise, x and y both subject to error, the line that one gets by the exact solution given in Exercise 6a lies between the two false lines that one gets by i. throwing the adjustment all on to y, using the equations of Exercise 1; and ii. throwing the adjustment all on to x, using the equations of Exercise 7a; but that these two false lines *differ only in the effect of the squares* of the x residuals and of the y residuals, respectively. (*Hint:* Both terms of $1/W$ in Exercise 4 are constant over all points when w_x and w_y are constant; hence, so far as the values of a and b or p and q are concerned, W can be put equal to unity at every point in all three solutions — in the correct solution, and in the two false solutions. The normal equations of Exercise 4 will then give identical results for all three. But the normal equations of Exercise 4 can be in error at most by the neglect of higher powers of the residuals, hence the false solutions i. and ii. can differ from the true solution only through the neglect of such terms. This means that when x has the same weight over all points, and y likewise, the false solutions will hardly be distinguishable from the true solution if the residuals are all fairly small.[4])

> *Remark 1.* If W is constant from one point to another, it is advisable for convenience of computation to choose the system of weighting so that $W = 1$ at all points. This is only saying that the arbitrary factor σ^2 in Eq. 13 of Section 11 is to be chosen so that $W = 1$. Then S in the extreme left entry of Row III in the solution of the normal equations comes out in the same system, and $\sigma^2(ext) = S/(n - 2)$ is the external estimate of σ^2 in the same units as were arbitrarily chosen for it.

(c) All three lines of part (b) pass through the center of gravity $\bar{x}, \bar{y}$ (called also the centroid).

> *Remark 2.* Statements similar to those of part (b) will hold for any curve when the combination of the form of the function and the weighting of the coordinates causes both terms of $1/W$ to be constant over all n points. Example 3 of the next chapter is an illustration in three dimensions (three terms in $1/W$).

Exercise 9. For the line $y = a + bx$ fitted to n points, the following expressions hold (all due to Karl Pearson, *Phil. Mag.,* vol. 2, 1901: pp. 559–572).

(a) $\sum res^2 = n(1 - r^2)s_y{}^2$

> x free of error, the y coordinates all of equal weight (unity); the deviations measured in the vertical. (This result was given in Exercise 3b.)

[4] This fact was noted by the author without proof in the *Proc. Physical Soc.* (London), vol. 47, 1935: p. 107.

(b) $\sum res^2 = n(1 - r^2)s_x^2$

y free of error, the x coordinates all of equal weight (unity); the deviations measured in the horizontal.

(c) $\sum res^2 = \frac{1}{2}n\{s_x^2 + s_y^2 - \sqrt{(s_x^2 - s_y^2)^2 + 4r^2 s_x^2 s_y^2}\}$

The x and y coordinates of equal weight (unity), the deviations measured perpendicular to the fitted line.

In these formulas, s_x^2, s_y^2, and r have the meaning ascribed to them in Exercise 3, page 177.

66. The parabola

Exercise 10.   Given

$$y = a + bx + cx^2$$

to be fitted to n points, x and y having weights w_x and w_y at any point.   Here we take

$$F = y - (a + bx + cx^2)$$

$$F_0 = y_{obs} - (a_0 + b_0 x_{obs} + c_0 x_{obs}^2)$$

The derivatives of F are

$$F_x = -(b + 2cx), \quad F_y = 1$$

$$F_a = -1, \quad F_b = -x, \quad F_c = -x^2$$

$$L \quad \text{or} \quad \frac{1}{W} = \frac{(b + 2cx)^2}{w_x} + \frac{1}{w_y}$$

The headings of Table 1 in Section 60 will be these:

h, or Point No.	$F_x = -(b + 2cx)$	w_x	w_y	L	$\sqrt{L}$	F_b	F_c	F_0

It is understood that in calculating all quantities under these headings, x and y are to be replaced by their observed values, and a, b, c, by a_0, b_0, c_0 (cf. the note at the beginning of Sec. 65, p. 173). It is not necessary to tabulate F_y and F_a because they remain constant from point to point.

The headings of Table 2 will be as shown below.

h, or Point No.	$F_a/\sqrt{L}$ $= -\sqrt{W}$	$F_b/\sqrt{L}$ $= -\sqrt{W}\cdot x$	$F_c/\sqrt{L}$ $= -\sqrt{W}\cdot x^2$	$F_0/\sqrt{L}$ $= \sqrt{W}\cdot F_0$	Sum

The usual process of cumulating sums of squares and cross-products in Table 2 yields the following normal equations.

Row	A	B	C	$= $	1	C_1	C_2	C_3	Sum	
I	$[W]$	$[Wx]$	$[Wx^2]$		$-[WF_0]$	1	0	0	...	
2		$[Wx^2]$	$[Wx^3]$		$-[WxF_0]$	0	1	0	...	(Set 1,
3			$[Wx^4]$		$-[Wx^2F_0]$	0	0	1	...	Exercise 10)
4					$+[WF_0F_0]$	0	0	0	...	

The solution, carried out by the usual routine procedure, gives A, B, and C, whence the adjusted values of a, b, and c are

$$a = a_0 - A$$
$$b = b_0 - B$$
$$c = c_0 - C$$

The minimized value of S or $\sum (w_x V_x^2 + w_y V_y^2)$ will appear in Row IV, column " 1." This will be simply $\sum w_x V_x^2$ if y is free of error, and $\sum w_y V_y^2$ if x is free of error. Directly above, in Row 8, appears the sum of squares that is removed from $[WF_0F_0]$ by shifting the y intercept from a_0 to a; in Row 9 appears the further decrease brought about by allowing the second parameter to shift from b_0 to b; and in Row 10, just above S, appears the portion of the sum of squares that is finally removed by adjusting the parabolic term from c_0x^2 to cx^2 (see Exercise 3 of Sec. 61).

The reciprocal matrix Δ^{-1} will appear in the C_1, C_2, C_3 columns of Rows 11, 12, and 13 (the "back solution"), containing the variance and product-variance coefficients for a, b, and c. (See Exercise 12 for the matrix Δ^{-1} in a special case.)

Note the similarity between Set 1 of Exercise 4 (p. 179), and Set 1 of Exercise 10. Note also that if x is free of error, a_0, b_0, and c_0 *may* be taken as 0, so far as F_0 is concerned, in which event F_0 becomes simply

$$F_0 = y_{obs}$$

The normal equations then give a, b, and c directly, and would appear as shown below.

Row	a	b	c	$=$	1	C_1	C_2	C_3	Sum	
I	$[W]$	$[Wx]$	$[Wx^2]$		$[Wy]$	1	0	0	...	
2		$[Wx^2]$	$[Wx^3]$		$[Wxy]$	0	1	0	...	(Set 2,
3			$[Wx^4]$		$[Wx^2y]$	0	0	1	...	Exercise 10)
4					$[Wyy]$	0	0	0	...	

More decimals will be required here than if good values of a_0, b_0, and c_0 had been used in the calculation of F_0, and the previous normal equations (Set 1 of this exercise) had been used to find A, B, and C. Why?

> The reciprocal matrix is the same, in both sets, and the minimized value of $\sum (w_x V_x^2 + w_y V_y^2)$ again comes in the extreme left entry of Row IV; but, as in Remark 5 of Exercise 4, the entries directly above it in Rows 10 and 9 do *not* show the increments in the sum of the weighted squares that would result from setting $c = 0$ and $b = c = 0$, respectively, unless b and c are very small, or x free of error.

> Note the similarity between Set 2 of Exercise 4, and Set 2 of Exercise 10. The remarks at the end of Exercise 4 apply here with obvious modifications. For example, approximate values of b and c *must* be used in the calculation of W at each point where x is subject to error.

Exercise 11.   Given[5]

$$y = a + bx + cx^2$$

to be fitted to n points, x free of error, all y coordinates of equal weight (unity). If a_0, b_0, and c_0 all be taken as 0, the normal equations giving a, b, and c directly are

Row	a	b	c	$=$	1	C_1	C_2	C_3	Sum
I	n	$[x]$	$[x^2]$		$[y]$	1	0	0	...
2		$[x^2]$	$[x^3]$		$[xy]$	0	1	0	...
3			$[x^4]$		$[x^2y]$	0	0	1	...
4					$[yy]$	0	0	0	...

[5] See the reduced type at the beginning of this chapter for references to special methods involving orthogonal polynomials, applying to problems wherein x is equally spaced.

These arise immediately from the last set of normal equations of the preceding exercise by noting that under the conditions $w_x = \infty$ and $w_y = 1$ throughout, $W = 1$ throughout. Row IV in the solution of the normal equations will contain the minimized value of $\sum (y_{obs} - y_{calc})^2$ in the " 1 " column. The sum of squares successively removed by the constant, linear, and parabolic terms will appear in the " 1 " column of Rows 8, 9, and 10 (see Exercise 3 of Sec. 61; also Exercises 1, 4, 5, and 10 of this chapter).

Note the similarity between these normal equations and those of Exercise 1, Set 2 (p. 175).

Exercise 12.   (a) In the preceding exercise, let the origin of x be taken at the mean value of x, and let $n\mu_2$ be written for $[x^2]$ and $n\mu_4$ for $[x^4]$.   Then the normal equations are

Row	a	b	c	$=$	1	C_1	C_2	C_3
I	n	0	$n\mu_2$		$[y]$	1	0	0
2		$n\mu_2$	0		$[xy]$	0	1	0
3			$n\mu_4$		$[x^2y]$	0	0	1
4					$[yy]$	0	0	0

Show that the reciprocal matrix is

$$\Delta^{-1} = \begin{vmatrix} \dfrac{\mu_4}{n\mu_4 - n\mu_2{}^2} & 0 & -\dfrac{\mu_2}{n\mu_4 - n\mu_2{}^2} \\[2ex] 0 & \dfrac{1}{n\mu_2} & 0 \\[2ex] -\dfrac{\mu_2}{n\mu_4 - n\mu_2{}^2} & 0 & \dfrac{1}{n\mu_4 - n\mu_2{}^2} \end{vmatrix}$$

From this matrix, one can write down the standard error of the fitted curve, or of any function of a, b, c, in terms of σ (see Sec. 62; also Exercise 2 of this section).   In particular, the

$$(\text{S. E. of } a)^2 = \frac{\sigma^2}{n(1 - \mu_2{}^2/\mu_4)}$$

$$(\text{S. E. of } b)^2 = \frac{\sigma^2}{n\mu_2} \qquad \text{(Compare with Exercise 2, p. 176.)}$$

$$(\text{S. E. of } c)^2 = \frac{\sigma^2}{n(\mu_4 - \mu_2{}^2)}$$

The (S. E. of y_{calc})^2 at the center of gravity is
$\sigma^2/n(1 - \mu_2^2/\mu_4)$, which exceeds the value σ^2/n found in Exercise 2
for the line.

(b) Show that the determinant Δ of the coefficients is equal to
$n^3\mu_2(\mu_4 - \mu_2^2)$; hence that near indeterminacy (small Δ) will
result not only in instability but also in high standard errors for a,
b, and c, and rapid fanning out of the standard error of y_{calc} (see
Exercise 2c, p. 176; also Exercise 2a of Sec. 61, p. 162).

67. The exponential and its logarithmic form

Exercise 13.   Given the equation

$$y = ae^{bx}$$

to be fitted to n points, x free of error, all y coordinates of equal
precision (unit weight).   Here we take

$$F = y - ae^{bx}$$

Good approximate values of a and b can usually be found by
plotting log y against x.   Assuming that they can be obtained, we
write

$F_0 = Y - a_0 e^{b_0 X}$ (Y denotes an observed y as in Fig. 17, p. 133.)

The derivatives of F are

$$F_y = 1, \quad F_a = -\frac{y}{a}, \quad F_b = -xy$$

$W = 1$ at all points; hence Tables 1 and 2 of Section 60 coalesce.
They will be made up as follows.   For convenience in writing, the
subscript 0 will be withheld from the a and b. X_1, Y_1, etc., are
the observed x and y coordinates of the n points.

TABLES 1 AND 2

h	F_a	F_b	F_0	Sum
1	$-Y_1/a$	$-X_1Y_1$	$Y_1 - ae^{bX_1}$	...
2	$-Y_2/a$	$-X_2Y_2$	$Y_2 - ae^{bX_2}$	...
.	.	.	.	
.	.	.	.	
.	.	.	.	
etc.				

The normal equations are formed from this table by summing squares and cross-products:

Row	A	B	$=$	1	C_1	C_2	Sum
I	$[Y^2/a^2]$	$[XY^2/a]$		$-[YF_0/a]$	1	0	...
2		$[X^2Y^2]$		$-[XYF_0]$	0	1	...
3				$[F_0F_0]$	0	0	...

The solution of the normal equations by the usual routine described in Section 61 gives A and B, also the reciprocal matrix, and the minimized value of $\sum res^2$. The adjusted values of a and b are then

$$a = a_0 - A$$

$$b = b_0 - B$$

The extreme left entry in Row III of the solution of the normal equations gives S or $\sum res^2$, the residuals all being measured entirely in the vertical (i.e., parallel to Oy). Directly above S, in Row 5, appears the sum of squares removed by the shift from a_0 to a, and in Row 6 the further decrease brought about by adjusting the exponent from b_0x to bx.

Exercise 14. If in the preceding exercise, the x coordinates are free of error but the y coordinates have unequal precision, designated by weight w (varying from point to point), W is no longer unity, but is equal to w, which may vary from point to point. Table 2 of Section 60 then runs as follows:

h	$F_a/\sqrt{L}$	$F_b/\sqrt{L}$	$\sqrt{w} \cdot F_0$	Sum
1	$-\sqrt{w_1}Y_1/a$	$-X_1Y_1\sqrt{w_1}$	$\sqrt{w_1}(Y_1 - ae^{bX_1})$	...
2	$-\sqrt{w_2}Y_2/a$	$-X_2Y_2\sqrt{w_2}$	$\sqrt{w_2}(Y_2 - ae^{bX_2})$	...
.	.	.	.	
.	.	.	.	
.	.	.	.	
etc.				

The approximate values a_0 and b_0 are inserted for a and b.

The normal equations, formed from Table 2 in the usual manner, can be symbolized as follows:

Row	A	B	=	1	C_1	C_2	Sum
I	$[wY^2/a^2]$	$[wXY^2/a]$		$-[wYF_0/a]$	1	0	...
2		$[wX^2Y^2]$		$-[wXYF_0]$	0	1	...
3				$[wF_0F_0]$	0	0	...

In the solution of the normal equations by the routine of page 158, the minimized value of $\sum w(y_{obs} - y_{calc})^2$ comes in the extreme left entry of Row III. Just above, in Rows 5 and 6, will appear the portions of the weighted sums of squares removed successively by adjusting a and then b (see Exercise 3 of Sec. 61; also Exercises 1, 4, 5, 10, 11, 12, and 13 of this chapter).

The adjusted values of a and b are, as usual,

$$a = a_0 - A$$
$$b = b_0 - B$$

A and B being found by solving the normal equations. Naturally these normal equations become the same as those of Exercise 13 if $w = 1$ throughout.

Exercise 15. (a) The formula to be fitted in the two previous exercises can be taken in the logarithmic form

$$\log y = \log a + bx \log e$$

Suppose now that y' be written for $\log y$, a' for $\log a$, b' for $b \log e$; then

$$y' = a' + b'x$$

We now take

$$f = y' - (a' + b'x)$$
$$f_0 = Y' - (a_0' + b_0'X) \quad (Y' = \log Y_{obs})$$

wherein a_0' means $\log a_0$, and b_0' means $b_0 \log e$. The derivatives of f are as follows:[6]

$$f_x = -b', \quad f_{y'} = 1, \quad f_y = \frac{df}{dy'}\frac{dy'}{dy} = \frac{0.434}{y}$$

$$f_{a'} = -1, \quad f_{b'} = -x$$

$$L \text{ or } \frac{1}{W} = \frac{f_x f_x}{w_x} + \frac{f_y f_y}{w_y} = \frac{b'^2}{w_x} + \frac{0.434^2}{y^2 w_y}$$

Suppose that x is free of error, but that the weight of an observed y coordinate is w, which may vary from point to point. (If all y coordinates have equal weight, it is easy to put w equal to 1 in what follows.) With $w_x = \infty$, the first term in L drops out, leaving

$$L \quad \text{or} \quad \frac{1}{W} = \frac{0.434^2}{y^2 w}$$

It will be noticed from the result of Exercise 8e, page 45, that if w is the weight of y, then $y^2 w / 0.434^2$ is the weight of y' or log y. Suppose that on this account we set

$$w' = \frac{y^2 w}{0.434^2} = (2.30 y)^2 w$$

Then w' is the weight of y', and

$$W = w'$$

If w (the weight of y) is constant throughout, then $w_{y'}$ is not, and vice versa. (Cf. the remark appended to Exercise 18.)

Table 2 of Section 60 will have headings as follows:

h, or Point No.	$f_{a'}/\sqrt{L}$ $= -\sqrt{w'}$	$f_{b'}/\sqrt{L}$ $= -x\sqrt{w'}$	$\sqrt{w'}f_0$	Sum

The normal equations will be

Row	A'	B'	$= 1$	C_1	C_2	Sum
I	$[w']$	$[xw']$	$-[w'f_0]$	1	0	$\cdots$
2		$[x^2 w']$	$-[xw'f_0]$	0	1	$\cdots$
3			$[w'f_0f_0]$	0	0	$\cdots$

[6] It is convenient to remember that log e = 1/ln 10 = 0.434 $\cdots$ = 1/2.30 $\cdots$. The symbol log means base 10, and the symbol ln means base e (logarithme naturel).

We perceive that these are similar to the normal equations of Exercise 5, but with w' in place of w, and f in place of F. More precisely, the comparison is this:

In Exercise 5, $y = a + bx$, x free of error, y of weight w.

Here, $y' = a' + b'x$, " " " " y' " " w'.

This means that we may fit the equation $y = ae^{bx}$ by writing it in the logarithmic form

$$\log y = \log a + bx \log e$$

and treating it as a linear equation in $\log y$ and x, at the same time giving $\ln y$ a weight just y^2 times the weight of y, or $\log y$ a weight $(2.30y)^2$ times the weight of y.

> *Remark.* It is customary among computers to fit the exponential equation $y = ae^{bx}$ by taking logarithms and treating it as linear in $\log y$ and x, but it is not so usual for them to change the weighting to correspond to the logarithms. The neglect of the factor $(2.30y)^2$ not only distorts the results for a and b, but also invalidates the reciprocal matrix and all calculations made with it on the standard error of a function of the parameters; moreover, under such circumstances, the extreme left entry of Row III no longer contains S. See also the reduced type at the conclusion of Exercise 18, page 201.

(b) The extreme left entry of Row III in the solution of the normal equations contains $\sum w(y_{obs} - y_{calc})^2$. The extreme left numbers appearing in Rows 5 and 6 are the weighted sums of squares removed successively by adjusting a and then b (see Exercise 3 of Sec. 61, and Exercises 1, 4, 5, 10–14 of this chapter). These statements would not be true if one were to neglect the factor $(2.30y)^2$ for the weight of $\log y$.

Note that in the normal equations of part (a) it is permissible to use $a_0' = 0$ and $b_0' = 0$, in which event

$$f_0 = Y' \quad \text{or} \quad \log y_{obs}$$

whereupon the normal equations will be as written below.

Row	a'	b'	$=$	1	C_1	C_2	Sum
I	$[w']$	$[w'X]$		$[w'Y']$	1	0	$\cdots$
2		$[w'X^2]$		$[w'XY']$	0	1	$\cdots$
3				$[w'Y'Y']$	0	0	$\cdots$

$w' = 2.30^2 y^2 w$ as on the preceding page.

These normal equations give a' and b' directly. As in Exercises 1 and 5, no question of an approximate value of b' enters for the calculation of the w', since w_x is infinite (x free of error), but more decimals are required than when good approximate values of a' and b' are used. (See Exercise 1d.)

In the solution of these normal equations by the routine exhibited in Section 60, the minimized $\sum w(y_{obs} - y_{calc})^2$ appears in the extreme left entry of Row III, as usual. Directly above it in Row 5 comes the reduction brought about by changing a from 1 to its final value, and in Row 6 appears the further reduction accomplished by turning the logarithmic line from the horizontal through the angle arc tan b'.

Exercise 16. In fitting the equation

$$y = ae^{bx}$$

with x and y *both* subject to error, we may take F as in Exercise 13, whereupon

$$F_0 \equiv Y - a_0 e^{b_0 X} \quad (X \text{ and } Y \text{ observed})$$

Here we have use for the additional derivative $F_x = -by$, whence

$$L \quad \text{or} \quad \frac{1}{W} = \frac{b^2 y^2}{w_x} + \frac{1}{w_y}$$

If x is free of error, the first term of $1/W$ drops out and leaves $W = w_y$, the situation assumed for Exercise 14; if y is free of error, the second term drops out and leaves $W = w_x/b^2 y^2$.

Since we are here taking the case where x and y may both be in error, we set up Table 1 of Section 60 with headings as follows:

Point No.	$F_x = -by$	w_x	w_y	L or $\sqrt{L}$ or $1/W$ $1/\sqrt{W}$	$F_a = -y/a$	$F_b = -xy$	F_0

From this is formed Table 2 with headings exactly like those of Exercise 14 but with w replaced by W. Likewise, the normal equations will be symbolized as in Exercise 14, w replaced by W. In fact, once Table 2 is set up, from then on it is immaterial to the computer whether one or both coordinates are subject to error — a statement that holds good in any problem of curve fitting.

The solution of the normal equations will give A and B. The minimized sum of weighted squares (S) will appear in the extreme left entry of Row III, the portions removed by the successive adjustments of a and b falling in Rows 5 and 6 directly above S. (Cf. Exercise 3 of Sec. 61 and Exercises 1, 4, 5, 10–15 of this chapter.)   Here, $S = \sum (w_x V_x{}^2 + w_y V_y{}^2)$, both x and y residuals being present.

Exercise 17. To use the logarithmic form of the exponential (see the preceding exercise) we write

$$\log y = \log a + b'x \quad (b' = b \log e$$
$$= 0.434b)$$

or

$$y' = a' + b'x$$

for fitting the exponential $y = ae^{bx}$ when x and y are *both* subject to error, one would define f as in Exercise 15; whereupon

$$f_0 = Y' - (a_0' + b_0'X)$$

The derivatives of f are as in Exercise 15. L or $1/W$ will now have two terms, both coordinates being subject to error; in fact

$$L \quad \text{or} \quad \frac{1}{W} = \frac{b'^2}{w_x} + \frac{1}{w_{y'}}$$

$w_{y'}$ being the weight of $\log y$. The normal equations will be symbolized exactly like those of Exercise 15a, but with W in place of w'. The extreme left entry in Row III will be the minimized sum of squares S, with the remarks at the end of Exercise 16 applying here as well.

The analogy with Exercise 4 is perfect throughout, as shown by the following summary:

Exercise 4	*Exercise 17*
$y = a + bx$	$y' = a' + b'x$
$\dfrac{1}{W} = \dfrac{b^2}{w_x} + \dfrac{1}{w_y}$	$\dfrac{1}{W} = \dfrac{b'^2}{w_x} + \dfrac{1}{w_{y'}}$

All the remarks and notes of Exercise 4 apply here if y is replaced by y' or $\log y$, a by a', b by b', and w_y by $w_{y'}$.

It is possible that in some problems, $w_{y'}$ might be constant from one point to another (in which case w_y is *not* constant); then if w_x is also constant, we have a situation toward which Remark 2 at the end of Exercise 8 (p. 186) is directed.

Exercise 18. (a) Take

$$f = \log y - (\log a + b'x) \quad \text{(as in Exercise 15)}$$
$$F = y - ae^{bx} \quad\quad\quad (\text{ " "} \quad\quad \text{ " } 13)$$

and suppose that x, y, a, and b take on small increments denoted by δx, etc. Prove that

$$\delta F = y\, \delta f \log e;$$

hence at any point, $F_0 = y f_0 \log e$ to within higher powers of f_0 or F_0.

(b) Thence prove that the normal equations in Exercise 14 for fitting $y = ae^{bx}$ will give the same curve, i.e., the same results for **a** and **b** and for $\sum w(y_{obs} - y_{calc})^2$, as the normal equations in Exercise 15a for the equivalent logarithmic form, except for discrepancies involving the squares and higher powers of residuals, the logarithmic form being slightly more accurate.[7] (*Hint:* Note that if A is small, $A' = 0.434/a$. Also, so far as a and b are concerned, the top normal equation in Exercise 14 may be multiplied through by a.)

The same comparison holds between Exercises 16 and 17. But with $b \neq 0$, and x and y both subject to error, there is not so much advantage in the logarithmic form.

Remark. It may be worth while to pause for a comment on the factor $(2.30y)^2$ which is required for the proper weighting of $\log y$. Take the one-parameter curve[8]

$$y = 10^{bx}$$

[7] Mr. K. A. Norton pointed this out in one of the author's classes.

[8] This illustration was developed in some correspondence with Professor W. L. Gaines of the University of Illinois, extending between 1932 and 1938; also in conversations with Mr. G. R. Gause, lately of the Aberdeen Proving Ground, now with the War Department in Washington.

and, to make the problem simple, let it be fitted to just two points in the xy plane, x being free of error and both y observations of equal weight (unity for convenience).

x	y	$\log y$
1	10	1
2	95	1.9777

To arrive at the least squares solution, we may write

$$F = \log y - bx$$

$$F_0 = \log y_{obs} - b_0 x$$

$$F_b = -x$$

$$F_x = -b_0 \text{ (not needed because the weight of } x \text{ is infinite)}$$

$$F_y = \frac{1}{2.30y}$$

$$w = 1$$

$$L = \frac{F_y F_y}{w} = \frac{1}{(2.30y)^2}$$

There is only one normal equation, namely,

$$B = \left[\frac{F_b F_0}{L}\right] \div \left[\frac{F_b F_b}{L}\right] = -\frac{\sum w'x(\log y_{obs} - xb_0)}{\sum w'x^2}$$

wherein $w' = (2.30\,y)^2$.

Note: The same equation for B can be derived by saying that we seek to minimize

$$S = \sum w'(\log y_{obs} - \log y_{calc})^2, \quad w' = (2.30\,y)^2$$

Replace $\log y_{calc}$ by bx, or, rather, its equivalent $(b_0 - B)x$, and get

$$S = \sum w'(\log y_{obs} - [b_0 - B]x)^2$$

B is the (unknown) quantity which, when subtracted from b_0, gives the final b. Now differentiate S with respect to B, and set this derivative equal to zero. The result is

$$\sum w'x(\log y_{obs} - [b_0 - B]x) = 0$$

Solve for B, and the result will agree precisely with that shown above.

To continue, we may take $b_0 = 1$, derived from inspection. We also replace w' by the correct weighting function y_{obs}^2, and get

$$B = -\frac{1 \times 10^2(1 - 1) + 2 \times 95^2(1.97772 - 2 \times 1)}{1^2 \times 10^2 + 2^2 \times 95^2}$$

$$= \frac{402.15}{36,200} = 0.01111$$

whence

$$b = b_0 - B = 1 - 0.01111 = 0.98889$$

This is the least squares value of b.

Now if in performing the solution we had inadvertently taken $w' = 1$, forgetting that the weight of log y is not the same as the weight of y, L would have appeared to be constant (unity), instead of proportional to y^2, and the result would have been

$$B = -\frac{\sum x \ (\log y_{obs} - xb_0)}{\sum x^2}$$

$$= -\frac{(1 - 1) + 2(1.97772 - 2)}{1^2 + 2^2}$$

$$= \frac{0.04456}{5} = 0.008912$$

and b would have been

$$b = b_0 - B = 1 - 0.00891 = 0.99109$$

The comparison of the sum of squares for the two different solutions is shown below.

x	y_{obs}	Correct weighting $b = 0.98889$				False weighting $b = 0.99109$			
		$\log y_{calc} = 0.98889x$	y_{calc}	$y_{obs} - y_{calc}$	$(y_{obs} - y_{calc})^2$	$\log y_{calc} = 0.99109x$	y_{calc}	$y_{obs} - y_{calc}$	$(y_{obs} - y_{calc})^2$
1	10	0.98889	9.7474	0.253	0.064	0.99109	9.797	0.203	0.041
2	95	1.97778	95.012	−0.012	0.000	1.98218	95.966	−0.966	0.933
		Sum of squares, $S = 0.064$				Sum of squares, $S = 0.974$			

Thus, by weighting log y in proportion to $y_{obs}{}^2$ we obtain a sum of squares that is only a fifteenth that obtained by ignoring the change in weight.

The only circumstance under which the factor y^2 may be ignored is where the fitted logarithmic line is nearly horizontal, for then the weighting factor y^2 is nearly constant from one point to another and can be omitted without serious error in the formation of the normal equations, the parameters a, b, c, etc., being left practically unaltered.

Even so, the last entry in the " 1 " column (Row IV, p. 158) is not S, but requires multiplication by an average value of $(2.30y)^2$, which might be denoted by $\overline{(2.30y)^2}$. Moreover, each element of the reciprocal matrix requires division by $\overline{(2.30y)^2}$ before it is to be interpreted as a variance coefficient (cf. the remark on p. 195). However, it is interesting to note that, owing to compensation, the uncorrected elements when used in Eq. 24 (p. 168), along with the external estimate of σ made from the uncorrected sum of squares, will give the correct value for the estimated standard error of a function.

The factor y^2 takes care of the change in scale that accompanies the transfer to logarithms. The student may find it helpful to refer back to Fig. 9 on page 45. The y values may all have the same weight, but their logarithms do not. No matter what function is being fitted, the two terms $F_x F_x / w_x$ and $F_y F_y / w_y$ in L or $1/W$ (cf. Eq. 8, p. 134) can be relied upon to perform the same service as $(2.30y)^2$ does for the logarithmic scale.

This example is an illustration of the fact that if the procedure of Section 60 is followed, it makes no difference how a formula is written. One form will give the same curve as another, except for disturbances arising from the neglect of second and higher powers of the residuals, but these are not usually of much consequence if the data are worth fitting.

Of course, in some lines of work, the weight of y is approximately inversely proportional to y^2, whence the weight of log y is practically constant, independent of y. When this is so, the weighting factor y^2 is to be omitted.

Exercise 19.   (Yntema's refinement.)[9]   In fitting the curve

$$y = ae^{bx}$$

[9] This device has been taught by Professor Theodore Yntema at the University of Chicago for years. It was first called to my attention by Dr. John H. Smith of the University of Chicago (more recently of the Bureau of Labor Statistics in Washington).

with x free of error, we seek to minimize

$$S = \sum w(y - y_c)^2$$

where w is the weight of the observed y coordinate at a particular point, and y_c is the calculated ordinate, ae^{bx}. The normal equations will be obtained by equating to zero the derivatives of S with respect to a and b, by which process we find that

$$\left. \begin{array}{c} \sum w(y - y_c)\dfrac{dy_c}{da} = 0 \\[3mm] \sum w(y - y_c)\dfrac{dy_c}{db} = 0 \end{array} \right\}$$

Now we may use the logarithmic form by rewriting these equations as

$$\left. \begin{array}{c} \sum \theta(y)(y' - y_c')\dfrac{d}{da'}\, y_c' = 0 \\[3mm] \sum \theta(y)(y' - y_c')\dfrac{d}{db'}\, y_c' = 0 \end{array} \right\}$$

wherein $y' = \log y$, $y_c' = \log y_c$, $a' = \log a$, $b' = b\ \log e$, and $\theta(y)$ is such a function of y that the two forms of the equations are the same. Evidently it must be that

$$\theta(y) = w\frac{\dfrac{dy_c}{da}}{\dfrac{dy_c'}{da'}}\frac{y - y_c}{y' - y_c'} = w\frac{dy_c}{dy_c'}\frac{y - y_c}{y' - y_c'}$$

$$= 2.30^2 w y_c^{\frac{3}{2}} y^{\frac{1}{2}} \quad (y \text{ here denotes } y_{obs}.)$$

The last equality is not exact, but is very close, as Professor Yntema discovered, and as the student may wish to demonstrate for himself.

The normal equations are exactly like those in Exercise 15, $\theta(y)$ now replacing w'. It will be observed that the Yntema refinement has merely replaced y^2 in w' by $y_c^{\frac{3}{2}} y^{\frac{1}{2}}$ in $\theta(y)$. There will be scarcely any distinction if the residuals are all very small, in which event y_c and y (the calculated and observed y values) will be very nearly equal, and $y_c^{\frac{1}{2}}y^{\frac{1}{2}}$ will be very nearly the same as y^2. When the curve does not fit well, it may be important to take account of the Yntema refinement.

68. The exponential with a linear component

Exercise 20.   Given the equation

$$y = ae^{bx} + cx + d$$

to be fitted to n points.   Write

$$F \equiv y - ae^{bx} - cx - d$$

The derivatives are

$$F_a = -e^{bx}, \quad F_b = -xae^{bx}, \quad F_c = -x, \quad F_d = -1$$
$$F_x = -abe^{bx} - c, \quad F_y = 1$$
$$\frac{1}{W} = \frac{(abe^{bx} + c)^2}{w_x} + \frac{1}{w_y}$$

(The first term of $1/W$ is missing if x is free of error, the second if y is free of error.)

The formation of Tables 1 and 2 of Section 60, and the formation of the normal equations and their solution, proceed in much the same fashion as heretofore.   The only novelty is that here there are four parameters, and hence four unknown parameter-residuals, A, B, C, and D.   The numerical values of F_0 and the derivatives F_a, F_b, F_x, etc., for use in Tables 1 and 2, are calculated with the approximate values a_0, b_0, c_0, and d_0, arrived at somehow (see the reduced type at the end of Sec. 55).

The extreme left entry in Row V of the solution of the normal equations will give the minimized $\sum (w_x V_x^2 + w_y V_y^2)$.   The entries just above it in Rows 12, 13, 14, and 15 will show the reductions in the weighted sum of squares arising from the successive adjustments of a, b, c, and d.

If only the y coordinates are subject to error, the extreme left entry in Row V will give $\sum w \cdot res^2$, the deviations being measured in the vertical (i.e., parallel to the y axis).   Moreover, if all y coordinates have the same weight (unity), then $W = 1$ throughout, and Tables 1 and 2 of Section 60 coalesce.

With a formula of this kind, there is no possibility of making it linear by such a device as taking logarithms, for which reason, this problem and others like it have been called insoluble. Fortunately, the solution is entirely straightforward.

69. The generalized hyperbola and its logarithmic form

Exercise 21. Given the equation

$$y = ax^b$$

to be fitted to n points. Here we write

$$F \equiv y - ax^b$$

whence

$$F_0 = y_{obs} - ax_{obs}{}^b \quad (a \text{ and } b \text{ being replaced by } a_0 \text{ and } b_0)$$

The derivatives of F are

$$F_x = \frac{-by}{x}, \quad F_y = 1,$$

$$F_a = \frac{-y}{a}, \quad F_b = -y \ln x$$

$$L \quad \text{or} \quad \frac{1}{W} = \frac{b^2 y^2}{a^2 w_x} + \frac{1}{w_y}$$

The headings for Table 1 of Section 60 in the general case would be

h	$F_x = -by/x$	w_x	w_y	L or $1/W$	$\sqrt{L}$ or $1/\sqrt{W}$	$F_a = -y/a$	$F_b = -y \ln x$	F_0

It is easy to make the necessary modifications for special cases. Thus, if x is free of error, then $W = w_y$ and the F_x and w_x columns are superfluous; if further, all y coordinates have equal weight (unity), then $W = 1$ for all points, and Tables 1 and 2 will coalesce. On the other hand, if y is free of error, then $1/W = b^2 y^2/a^2 w_x$ and the w_y column is omitted. From Table 1 is formed Table 2 with these headings:

h	$\sqrt{W} \cdot F_a$ or $F_a/\sqrt{L}$	$\sqrt{W} \cdot F_b$ or $F_b/\sqrt{L}$	$\sqrt{W} \cdot F_0$ or $F_0/\sqrt{L}$	Sum

The usual sums of squares and cross-multiplications from Table 2 give the normal equations

Row	A	B	$=$	1	C_1	C_2	Sum
I	$[WF_aF_a]$	$[WF_aF_b]$		$[WF_aF_0]$	1	0	...
2		$[WF_bF_b]$		$[WF_bF_0]$	0	1	...
3				$[WF_0F_0]$	0	0	...

Exercise 22. The equation $y = ax^b$ of the preceding exercise may be turned into the logarithmic form

$$\log y = \log a + b \log x$$

or $\qquad y' = a' + bx' \quad$ (as in Exercise 15.)

Let $\qquad f = y' - (a' + bx')$

$\qquad\qquad f_0$ as usual

The derivatives of f are

$$f_x = -\frac{0.434b}{x}, \quad f_y = \frac{0.434}{y}$$

$$f_{a'} = -1, \qquad f_b = -x'$$

Then

$$L \quad \text{or} \quad \frac{1}{W} = 0.434^2\left(\frac{b^2}{x^2 w_x} + \frac{1}{y^2 w_y}\right)$$

$$= \frac{b^2}{w_{x'}} + \frac{1}{w_{y'}}$$

wherein

$$\frac{1}{w_{x'}} = \frac{0.434^2}{x^2 w_x} = \frac{1}{\text{wt. of } x' \text{ or } \log x} \quad \text{(See Exercise 8}e\text{ on p. 45.)}$$

$\dfrac{1}{w_{y'}}$ similarly defined. The headings for Table 1 of Section 60 will be these:

h, or Point No.	w_x	$w_{x'}$	w_y	$w_{y'}$	L or $1/W$	$\sqrt{L}$	f_x	f_b	f_0

(See the remarks under Table 1 of the preceding exercise. $f_{a'}$ is not listed, being constant.)

The headings of Table 2 will be the usual ones, as in Table 2 of the preceding exercise with f in place of F.

The normal equations will be symbolized precisely like those of Set 1 in Exercise 4. In fact all the remarks and notes of Exercise 4 can be translated directly to the present problem. The reason is obvious: we have here a line in the variables x' and y', with weights $w_{x'}$ and $w_{y'}$. The two terms of L or $1/W$ seen above take care of the change in the form of the function from exponential to logarithmic. In fact, we could say that

$$\frac{1}{W} = \frac{f_{x'}f_{x'}}{w_{x'}} + \frac{f_{y'}f_{y'}}{w_{y'}} = \frac{f_x f_x}{w_x} + \frac{f_y f_y}{w_y}$$

as in Exercise 11b, page 46.

Exercise 23. Prove that the normal equations of Exercise 21 for fitting $y = ax^b$ will give the same curve, i.e., the same results for a and b and hence for S, as the normal equations of Exercise 22 for the equivalent logarithmic form, $\log y = \log a + b \log x$, except for discrepancies involving the squares and higher powers of residuals, the logarithmic form being slightly more accurate, especially if x is free of error. (Refer back to Exercises 18 and 22.)

70. The hyperbola with a linear component

Exercise 24. Given the equation

$$y = ax^b + c + dx$$

to be fitted to n points. Write

$$F \equiv y - ax^b - c - dx$$

F_0 at any point is found, as usual, by giving x and y their observed values at that point, and a, b, c, d their approximate values a_0, b_0, c_0, d_0 (found somehow; Sec. 55). The derivatives of F are

$$F_x = -abx^{b-1} - d, \quad F_y = 1, \quad F_a = -x^b, \quad F_b = -ax^b \ln x,$$

$$F_c = -1, \quad F_d = -x$$

whence

$$L \quad \text{or} \quad \frac{1}{W} = \frac{(abx^{b-1} + d)^2}{w_x} + \frac{1}{w_y}$$

$$(W = w_y \text{ if } x \text{ is free of error})$$

Tables 1 and 2 of Section 60 are made up, and the normal equations formed and solved, by the usual routine. Row V in the " 1 " column will give the minimized value of S or $\sum (w_x V_x{}^2 + w_y V_y{}^2)$, the successive reductions in the weighted sum of squares appearing in Rows 12, 13, 14, and 15, as usual (see Exercises 1, 4, 5, 10–16).

The reader should refer back to the reduced type appended to Exercise 20, which applies here as well.

Exercise 25. Given the equation

$$u = ax + by^c + dz$$

u, x, y, and z possibly all being observed. (This equation is used by Professor W. L. Gaines at the University of Illinois in his work on nutrition and lactation.) Take

$$F = u - (ax + by^c + dz)$$

F_0 as usual

The derivatives of F are

$$F_u = 1, \quad F_x = -a, \quad F_y = -cby^{c-1}, \quad F_z = -d$$

$$F_a = -x, \quad F_b = -y^c, \quad F_c = -by^c \ln y, \quad F_d = -z$$

$$\frac{1}{W} = \frac{1}{w_u} + \frac{a^2}{w_x} + \frac{(cby^{c-1})^2}{w_y} + \frac{d^2}{w_z}$$

Here we have a problem in four dimensions; $1/W$ contains four terms. The first term is absent if u is free of error, the second if x is free of error, etc.

The headings for Table 1 in Section 60 would be these:

h, or Point No.	w_u w_x by^c F_y w_y w_z	$1/W$ $1/\sqrt{W}$	$F_a = -x$	$F_b = -y^c$	$F_c = -by^c\ln y$	$F_d = -z$	F_0

Some of these headings will be omitted if any of the u, x, y, or z values are free of error throughout.

Table 2 will be formed by divisions in Table 1, and the headings would be as shown below:

h, or Point No.	$\sqrt{W \cdot F_a}$	$\sqrt{W \cdot F_b}$	$\sqrt{W \cdot F_c}$	$\sqrt{W \cdot F_d}$	$\sqrt{W \cdot F_0}$	Sum

The normal equations will be formed and solved in the usual routine manner (p. 158). Row V will contain the minimized value of S, being in this case $\sum (w_u V_u^2 + w_x V_x^2 + w_y V_y^2 + w_z V_z^2)$ in the " 1 " column, the successive reductions in the weighted sum of squares appearing in Rows 12, 13, 14, and 15, as usual (see Exercises 1, 4, 5, 10–16, 24).

If only the u coordinates are subject to error, $S = \sum w_u V_u^2$. Moreover, if all the u coordinates have the same weight (unity), then $W = w_u = 1$ throughout, and Tables 1 and 2 coalesce.

The second paragraph in reduced type appended to Exercise 20 applies here (p. 204).

71. Miscellaneous

Exercise 26. (a) Given the equation

$$u = ax + by + cz$$

to be fitted to n observed points. Take

$$F = u - (ax + by + cz)$$

and show that

$$\frac{1}{W} = \frac{1}{w_u} + \frac{a^2}{w_x} + \frac{b^2}{w_y} + \frac{c^2}{w_z}$$

Then the normal equations will be symbolized in the form shown.

Row	A	B	C	$=$	1	C_1	C_2	C_3	Sum
I	$[Wxx]$	$[Wxy]$	$[Wxz]$		$-[WxF_0]$	1	0	0	...
2		$[Wyy]$	$[Wyz]$		$-[WyF_0]$	0	1	0	...
3			$[Wzz]$		$-[WzF_0]$	0	0	1	...
4					$[WF_0F_0]$	0	0	0	...

(b) If it is desired to solve for a, b, c directly, the unknowns in the normal equations would be a, b, and c, and the " 1 " column would be

$$[Wxu]$$

$$[Wyu]$$

$$[Wzu]$$

$$[Wuu]$$

Extra decimals will be required for accuracy, as mentioned on page 175.

(c) Prove that the minimized sum of the weighted squares is

$$S = [WF_0F_0] - [WxF_0]A - [WyF_0]B - [WzF_0]C$$

If the normal equations are set up to give a, b, and c directly, as in part (b), then

$$S = [Wuu] - [Wxu]a - [Wyu]b - [Wzu]c$$

(See Exercise 3a in Sec. 61.)

> *Remark.* If u alone is subject to error, and of uniform precision (unit weight) throughout, the only change in the normal equations would be that W would not appear, being unity throughout. The minimized sum of squares would be
>
> $$S = [uu] - [xu]a - [yu]b - [zu]c$$
>
> This equation is used a good deal in some kinds of statistical work; see, e.g., p. 160 of the 6th edition of Fisher's *Statistical Methods for Research Workers*, on which the above equation appears as
>
> $$S(y - Y)^2 = S(y^2) - b_1S(x_1y) - b_2S(x_2y) - b_3S(x_3y)$$
>
> this being the sum of squares after fitting
>
> $$Y = b_1x_1 + b_2x_2 + b_3x_3$$
>
> Example 3 in Chapter XI is an illustration.

Exercise 27. In pharmacology and toxicology, experiments are made on a certain number n of organisms or animals to test the lethal action of a drug or dosage of X-rays, for various concentrations, or various times of exposure. The proportion killed is usually designated by the letter p, and the proportion surviving by the letter q. Under the assumption that the susceptibility of an individual to a poison is a normally distributed variate, the relation of p and q to the deviation y from the average susceptibility may be expressed in terms of the normal integral by the equation

$$q = \frac{1}{\sqrt{2\pi}} \int_y^\infty e^{-\frac{1}{2}t^2} \, dt = 1 - p$$

By using a table of the normal probability integral it is possible to express q in terms of y. To avoid the use of the negative normal deviates that arise when the observed survival q is more than half of the animals tested, Bliss[10] has introduced the term probit, and has provided tables for conversion. Probits are simply normal deviates to which the constant number 5 has been added. If Y denotes a probit, then $Y = y + 5$. The scale in probits runs practically from 1 to 9, the 5 in the middle corresponding to the center of the normal curve, where $y = 0$.

It has been found that when the dosage is expressed in logarithms, and the observed proportion q surviving is transformed into probits, then the relation between the log-dosage and the probits surviving is approximated by a straight line. The fitting of this line, with proper weighting of the points, constitutes an important application of least squares. To fit the line by least squares, the weights of the probits must be obtained. Now q is a proportion, and the assumption is made that the n animals or organisms are drawn randomly from some universe, wherefore the theoretical variance of q is pq/n. Then by Eq. 8 on page 40, the variance of the probit Y can be written

$$\sigma_Y{}^2 = \left(\frac{dY}{dq}\right)^2 \sigma_q{}^2$$

Show by differentiating the equation relating q to y that

$$\sigma_y{}^2 = \sigma_Y{}^2 = \frac{pq}{nz^2}$$

[10] C. I. Bliss, " The calculation of the dosage-mortality curve," *The Annals of Applied Biology*, vol. 22, 1935: pp. 134–167.

where z is the ordinate of the normal curve at the probit Y.   Then

$$w_Y = \frac{nz^2}{pq}$$

is the weight to be applied to the probit Y in fitting the dosage-mortality curve.   Note that the probit Y is a quantity called a percentile of a distribution.   If the standard deviation of the sampled universe is σ, then the

$$\text{Variance of the percentile} = \frac{pq\sigma^2}{nz^2}$$

Since probits are by definition expressed in terms of the standard deviation of the assumed normal curve, the quantity σ^2 in this problem is equal to unity.

CHAPTER XI

FOUR EXAMPLES IN CURVE FITTING

EXAMPLE 1. FITTING AN ISOTHERM

72. Formation and solution of the normal equations. For this example, data taken by the Michels[1] *et al.* on carbon dioxide will be used. The equation to be fitted is

$$y = a + bx + cx^2 + dx^4 \qquad \begin{matrix} (y \text{ denotes } pv, \text{ pressure times} \\ \text{volume; } x \text{ denotes density)} \end{matrix}$$

The parameters are not independent but are subject to the condition that

$$y = 1 \text{ when } x = 1$$

This condition arises because of the definition of the unit of volume. Because of this condition,

$$a = 1 - b - c - d$$

and

$$y = 1 + (x - 1)b + (x^2 - 1)c + (x^4 - 1)d$$

Weights: All y coordinates have equal weight; x is free of error. Let

$$F = y - \{1 + (x - 1)b + (x^2 - 1)c + (x^4 - 1)d\}$$

Derivatives:

$$F_b = -x + 1, \quad F_c = -x^2 + 1, \quad F_d = -x^4 + 1$$

$$F_y = 1, \qquad F_x \text{ is not needed since } x \text{ is free of error.}$$

$$W = 1 \quad \text{at every point.}$$

[1] A. Michels, C. Michels, and H. Wouters, *Proc. Royal Soc.* (London), vol. 153A, 1935: pp. 201–224.

The following approximate values are known from previous experience:

$$b_0 = -0.006837046$$
$$c_0 = 0.000011392$$
$$d_0 = 0.0^9\ 1514$$

Then

$$F_0 = y_{obs} - \{1 - 0.00683705(x - 1) + 0.000011392(x^2 - 1)$$
$$+ 0.0^9\ 15(x^4 - 1)\}$$

TABLES 1 AND 2

(FORMED FROM THE ORIGINAL DATA)

Point No.	$-F_b$	$-F_c$	$-F_d$	$-F_0$	Sum
1	1.77×10	3.51×10^2	1.24×10^5	0.55×10^{-4}	7.07
2	2.25	5.49	3.03	0.79	11.56
3	2.72	7.93	6.30	2.07	19.02
4	3.18	10.74	11.55	3.09	28.56
5	3.66	14.15	20.04	6.22	44.07
6	4.14	17.99	32.39	10.05	64.57
7	4.61	22.20	49.31	14.84	90.96
Sum	22.33	82.01	123.86	37.61	265.81 √

In this example, $W = 1$ throughout, with the result that Tables 1 and 2 mentioned in Section 60 are identical. The minus signs in the headings avoid minus signs in the table. The powers of 10 bring uniformity in the denominations of the columns.

The original data were listed to more decimals than are indicated by the above table, and the normal equations shown here, it so happens, were formed from the original data, retaining all decimals, then rounding them off to the number shown. Exact agreement can not be expected, therefore, with the accumulated squares and cross-products that one would form in the usual manner from the table above. The effect on the parameters, arising from the use of the extra decimals, is negligible, and the conclusions are the same either way.

The Sum column provides a check, which should never be omitted; it is formed regardless of the powers of 10; in fact no attention is paid to the powers of 10 until the end, when the solution is decoded. After the normal equations are formed,

NORMAL EQUATIONS (THE SOLUTION FOLLOWS THE FORM OUTLINED ON PAGE 158)

Row	Unknowns 10B	10²C	10⁵D	=	1	C₁	C₂	C₃	Sum
I	77.53	302.94	497.86	=	151.06×10^{-4}	100	0	0	1129.38 ✓
2		1236.98	2155.67		654.02	0	100	0	4449.61 ✓
3			4066.38		1233.79	0	0	100	8053.70 ✓
4					374.68	0	0	0	2413.55 ✓
	Factors								
5	3.907377	−1183.68	−1945.32		−590.23	−390.74	0	0	−4412.90
II		53.30	210.35		63.79	−390.74	100	0	36.70 ✓
6	6.421556		−3197.02		−970.01	−642.16	0	0	−7252.36
7	3.946701		−830.20		−251.75	1542.12	−394.67	0	−144.85
III			39.16		12.03	899.97	−394.67	100	656.49 ✓
8	1.948379				−294.31	−194.84	0	0	−2200.46
9	1.196797				−76.34	467.63	−119.68	0	−43.93
10	0.3071320				−3.69	−276.41	121.22	−30.71	−201.63
IV					0.33	−3.61	1.54	−30.71	−32.46 ✓

Therefore $\sum (wV^2) = 0.33 \times 10^{-8}$; $\sigma^2(ext) = 0.33 \times 10^{-8} = 0.33 \times 10^{-8}/4 = 0.082 \times 10^{-8}$

Row					1	C₁	C₂	C₃	Sum
13	10B =				0.036136	236.75	−98.03	22.98	
12	10²C =				−0.015361	−98.03	41.65	−10.08	
11	10⁵D =				0.3071320	22.98	−10.08	2.55	16.76 ✓

the sums in Rows I, 2, 3 are each raised by 100 to take account of the entries in the C columns.

Why is it better to start off with 100 rather than 1 in the C columns, for the calculation of the reciprocal matrix? Perhaps 1000 would have been better than 100.

Note the symmetry in the reciprocal matrix, which is found between the vertical lines in Rows 11, 12, and 13.

From the normal equations one may make up the following tabulation of results.

$B = +0.036 \times 10^{-5}$ $b = -0.00683705 - 0.0^6 36 = -0.00683741$

$C = -0.015 \times 10^{-6}$ $c = 0.0^4 11392 + 0.0^7 15 = 0.0^4 11407$

$D = +0.307 \times 10^{-9}$ $d = 0.0^9 151 - 0.0^9 307 = -0.0^9 156$

$$\therefore a = 1 - b - c - d = 1.00682600$$

Est'd S.E.^{2} of $b = 236.75 \times 10^{-2-2} \sigma^2 (ext) = 19.3 \times 10^{-12}$

"   "   " $c = 41.65 \times 10^{-2-4} \sigma^2 (ext) = 3.40 \times 10^{-14}$

"   "   " $d = 2.55 \times 10^{-2-10} \sigma^2 (ext) = 0.209 \times 10^{-20}$

"   "   " $a = \sigma^2 (ext) (236.75 \times 10^{-4} + 41.65 \times 10^{-6}$
$+ 2.55 \times 10^{-12} - 2 \times 98.03 \times 10^{-5}$
$+ 2 \times 22.98 \times 10^{-8} - 2 \times 10.08 \times 10^{-9})$
$= 17.7 \times 10^{-12}$

See Eqs. 21 and 22, p. 167; remember that a is a function of b, c, and d.

See also Exercise 1 ahead.

Final results for the parameters:

$a = 1.0068260 \pm 0.0000042$
$b = -0.0068374 \pm 0.0000044$ Standard errors estimated
$c = 0.0^4 1141 \pm 0.0^6 18$ from 4 degrees of freedom.
$d = -0.0^9 156 \pm 0.0^9 046$

These standard errors appear to be small compared with the parameters. However, it must be noted that they are calculated from only 4 degrees of freedom. There is really not much that one can say in the way of the prediction of future data, purely on the basis of standard errors that have been calculated from a single experiment, and in particular if this experiment yields only 4 degrees of freedom, as is true here. A consistent pattern of small standard errors, in experiment after experiment, would begin to assume scientific significance, and such is in fact the actual situation with compressibility data, though the other experiments, and the calculations therefor can not be shown here.

An important consideration was voiced at the outset in Chapter VIII, wherein it was stated that the real test of a calculated curve comes when it is used as a basis for action. The form of equation used here, and the method of fitting, have been tested severely in this way. For instance, by means of this equation, the Michels have calculated various physical properties of carbon dioxide, and they and others have carried out similar calculations for other gases, and always the results of these calculations have tied up closely with whatever direct experimental work exists on the index of refraction, Joule-Thomson coefficient, heat capacities, entropy, and other properties, most of which are difficult to measure directly. Manufacturing processes designed on the basis of these calculated physical properties have turned out to be correct, thus bearing out the usefulness of the parameters so calculated.

This statement does not contain any argument that these particular parameters are better than any other set that could be obtained from the given observations. It would take a long run of experience in the use of various alternative procedures for fitting, in order to decide just what method is better than another. Such comparisons probably do not exist.

It is interesting to see what would be the sum of squares if the term dx^4 had been dropped. From Row III we find [cc.2] $= 39.16 \times 10^{10}$; this multiplied by d^2 or $(-0.0^9156)^2$ gives 0.9×10^{-8}, which added to 0.33×10^{-8} gives 1.23×10^{-8} for the sum of the $(y_{obs} - y_{calc})^2$ that would be obtained from fitting the curve $y = a + bx + cx^2$. We then find

$$\sigma^2(ext) = 1.23 \times \frac{10^{-8}}{5} = 0.256 \times 10^{-8} \quad (dx^4 \text{ omitted})$$

We already had

$$\sigma^2(ext) = 0.082 \times 10^{-8} \qquad\qquad (dx^4 \text{ included})$$

Since the sum of squares, and hence $\sigma(ext)$, is so much lower when the term dx^4 is included, it appears from the meagre evidence afforded by the four degrees of freedom of this one experiment, that one is warranted in carrying this term.

One may also use Eq. 17 on page 165 for computing the effect of dropping d. One thus finds

$$\delta S = \sigma^2 \, (ext) \left(\frac{d - 0}{\text{S.E. of } d} \right)^2$$

$$= 0.082 \times 10^{-8} \left(\frac{0.0^9156}{0.0^9046} \right)^2 = 0.94 \times 10^{-8}$$

Exercise 1. Show that when corrected for powers of 10 the reciprocal matrix is

$$\Delta^{-1} = \begin{vmatrix} 236.75 \times 10^{-4} & -98.03 \times 10^{-5} & 22.98 \times 10^{-8} \\ -98.03 \times 10^{-5} & 41.65 \times 10^{-6} & -10.08 \times 10^{-9} \\ 22.98 \times 10^{-8} & -10.08 \times 10^{-9} & 2.55 \times 10^{-12} \end{vmatrix}$$

These are the figures that were used in writing down the standard errors of a, b, c, and d. Evaluated as a determinant, this gives $\Delta^{-1} = 4.6 \times 10^{-22}$.

Exercise 2. The evaluation of the determinant of the coefficients is

$$\Delta = (77.53 \times 10^2)(53.30 \times 10^4)(39.16 \times 10^{10}) = 0.162 \times 10^{22}$$

(See Exercise 1 of Sec. 61, p. 161.) This result is not exact; the discrepancy arises from instability, and could be overcome by carrying more decimals.

Exercise 3. (a) Prove that the standard error of the curve at $x = 1$ is 0, and that at $x = 0$ it is the same as the standard error of a.

(b) Why is the standard error of the y intercept practically equal to the standard error of b? Argue geometrically and analytically.

73. A note on instability. As often happens in curve fitting, these normal equations are unstable. One of the most sensitive tests for instability is to compare the direct solution (already found in the " 1 " column of Rows 11, 12, and 13) with that given by using the reciprocal matrix as a multiplier; by such means we get the *reciprocal solution* (pp. 165–166)

$$10B = \{ 151.06 \times 236.75 - 654.02 \times 98.03 + 1233.8 \times 22.98 \} \, 10^{-4-2}$$
$$= 0.0260 \times 10^{-4}$$

and in like manner (which the student should undertake as an exercise),

$$10^2 C = -0.0508 \cdot 10^{-4}, \quad 10^5 D = 0.2500 \cdot 10^{-4}$$

These are in disagreement with the direct solution found in Rows 11, 12, and 13, and thus instability is indicated. The direct solution satisfies the normal equations to the last decimal, but, when there is instability, many other solutions not too far away could do the same thing.[2] The reciprocal solution, however, does not satisfy the normal equations, the actual numbers being 111 against 151.06, 483 against 654.02, 919 against 1233.79. As indicated in Exercise 2, these discrepancies could be overcome by carrying more decimals.

The insidious thing about instability is that its presence may go undetected. For instance, if here we had only the " reciprocal solution," and had not tried to check it by substitution, we might have accepted it. The use of the reciprocal matrix as a multiplier is in theory very fascinating, but as a practical matter in curve fitting we should not wax too enthusiastic about it. Fortunately it does work to good advantage in many problems, as seen for instance in Chapter V of R. A. Fisher's *Statistical Methods for Research Workers*. In Section 36 also, the equations were stable and no difficulties arose.

EXAMPLE 2. ANOTHER POLYNOMIAL

BOTH x AND y OBSERVATIONS SUBJECT TO ERROR

74. The observations and their weights. The polynomial

$$y = a + bx + cx^2 \tag{1}$$

is to be fitted to points in the xy plane, x and y both subject to error. The observations on the coordinates are shown in the accompanying table.

---

[2] See footnotes 10 and 12 in Chapter IX (pp. 160 and 161) for references to Tuckerman's paper and a note by the author on this subject.

TABLE OF OBSERVATIONS (EXAMPLE 2)

N denotes the number of observations at a point, s their standard deviation, defined by

$$s^2 = \frac{1}{N} \sum (x_i - \bar{x})^2 = \frac{1}{N} \sum res^2 \qquad (2)$$

with a similar equation for the standard deviation of the y observations.

Point No. h	For the x coordinates				For the y coordinates			
	True value	Obs'd	N	s^2	True value	Obs'd	N	s^2
1	−2	−2.28	5	0.154	0.11	0.129	10	0.00447
2	−1	−1.13	6	.152	.15	.131	9	177
3	0	−0.44	7	.202	.20	.198	8	264
4	1	1.44	8	.315	.25	.247	7	182
5	2	1.90	9	.176	.31	.312	6	105
6	3	2.93	10	.124	.38	.380	5	100
7	4	3.81	7	.307	.45	.441	7	294
8	5	5.07	4	.032	.53	.529	12	286
9	6	6.11	10	.343	.61	.590	4	015
10	7	7.17	9	.016	.70	.728	4	082
11	8	7.83	7	.176	.79	.791	7	244
12	9	9.32	5	.154	.89	.922	5	442

75. A note on the observed values.   This is an artificial example, carried out under ideal conditions, in order to combine special features of a number of practical examples that might have been chosen for illustration.   The coordinates observed (the " true " points) were taken along the curve

$$y = 0.2 + 0.05x + 0.003x^2 \qquad (3)$$

The standard error of a single observation on an x coordinate was assumed to be 0.5 cm., and the standard error of a single observation on a y coordinate was assumed to be 0.05 lb.   Artificial observations were taken by using Tippett's numbers, assuming that the observations are normally distributed, according to the table shown in the appendix.   Considerable departure from the normal distribution would not affect the results appreciably.   The procedure can be described as follows:

i. Read out N numbers systematically (i.e., read up, or down, or diagonally) from Part A of the appendix (p. 252). Each number is a deviation, in units of σ_x or σ_y, as the case may be, from the true value of whatever coordinate is being observed. If desired, Tippett's *Random Sampling Numbers* (Tracts for Computers, No. 15, Cambridge 1927) can be used, in conjunction with the table in Part B of the appendix. N is the number of observations on a coordinate, as shown in the accompanying *Table of Observations*.

ii. Take the average of these N deviations, and multiply it by σ_x if an x coordinate is being measured, or by σ_y if a y coordinate is being measured. (The numerical values of σ_x and σ_y are to be discussed shortly. Assume for the moment that they have been settled upon.)

iii. Add this deviation to the true coordinate to get the observed coordinate, and enter it in the table.

iv. Compute the variance, or the square of the standard deviation, for the observations on each coordinate. These are shown as s^2 in the table. The formula is in the heading.

The question arises how to weight the various values of X and Y. For one thing, the weight of any coordinate will be proportional to N, but that is not enough; the precisions of single observations are evidently not the same for the y coordinates as they are for the x coordinates, judging from the s^2 columns. In order to check the x and y precisions for this particular set of observations, as one might wish to do in practice, we may plot Fig. 21 to show the successive values of $s^2N/(N-1)$ for x, and of the same thing for y, both plotted against x (y would do as well). $s^2N/(N-1)$ for x (or y) at any point is an estimate of the square of the standard error of the single observations on x (or y) at that point.

Although there is fluctuation of the estimates, there is not too much, and there is no trend.[3] Now the weighted average on the x plot is not far from 0.25, and the weighted average on the y plot is not far from 0.0025, so it seems reasonable to conclude that the prior values of precision (viz., $\sigma_x = 0.5$ cm., $\sigma_y = 0.05$ lb.) should not be changed. In practice, standard errors are usually

---

[3] In practice one must have enough estimates to enable him to plot a Shewhart control chart, before making such statements. However, here we have a method (the use of Tippett's numbers) that in the past has demonstrated randomness, and these statements can safely be made.

known pretty definitely from previous experience. Accordingly we take 0.5 for the standard error of single observations on x and 0.05 for the standard error of single observations on y, over the entire range. By recalling that weights are inversely proportional to the variances (p. 21), we see that a single observation on a y coordinate has 100 times the weight of a single observation on an x coordinate (Eq. 16, p. 22). As a matter of convenience,

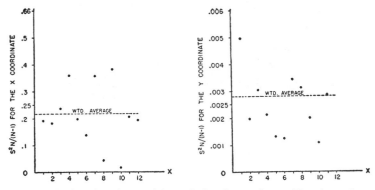

Fig. 21. Estimating the precisions of the observations. The chart shows estimates of the squares of the standard errors of single observations. A chart of this kind will disclose trends and abnormal variations in the precisions, though one should have more points than this at his disposal.

then, we take unity for the weight of a single observation on x, and 100 for the weight of a single observation on y. This is equivalent to setting $\sigma = 0.5$ for observations of unit weight. The values of w_x are then the same as the numbers N referring to x, in the table of observations, and the values of w_y are 100 times the numbers N referring to y. (If the precision of single observations on either x or y coordinates were variable over the range of the points, obvious modifications could be made in the weighting.)

76. Formation and solution of the normal equations. We shall carry out the steps called for in Section 60.

1st step: get approximate values for a, b, c. By passing the curve through three selected points, approximate values for a_0, b_0, c_0 could be found (see the reduced type on the method of selected points, Sec. 55). In this particular case, however, we shall instead use the true values of the parameters as approximations. They are found in Eq. 3. Accordingly, we write

$$\left.\begin{array}{l} a_0 = 0.2 \\ b_0 = 0.05 \\ c_0 = 0.003 \end{array}\right\} \tag{4}$$

Of course, the final results will be the same, no matter what values we choose (within reason) for the approximations a_0, b_0, c_0 (cf the reduced type on pp. 137 and 138).

2d step: the derivatives. For the function being fitted (Eq.1) we write

$$F = y - (a + bx + cx^2) \tag{5}$$

and then find the following derivatives:

$$\left.\begin{array}{l} F_x = -(b_0 + 2c_0X), \quad F_y = 1 \\ F_a = -1, \, F_b = -X, \quad F_c = -X^2 \end{array}\right\} \tag{6}$$

whence (see Eq. 8, p. 134),

$$L \text{ or } \frac{1}{W} = \frac{(b_0 + 2c_0X)^2}{w_x} + \frac{1}{w_y} \tag{7}$$

Also we write

$$F_0 = Y - (a_0 + b_0X + c_0X^2) \tag{8}$$

3d step: numerical values; Table 1. We are now ready to calculate the numerical values of $1/W$, $1/\sqrt{W}$, F_a, F_b, F_c, and F_0, and to compute Table 1, which precedes the matrix, Table 2.

4th step: preparation of the matrix; Table 2. Now divide the values of F_a, F_b, F_c, and F_0 in any row by the corresponding value of $1/\sqrt{W}$, and form the sums at the right and at the bottom for checks.

5th step: the formation of the normal equations. The normal equations are formed by the usual accumulation of squares and cross-products from Table 2. The solution is carried out by the routine outlined on page 158, and used previously on pages 82 and 83, and in the preceding example.

TABLE 1

THE THIRD STEP: NUMERICAL VALUES OF $1/W$, $1/\sqrt{W}$, F_a, F_b, F_c, AND F_0

Point No.	$-F_x = b_0 + 2c_0X$	$(F_x)^2 = (b_0 + 2c_0X)^2$	w_x	w_y	L or $1/W$	$1/\sqrt{W}$	$-F_a$	$-F_b = X$	$-F_c = X^2$	F_0
1	0.03632	0.0013191	5	1000	0.001264	0.035552	1	−2.28	5.1984	+0.02741
2	4322	18680	6	900	1422	37709	1	−1.13	1.2769	−0.01633
3	4736	22430	7	800	1570	39623	1	−0.44	0.1936	+0.01942
4	5864	34386	8	700	1858	43105	1	1.44	2.0736	−0.03122
5	6140	37700	9	600	2086	45667	1	1.90	3.6100	+0.00617
6	6758	45671	10	500	2457	49568	1	2.93	8.5849	+0.00775
7	7286	53086	7	700	2187	46765	1	3.81	14.5161	+0.00694
8	8045	64722	4	1200	2451	49508	1	5.08	25.7556	−0.00202
9	8666	75100	10	400	3251	57018	1	6.11	37.3321	−0.02750
10	9302	86527	9	400	3461	58830	1	7.17	51.4089	+0.01527
11	9698	94051	7	700	2772	52650	1	7.83	61.3089	+0.01557
12	10592	112190	5	500	4244	65146	1	9.32	86.8624	−0.00459

Since $-F_a = +1$ all the way through, it would ordinarily not be listed in a column.

TABLE 2

(*This comes by divisions performed on Table 1.*)

Point No.	$-\sqrt{W}\cdot F_a$	$-\sqrt{W}\cdot F_b$	$-\sqrt{W}\cdot F_c$	$\sqrt{W}\cdot F_0$	Sum
1	28.13	-6.4136×10	1.4623×10^2	$+7.7104\times10^{-1}$	30.8891
2	26.52	-2.9968	0.3386	-4.3307	19.5311
3	25.24	-1.1106	0.0489	$+4.9016$	29.0799
4	23.20	3.3408	0.4811	-7.2430	19.7789
5	21.90	4.1610	0.7906	$+1.3512$	28.2028
6	20.17	5.9098	1.7316	$+1.5632$	29.3746
7	21.38	8.1458	3.1035	$+1.4838$	34.1131
8	20.20	10.2515	5.2026	-0.4080	35.2461
9	17.54	10.7169	6.5481	-4.8235	29.9815
10	17.00	12.1890	8.7395	$+2.5959$	40.5244
11	18.99	14.8692	11.6426	$+2.9567$	48.4585
12	15.35	14.3062	13.3334	-0.7046	42.2850
Sum	255.62	73.3692	53.4228	5.0530	387.4650$\sqrt{}$

Cleared of minus signs and powers of 10, Rows 11, 12, and 13 lead to the following values of the parameter-residuals A, B, C, and to the reciprocal matrix shown below.

$$\left.\begin{array}{l} A = -0.00241 \\ B = 0.004306 \\ C = -0.000577 \end{array}\right\} \qquad (9)$$

$$\Delta^{-1} = \left|\begin{array}{ccc} 0.0^3 2767 & 0.0^6 3 & -0.0^5 57 \\ 0.0^6 3 & 0.0^4 638 & -0.0^5 84 \\ -0.0^5 57 & -0.0^5 84 & 0.0^5 14 \end{array}\right| \qquad (10)$$

The adjusted parameters will be found by subtracting each residual from the corresponding approximate value, according to Eqs. 6 in Chapter IV, page 52. The numerical results follow.

$$\left.\begin{array}{l} a = a_0 - A = 0.2 + 0.00241 = 0.20241 \\ b = b_0 - B = 0.05 - 0.004306 = 0.045694 \\ c = c_0 - C = 0.003 + 0.000577 = 0.003577 \end{array}\right\} \qquad (11)$$

NORMAL EQUATIONS

Row	\[Unknowns \] −A	−10B	−100C	=	1*	C_1	C_2	C_3	Sum
I	5614.38	1278.30	975.38		147.18×10^{-1}	100	0	0	8115.24✓
2		975.38	623.87		−29.52	0	100	0	2948.03✓
3			475.40		28.95	0	0	100	2203.60✓
4					200.57	0	0	0	347.18✓
	Factors								
5	0.227683	−291.05	−222.08		−33.51	−22.77	0	0	−1847.70
II		684.33	401.79		−63.03	−22.77	100	0	1100.33✓
6	0.173729		−169.45		−25.57	−17.37	0	0	−1409.85
7	0.587129		−235.90		37.01	13.37	−58.71	0	−646.04
III			70.05		40.39	−4.00	−58.71	100	147.71✓
8	0.026215				−3.86	−2.62	0	0	−212.74
9	0.092105				−5.81	−2.10	9.21	0	101.35
10	0.576588				−23.29	2.31	33.85	−57.66	−85.17
IV					167.61	−2.41	43.06	−57.66	150.62✓
13		−A			0.024093	0.02767	0.00029	−0.05717	
12	Subst. 11 into Row II	−10B			−0.430636	0.00025	0.63821	−0.83814	
11	From Row III	−100C			0.576588	−0.05710	−0.83812	1.42752	

* The factor 10^{-1} holds all the way down the column.

The reciprocal matrix contains the variance and product variance coefficients, whence we may write the standard errors of the parameters a, b, c, and of any calculated y value or, in fact, of any function of a, b, c. The diagonal shows that the

$$\left. \begin{array}{l} \text{(S.E. of } a)^2 = 0.0002767\sigma^2 \\ \text{(S.E. of } b)^2 = 0.0000638\sigma^2 \\ \text{(S.E. of } c)^2 = 0.0000014\sigma^2 \end{array} \right\} \quad (12)$$

With $\sigma = 0.5$ (the standard error of observations of unit weight), it follows that the

$$\left. \begin{array}{l} \text{S.E. of } a = 0.0083 \\ \text{S.E. of } b = 0.0040 \\ \text{S.E. of } c = 0.00059 \end{array} \right\} \quad (13)$$

whence

$$\left. \begin{array}{l} a = 0.2024 \ \pm 0.0083 \\ b = 0.04569 \pm 0.0040 \\ c = 0.00358 \pm 0.00059 \end{array} \right\} \quad (14)$$

77. The reciprocal solution. The reciprocal solution for the unknowns A, B, C is obtained as follows:

$$-A = 147.18 \times 0.0277 - 29.52 \times 0.0003 \\ - 28.95 \times 0.0572 = 0.0241 \times 10^{-1} \quad (15)$$

$$-10B = 147.18 \times 0.0003 - 29.52 \times 0.6382 \\ - 28.95 \times 0.8381 = -0.4306 \times 10^{-1} \quad (16)$$

$$-100C = - 147.18 \times 0.0571 + 29.52 \times 0.8381 \\ + 28.95 \times 1.4275 = 0.5766 \times 10^{-1} \quad (17)$$

These values of A, B, and C substituted into the left-hand members of the normal equations give numbers that are to be compared with the right-hand members. The results are shown below.

Row	Value of the left-hand member	Value of the right-hand member
I	147.27	147.18
2	−29.60	−29.52
3	28.98	28.95

This close agreement, however, required more figures in Tables 1 and 2 than were advised on pages 79 and 155.

78. Adjusting the observations. The calculated point corresponding to the observed coordinates X, Y can now be found. We note that there will be a λ at every point, given by Eqs. 10, page 136.

$$\lambda_i = W_i(F_0{}^i - F_a{}^iA - F_b{}^iB - F_c{}^iC)$$

The superscripts on F refer to the point numbers, as they did on page 133. We use $A = -0.00241$, $B = 0.00431$, $C = -0.00058$, with the values of F_0, F_a, F_b, and F_c already entered in Table 1, page 223. We shall adjust the observations only at Points 10, 11, and 12, for illustration.

$$\lambda_{10} = \frac{1}{0.003461} \quad \{0.01527 - 0.00241 + 7.17 \times 0.00431$$
$$- 51.41 \times 0.00058\} = 4.029 \qquad (18)$$

$$\lambda_{11} = \frac{1}{0.002772} \quad \{0.01557 - 0.00241 + 7.83 \times 0.00431$$
$$- 61.31 \times 0.00058\} = 4.094 \qquad (19)$$

$$\lambda_{12} = \frac{1}{0.004244} \{-0.00459 - 0.00241 + 9.32 \times 0.00431$$
$$- 86.86 \times 0.00058\} = -4.055 \quad (20)$$

whence, by applying Eqs. 12, page 138, the residuals can be computed at once. The required values of F_x are in Table 1.

At point 10,

$$\left. \begin{array}{l} V_x = \dfrac{1}{w_x} \lambda_{10}F_x = \dfrac{1}{9} \times 4.029 \times -0.09302 = -0.0416 \\[2mm] V_y = \dfrac{1}{w_y} \lambda_{10}F_y = \dfrac{4.029}{400} = 0.01007 \end{array} \right\} \quad (21)$$

At point 11,

$$\left. \begin{array}{l} V_x = \dfrac{1}{7} \times 4.094 \times -0.09698 = -0.0567 \\[2mm] V_y = \dfrac{4.094}{700} = 0.0059 \end{array} \right\} \quad (22)$$

At point 12,

$$V_x = -4.055 \times - \frac{0.10592}{5} = 0.0859$$
$$V_y = \frac{-4.055}{500} = -0.00811$$

$$\left. \right\} \quad (23)$$

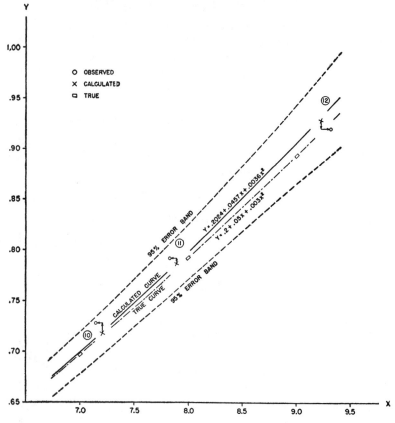

Fig. 22. An illustration of adjusted observations in curve fitting. The calculated curve and the 95 percent error band are shown in the neighborhood of points 10, 11, and 12. The error band is laid off above and below the calculated curve. The calculated or adjusted points lie on the calculated curve. Compare with Figs. 16 and 17, pages 132 and 133.

These residuals measured off from the observed points in the proper direction (see Fig. 22) give the *calculated points*, which lie on the *calculated curve*. Actually the points so calculated here do not fall exactly on the curve. Such discrepancies are trifling, being of second order from the neglect of second and higher powers of the residuals. One may simply manipulate the end decimal of V_x or V_y or both, in order to place the calculated point

$$\left. \begin{array}{l} x = X - V_x \\ y = Y - V_y \end{array} \right\} \quad \text{(Eqs. 13, p. 138)}$$

exactly on the curve. A precisely similar situation arises in problems of surveying wherein, for exact satisfaction of the geometrical conditions after adjustment, one often needs to manipulate the end decimal of one or more angles and sides (cf. p. 84).

By adjusting the observations, as is now possible (Eqs. 12, p. 138), the residuals can be inspected individually before any conclusion is based on S, the summation of $w_x V_x{}^2 + w_y V_y{}^2$.

Exercise. Compute the x and y residuals for the other nine points, and plot them.

79. The standard error of the calculated ordinates. In accordance with Eq. 22 on page 167, the variance of the function $f(a, b, c)$ is

$$\sigma_f{}^2 = \sigma^2 \left\{ 0.000\ 28 \left(\frac{df}{da}\right)^2 + 0.000\ 064 \left(\frac{df}{db}\right)^2 \right.$$
$$+ 0.000\ 0014 \left(\frac{df}{dc}\right)^2 + 2 \times 0.000\ 0003 \frac{df}{da} \frac{df}{db}$$
$$\left. - 2 \times 0.000\ 0057 \frac{df}{da} \frac{df}{dc} - 2 \times 0.000\ 0084 \frac{df}{db} \frac{df}{dc} \right\} \quad (24)$$

In particular, the calculated y with its standard error for this problem would be found by writing $a + bx + cx^2$ for $f(a, b, c)$, the result being

$$y = 0.2024 + 0.0457x + 0.0036x^2$$
$$\pm \sigma\{0.00028 + 0.000\ 0006x + 0.000\ 0526x^2$$
$$- 0.000\ 0168x^3 + 0.000\ 0014x^4\}^{\frac{1}{2}} \quad (25)$$

If the factor σ in front of the brace be replaced by 1.96σ, the double sign gives the 95 percent error band. This band, laid off from the true curve, is expected to embrace 95 percent of the calculated curves that would be obtained at any abscissa x in a large number of experiments like this one. Unfortunately, in practice, we do not have the true curve, and can only lay off the error band above and below the calculated curve, as is done in Fig. 22. The band so drawn will vary from one experiment to another (p. 170). Moreover, when σ is not known, we can only lay off a " confidence band " (p. 169), calculated from an estimated value of σ (next section). It is only when the number of degrees of freedom reaches 25 or 30 that the width of the confidence band can be interpreted as an error band, and even then only in randomness.

80. Calculation of the external estimate of σ. The external estimate of σ^2 (Sec. 13) is the sum (S) of the weighted squares of the residuals, divided by the number of degrees of freedom. Row IV in the solution of the normal equations gives

$$S = \sum (w_x V_x^2 + w_y V_y^2) = 1.68 \qquad (26)$$

The number of degrees of freedom is 9, this being the number of points (12) diminished by the number of parameters (3), whence

$$\sigma^2(ext) = \frac{S}{9} = \frac{1.68}{9} = 0.19 \qquad (27)$$

Now, in this example, we were furnished with a prior value of σ, (0.5; p. 221), and we are thus able to compute χ^2, which we recall is simply S/σ^2 (p. 15). We thus find

$$\chi^2 = \frac{S}{\sigma^2} = \frac{1.68}{0.5^2}$$
$$= 6.72 \qquad (28)$$

For 9 degrees of freedom the average value of χ^2 would be 9. The value just obtained is less than the average. Fisher's tables show

$$P(\chi^2) = 0.67 \quad \text{(approx.)}$$

which interpreted means that, in randomness, in 67 out of 100 experiments χ^2 would be greater than 6.72.

Example 3. A Formula Useful in Forestry[4]

81. The formula to be fitted. This example serves the purpose of illustrating three features: i. the fitting can be done with logarithms, the constant or nearly constant characteristic being suppressed or nearly suppressed to cut down the number of figures required; ii. W is constant throughout; iii. the prior value of σ can be expressed in terms of some of the parameters, so that, finally, the minimized S can be transformed into χ^2, and the fit of the formula judged on this criterion. All three features owe their existence both to the form of the fitted function and to the experimental material and procedure. One or more of them, however, is likely to be encountered in other work. If

x = the volume of a tree in board feet

y = the merchantable height of the tree

z = its diameter at breast height

then experience has shown that the equation

$$x = ay^b z^c \tag{29}$$

predicts satisfactorily[5] the values of x from observations on y and z.

The particular set of data for consideration in the present problem consists of 66 points — measurements on the volume, merchantable height, and diameter, of 66 trees. It will not be necessary to display the full set of points for the discussion intended here; the first six and the last will be sufficient. They come in no particular order of size. The logarithms are written in the three right-hand columns, for convenient inspection, since they will be needed in the fitting.

82. Rewriting the function to gain an advantage. Looking at the logarithms in the table of observations, we perceive that the

[4] This problem was furnished by Mr. Jesse H. Buell of the Forest Service, Asheville.

[5] Francis X. Schumacher and F. dos S. Hall, *J. Agric. Res.*, vol. 47, 1933: pp. 719–734; also Donald Bruce and Francis X. Schumacher, *Forest Mensuration* (McGraw-Hill, 1935), Art. 140.

first part of the figures, the "characteristics," do not vary much; in fact, in the Y' and Z' columns the characteristic is unity all the way down. What we need to do is to write the formula so that the variable part of the logarithms is brought into prominence. This can be accomplished by writing the formula as

$$x' = a' + by' + cz' \quad (x' = \log x, \text{ etc.}) \tag{30}$$

DATA FOR EXAMPLE 3

Point No.	Observations			Logarithms		
	Volume X (board feet)	Height Y (feet)	Diam. Z (inches)	$X' = \log X$	$Y' = \log Y$	$Z' = \log Z$
1	60	25	13.8	1.778	1.398	1.140
2	60	24	14.0	1.778	1.380	1.146
3	120	29	18.1	2.079	1.462	1.258
4	270	38	21.0	2.431	1.580	1.322
5	320	37	21.6	2.505	1.568	1.334
6	130	30	16.5	2.114	1.477	1.218
.	.	.	.	.	.	.
.	.	.	.	.	.	.
.	.	.	.	.	.	.
66	320	54	18.8	2.505	1.732	1.274
			Sums	152.136	102.451	84.090

and thereupon lowering the characteristics of x', y', and z' by the harmless device of subtracting unity from each logarithm, arriving finally at the form

$$x'' = a'' + by'' + cz'' \tag{31}$$

where the double primes denote suppressed logarithms, namely,

$$\left. \begin{aligned}
x'' &= x' - 1 = \log x - 1 \\
y'' &= y' - 1 = \log y - 1 \\
z'' &= z' - 1 = \log z - 1 \\
a'' &= a' - 1 + b + c = \log a - 1 + b + c
\end{aligned} \right\} \tag{32}$$

83. Formation and solution of the normal equations. By transposing the formula all to one side, we have the acceptable form

$$f = x'' - (a'' + by'' + cz'') \tag{33}$$

The derivatives of f are as follows:

$$\left. \begin{array}{ccc} f_{x'} = 1, & f_{y'} = -b, & f_{z'} = -c \\ f_{a''} = -1, & f_b = -y'', & f_c = -z'' \end{array} \right\} \tag{34}$$

Then

$$\begin{aligned} L = \frac{1}{W} &= \frac{f_{x'}f_{x'}}{w_{x'}} + \frac{f_{y'}f_{y'}}{w_{y'}} + \frac{f_{z'}f_{z'}}{w_{z'}} \qquad \text{(See Eq. 8, p. 134.)} \\ &= \frac{1}{w_{x'}} + \frac{b^2}{w_{y'}} + \frac{c^2}{w_{z'}} \\ &= 0.434^2 \left\{ \frac{1}{x^2 w_x} + \frac{b^2}{y^2 w_y} + \frac{c^2}{z^2 w_z} \right\} \end{aligned} \tag{35}$$

the last step coming from Exercise 8e on page 45.

In this investigation, and in related experience, the standard errors of x, y, and z have been found proportional to the quantities measured. To be specific

The S.E. of x is 7 percent of x

"   "   " y is 6   "   " y

"   "   " z is 5   "   " z

It follows, then, from Eq. 13 on page 21 that

$$\left. \begin{aligned} x^2 w_x &= \left(\frac{x\sigma}{\sigma_x} \right)^2 = \frac{\sigma^2}{0.07^2} \\ y^2 w_y &= \left(\frac{y\sigma}{\sigma_y} \right)^2 = \frac{\sigma^2}{0.06^2} \\ z^2 w_z &= \left(\frac{z\sigma}{\sigma_z} \right)^2 = \frac{\sigma^2}{0.05^2} \end{aligned} \right\} \tag{36}$$

wherefore

$$\frac{1}{W} = \left(\frac{0.434}{\sigma} \right)^2 \{ (0.07)^2 + (0.06b)^2 + (0.05c)^2 \} \tag{37}$$

which is constant throughout, independent of x, y, and z. This is the second of the three important features mentioned above.

Now σ is open to arbitrary choice, since weights are not absolute but are relative only (p. 22); and a convenient choice is to put

$$\sigma^2 = 0.434^2\{0.07^2 + (0.06b)^2 + (0.05c)^2\} \tag{38}$$

whereupon W *becomes unity at all points.* The value of σ, in this problem, is not needed until at the end, when it will be compared with $\sigma(ext)$. (See Sec. 14, p. 29.) What is more important at present, b and c will not be needed for the calculation of W, in spite of the fact that x, y, and z are all subject to error. From a computational standpoint, this is a fortunate situation, resting on the peculiar combination of the form of the fitted function and the standard errors of x, y, and z.

As it happens, W being constant (unity) throughout, the same results for a, b, and c would come from normal equations set up under the (incorrect) assumption that only the measurements on volume are subject to error, and that they are of unit weight. But estimates of the parameters, however important, are not the whole problem; one ought also to consider the adjustment of the observations for a study of the trends (if any) in the residuals; one ought also to know the minimized S for considerations of the fit of the formula, as, for example, by comparing $\sigma(ext)$ with the prior σ, which fortunately is at hand in this example as it was also in the preceding one. If the errors in the diameter and merchantable height are masked, none of the residuals in volume, merchantable height, or diameter can be found; moreover, the entry in Row IV of the solution, which should be S, is instead an unknown multiple of it, wherefore the possibility of reconciling the known experimental conditions with the fit of the curve is lost or put on a basis that is likely to do more harm than good.

Approximate values of a, b, and c (hence also of a''), after being found by some method or other (see pp. 137 and 138), or being known from previous experience, would be used in calculating the value of

$$f_0 = X'' - (a_0'' + b_0Y'' + c_0Z'')$$

at each of the 66 points. The capitals refer to the observed values of $\log x - 1$, $\log y - 1$, $\log z - 1$.

Since $W = 1$ throughout, Tables 1 and 2 of Section 60 coalesce, and the normal equations are symbolized as follows. A'', B, and C are the parameter-residuals.

		Unknowns				
Row	A''	B	C	=	1	Sum
I	66	$[Y'']$	$[Z'']$		$-[f_0]$	...
2		$[Y''Y'']$	$[Y''Z'']$		$-[Y''f_0]$	...
3			$[Z''Z'']$		$-[Z''f_0]$	...
4					$[f_0f_0]$	...

Since most of the adjustment is already contained in the approximate values of a, b, and c, a maximum of two figures would suffice in any column of X'', Y'', Z'', or f_0; and a maximum of three figures would likely suffice in the normal equations. Such simplification is our compensation for the trouble of computing f_0 at each point.

The solution would proceed as on page 158. Row IV will contain the minimized S. The reciprocal matrix found in Rows 11, 12, and 13 will contain the variance and product variance coefficients of a'', b, and c.

As an exercise, the reader might express the variance coefficients of a' and a in terms of c_{11}, c_{12}, etc., found in the reciprocal matrix in the solution of the normal equations for A'', B, and C.

84. Numerical results. Instead of using approximate values of a, b, and c, and computing an f_0 at each point, Mr. Buell had already adopted the somewhat longer process of using $a_0' = b_0 = c_0 = 0$, $f_0 = X'$, and solving for a', b, and c directly. His normal equations are symbolized as follows, directly in terms of the logarithms ($Y' = \log Y_{obs}$; etc.).

		Unknowns				
Row	a'	b	c	=	1	Sum
I	66	$[Y']$	$[Z']$		$[X']$	...
2		$[Y'Y']$	$[Y'Z']$		$[Y'X']$	...
3			$[Z'Z']$		$[Z'X']$	...
4					$[X'X']$	...

Numerically, his equations were these:

Unknowns

Row	a'	b	c	$=$	1
I	66	102.451000	84.090000		152.136000
2		159.921325	131.022337		237.985322
3			107.853544		195.795651
4					356.809522

The solution was found to be

$$\left.\begin{array}{l} a' = -1.78222 = \log a, \quad a = 0.01652 \\ b = 0.87476 \\ c = 2.14226 \end{array}\right\} \tag{39}$$

Hence the relation found was

$$x = 0.0165 y^{0.875} z^{2.14} \tag{40}$$

Not having at hand the complete form of solution, and in particular, not having S as it would appear in the form of solution shown in Section 61, page 158, we shall here make use of Exercise 3 of Section 61 (see also Exercise 25 of Sec. 70), thus getting

$$\begin{aligned} S = {} & 356.809522 + 152.136000 \times 1.78222 \\ & - 237.985322 \times 0.87476 \\ & - 195.795651 \times 2.14226 \end{aligned}$$
$$= 0.324 \tag{41}$$

It will be noted that S is here the small remainder left over from the addition and subtraction of relatively much larger numbers. To secure two figures in S, one must carry a, b, and c through the fourth decimal; this is so in spite of the fact that we can not possibly rely statistically on so many figures in a, b, and c, a fact that would be evident from their standard errors or from forest measurements in general. This situation is to be contrasted with the relatively few figures that would be required for the normal equations if good approximate values a_0'', b_0, and c_0 had been used for the calculation of f_0 at every point; with good approximations, the sum $[f_0 f_0]$ would itself be close to the minimized S, so that the correction terms need not be carried far. The reader will realize that this matter has been stressed earlier (see, e.g., pp. 153, 175, 180, 182, and 209).

We can now make the external estimate of σ from the value of S computed above, using Eq. 21, page 28, with the result that

$$\sigma^2(ext) = \frac{S}{66 - 3} = \frac{0.324}{63} = 0.00514 \tag{42}$$

This is to be compared with the prior σ^2, which from the choice made in terms of b and c on page 234 turns out to be

$$\sigma^2 = 0.434^2\{0.07^2 + (0.06 \cdot 0.875)^2 + (0.05 \cdot 2.142)^2\}$$
$$= 0.00356 \tag{43}$$

Thus $\sigma^2(ext)$ is about 50 percent larger than the prior σ^2. The possibility of this comparison is the third feature mentioned at the start.

A more exact comparison of the two estimates of σ can be made as follows. First of all, we need χ^2. By the definition of χ^2 on page 15,

$$\chi^2 = \frac{S}{\sigma^2} = \frac{0.324}{0.00356} = 91.0 \tag{44}$$

Since tables of chi-square do not run so high as 63 degrees of freedom, we use Fisher's function[6]

$$\sqrt{2\chi^2} - \sqrt{2k - 1}$$

which works out to be 2.3, giving P a little over 0.01. This is a little low, signifying that it might be well to look carefully at the data for inhomogeneities of various kinds.

It would be interesting to make a study of the residuals as functions of x, or y, or z, but we shall not stop here except to indicate how the residuals would be computed. From Eqs. 10, page 136, we have

$$\lambda = X'' - (a'' + bY'' + cZ'') \quad \text{(at any point)}$$

[6] This remarkable function is written at the bottom of Table III in Fisher's *Statistical Methods for Research Workers* (Oliver and Boyd), all editions. When k is large, say above 30, it is distributed very nearly as a normal deviate with unit standard deviation.

whence by Eqs. 12 on page 54 the logarithmic residuals would be

$$
\left.
\begin{aligned}
V_{x'} &= \frac{\lambda}{w_{x'}} f_{x'} = \frac{\lambda}{w_{x'}} = \left(\frac{0.434 \cdot 0.07}{\sigma}\right)^2 \lambda \\
V_{y'} &= \frac{\lambda}{w_{y'}} f_{y'} = -\frac{\lambda b}{w_{y'}} = -\left(\frac{0.434 \cdot 0.06}{\sigma}\right)^2 \lambda b \\
V_{z'} &= \frac{\lambda}{w_{z'}} f_{z'} = -\frac{\lambda c}{w_{z'}} = -\left(\frac{0.434 \cdot 0.05}{\sigma}\right)^2 \lambda c
\end{aligned}
\right\} \quad (45)
$$

since $\dfrac{df}{dx'} = \dfrac{df}{dx''}$, etc.

Certain special features peculiar to this problem have been mentioned, and the remaining details will be omitted; the reader, however, will profit from Professor Schumacher's comments on the foregoing.

85. Comments from Professor Francis X. Schumacher, Duke University

(a) The number of figures required in the solution of Mr. Buell's normal equations could be cut down by the calculation of an f_0 at every point, as emphasized in Section 84, but perhaps a more effectual saving of labor would follow upon transferring the origins of coordinates from the natural zeros to the logarithmic means $\overline{X'}$, $\overline{Y'}$, $\overline{Z'}$. We know from the first normal equation of either of the sets on page 235 that the fitted plane will pass through the logarithmic means, which is to say that the final values of a, b, and c will satisfy

$$\overline{X'} = a' + b\overline{Y'} + c\overline{Z'}$$

The transfer of the origins will not only cut down on the number of figures required, but will also eliminate the parameter a' and reduce the number of normal equations by one, leaving only b and c as the unknowns, a' to be found afterward by noting that

$$a' = \overline{X'} - b\overline{Y'} - c\overline{Z'}$$

The new sums and cross-products (to be denoted by appending the sign ° to the brackets) would be found by making the following reductions from Mr. Buell's equations:

$$[Y'Y']° = 159.921325 - 102.451^2/66 = 0.887880$$

$$[Y'Z']° = 131.022337 - 102.451 \times 84.090/66 = 0.490450$$

$$[Z'Z']° = 107.853544 - 84.090^2/66 = 0.715240$$

$$[Y'X']° = 237.985322 - 102.451 \times 152.136/66 = 1.826453$$

$$[Z'X']° = 195.795651 - 84.090 \times 152.136/66 = 1.960557$$

$$[X'X']° = 356.809522 - 152.136^2/66 = 6.122213$$

Four decimals will suffice, whereupon Mr. Buell's normal equations (p. 236) reduce to the following set, which can be solved as shown.

Row	b	c	=	1	Sum
I	0.8879	0.4904		1.8265	3.2048
2		0.7152		1.9606	3.1662
3	Factors			6.1222	9.9073
4	−0.55231	−0.2708		−1.0088	−1.7700
II		0.4444		0.9518	1.3962√
5	−2.05710			−3.7573	−6.5926
6	−2.14176			−2.0385	−2.9903
III		S	=	0.3264	0.3264√
8		b	=	0.8742	
7		c	=	2.1418	3.1418√

The values of b and c just obtained agree well enough with those on page 236, but with fewer figures and less trouble; and the same can be said for the sum of squares 0.3264 seen in Row III.   Otherwise obtained,

$$S = 6.1222 - 0.8742 \times 1.8265 - 2.1418 \times 1.9606$$
$$= 0.3263$$

affording an interesting check.   (The two figures 0.3264 and 0.3263 for S show a numerical comparison of the two expressions in parts c and a respectively of Exercise 3 on pp. 163 and 164.)

(b) The following suggestion is offered here in the hope of fostering first approximations as a preliminary to the real work of fitting by least squares. If the merchantable portion of the tree stem were of the same geometrical form in all tree sizes, the volume would vary directly with the height and as the square of the diameter. Hence useful approximations should be

$$b = 1$$

$$c = 2$$

$$a' = \overline{X'} - \overline{Y'} - 2\overline{Z'} \quad \text{(not needed in the plan just outlined)}$$

The problem is then seen as that of finding the effect of *changes produced by the form of the merchantable solid* upon tree volume.

Example 4. A Sample Survey of Canned Goods

86. Object of the survey. This example is described here, because the solution has a wide diversity of application in sample surveys; in fact, the solution given here has already been found useful in other fields. Of course, each new problem carried with it a multitude of theoretical and administrative details that are new and different, and these must be worked out and tailored to the new requirements.

In laying plans for allotments of canned goods for the year 1943, the question of current inventories of distributors arose and was referred to the Census, with the thought that sampling might be introduced to decrease the number of inquiries involved, and the expense attached thereto, and — what is more important oftentimes — to decrease the time interval between the collection of the data and the completion of the tables. A solution in the form of a sample was provided by Messrs. Morris H. Hansen and William N. Hurwitz, and was tried out in the Bureau of the Census. The country was divided into 24 areas; and within any one area, the establishments were divided into classes of five different sizes, depending on their inventories of canned goods on Date I. An inventory was taken of the stock in every store on Date I, but inventories of only a sample of stores were taken on

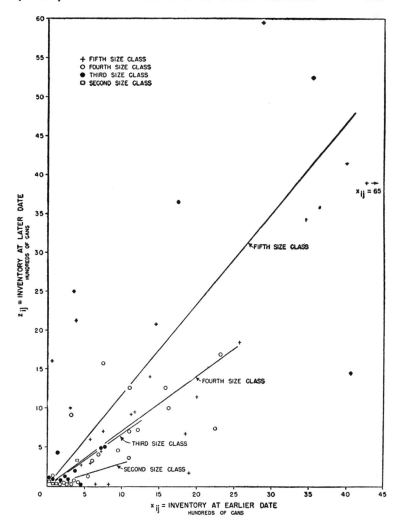

FIG. 23.   Inventories of canned peas on two dates for selected sample stores. Each point represents a store.   The four lines are drawn to show the calculated relations for the four different classes.   The first class is missing, because in this area no store of the first class had canned peas.

Date II, a month later. The sampling scheme diminishes the amount of reporting at Date II by requiring reports from all the stores in the 5th size class (the highest), but from only half of

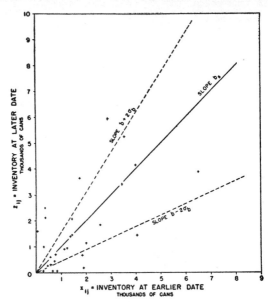

FIG. 24. Inventories for the fifth class, and the line through the centroid. Each point represents a store. The dashed wedge shows two standard deviations of the slope, calculated from Eq. 57.

them in the 4th size class, a quarter of them in the 3d, an eighth of them in the 2d, and a sixteenth of them in the 1st or lowest class.[7]

From the sample, it was possible to make a usable estimate, for each area, of the stock that would have been recorded by taking an

[7] In order to produce reliable estimates of inventories on Date II, by area, the sampling ratios were changed for smaller areas, depending on the sizes of the stocks on hand. The figures just given constitute a typical set of sampling ratios for one of the largest areas. The size class in which a store belongs is determined by the number of cans of all kinds of goods on hand — peas, beans, soup, meat, etc., — but the analysis is carried out for each commodity separately. This explains why the size classes for peas overlap in Figs. 23 and 24: a store with a large over-all inventory may be small in peas, and vice versa.

inventory of all the stores on Date II. Moreover, the design of the sample was such that the reliability of these estimates could be made on the basis of some initial trial samples, and sharpened by further trials. Some of the underlying theory can be approached in terms of curve fitting, and will be presented as such here. A forthcoming publication by Messrs. Hansen and Hurwitz will contain many other interesting aspects of the problem, particularly from the sampling angle.

87. What the sample gives. Let the subscript i denote the size class. There being five size classes in any area, i will run through the values 1, 2, 3, 4, 5. Let the subscript j refer to a particular store in the ith class. Then j will run through the values $1, 2, \cdots, n_i$.

n_i is the number of establishments sampled in the ith class

N_i is the total number of establishments in that class

x_{ij} is the inventory (number of cases of peas[8] on hand) in the jth establishment of the ith class on Date I (known for every store)

z_{ij} is the inventory of this same store on Date II (known only for the stores that are in the sample)

$$X_i = \sum_{j=1}^{N_i} x_{ij} =$$ the complete inventory of all stores in the ith class on Date I. (In this summation, j runs from 1 to N_i, to include all the stores in the class. X_i is known.)

$$x_i = \sum_{j=1}^{n_i} x_{ij} =$$ the inventory of just the sample stores in the ith stratum, on Date I. (In this summation, j runs from 1 only to n_i, since only the sample retailers are admitted in this sum. x_i is known.)

---

[8] For convenience, the analysis will be carried through with reference to canned peas, though obviously any other commodity or commodity group could be substituted.

$$Z_i = \sum_{j=1}^{N_i} z_{ij}, \quad \text{similar to } X_i, \text{ except that this is for Date II.}$$
$$(Z_i \text{ is to be estimated.})$$

$$z_i = \sum_{j=1}^{n_i} z_{ij}, \quad \text{similar to } x_i, \text{ except that this is for Date II.}$$
$$(z_i \text{ is known.})$$

$$Z = \sum_{i=1}^{5} Z_i = \text{ the established inventory on Date II for the}$$
$$\text{sum of all the five classes in this area.}$$

88. The estimated inventory and its standard error. One way to estimate the inventory for class i on Date II is to say that it is proportional to the inventory of that class on Date I, in accordance with which we write

$$Z_i = b_i X_i \tag{46}$$

Then

$$Z = \sum_{i=1}^{5} Z_i = Z_1 + Z_2 + Z_3 + Z_4 + Z_5 \tag{47}$$

is the estimated total inventory of all five classes in the area on Date II. Curve fitting enters the problem in the determination of usable values of b_i from the sample of stores in each class, and in the calculation of the variances of the estimated inventories.

The assumption will be that, except for accidental influences, such as weather, delayed shipping schedules, and mistakes in counting, all the stores of size class i would increase or decrease about the same relative amount between the two dates. This assumption, in this problem, has been found to lead to useful results. Of course, outside this particular field, or under other conditions, the same assumptions might lead to difficulty. It is only by careful investigation that one is able to say in advance under what conditions his assumptions will lead to usable predictions. Of course, the assumption that the inventories are each about the same on the two dates will be found violated by many individual stores, but on the whole it will be close enough for the purpose intended.

In evaluating the error in the slope b_i, we recognize the existence of accidental influence of variation in both x_{ij} and z_{ij}. The bigger the inventory, the bigger the standard error of the accidental variations. Hence we shall put

$$w_{x_{ij}} = \frac{1}{x_{ij}} \tag{48}$$

$$\sigma_{x_{ij}}^2 = x_{ij}\sigma^2 \tag{49}$$

wherein σ , as usual, is the standard error of observations of unit weight. We might write similar equations for the weight and standard error of z_{ij} (inventory of a sample store on Date II), but, if the two inventories x_{ij} and z_{ij} are not greatly different, it will be sufficient to make the x and z weights equal, thereby writing

$$w_{z_{ij}} = w_{x_{ij}} = \frac{1}{x_{ij}} \tag{50}$$

and

$$\sigma_{z_{ij}}^2 = x_{ij}\sigma^2 \tag{51}$$

The standard error resulting from the accidental influences on X_i on Date I can be found as follows:

$$X_i = \sum_{j=1}^{N_i} x_{ij} \tag{52}$$

Hence by the result obtained in Exercise 2 on page 42,

$$\sigma_{X_i}^2 = \sigma_{x_{i1}}^2 + \sigma_{x_{i2}}^2 + \cdots + \sigma_{x_{iN_i}}^2$$
$$= \left(x_{i1} + x_{i2} + \cdots + x_{iN_i}\right)\sigma^2 = \sigma^2 X_i \tag{53}$$

We here take

$$F \equiv z_{ij} - b_i x_{ij} \tag{54}$$

Then

$$L = \frac{F_x F_x}{w_x} + \frac{F_z F_z}{w_z} \quad \text{(at point } ij; \text{ Eq. 8, p. 134)}$$

$$= \frac{b_i^2}{w_x} + \frac{1}{w_z} = \frac{1 + b_i^2}{w_{ij}} \tag{55}$$

w_{ij} is here written for the weight of either x_{ij} or z_{ij}.

The normal equation for b_i is shown below. The subscript ij on w, x, and z is omitted for convenience, and the sums (Σ) are taken over the sample stores (i.e., j runs from 1 to n_i, while i remains constant).

b_i	$=$	1	C
$\dfrac{\sum wx^2}{1 + b_i^2}$		$\dfrac{\sum wxz}{1 + b_i^2}$	1

The resulting solution for the slope is

$$b_i = \frac{\sum wxz}{\sum wx^2} \qquad \text{(Compare with Eq. 34 on p. 31.)}$$

$$= \frac{\sum z_{ij}}{\sum x_{ij}} = \frac{z_i}{x_i} \tag{56}$$

since $w_{z_{ij}} x_{ij}$ is to be counted equal to unity (Eq. 50) and x_i is the inventory of the n_i sample stores on Date I. Note that by the value of b_i just obtained, the line is to be drawn from the origin to the centroid of the n_i points. The variance of b_i is seen from the normal equation to be

$$\sigma_{b_i}^2 = \frac{1 + b_i^2}{\sum wx^2}\,\sigma^2 = \frac{1 + b_i^2}{x_i}\,\sigma^2 \tag{57}$$

Now for the estimated inventory on Date II we recall that

$$Z = \sum_{i=1}^{5} Z_i = \sum_{i=1}^{5} b_i X_i \tag{47}$$

whereupon, by the result obtained in Exercise 3 on page 43, it follows that

$$\left(\frac{\sigma_Z}{Z}\right)^2 = \sigma^2 \sum_{i=1}^{5}\left[\left(\frac{\sigma_{b_i}}{b_i}\right)^2 + \left(\frac{\sigma_{X_i}}{X_i}\right)^2\right]$$

$$= \sigma^2 \sum_{i=1}^{5}\left[\frac{1 + b_i^2}{x_i b_i^2} + \frac{1}{X_i}\right] \tag{58}$$

The first term in the brackets arises from the sampling error in the slope b_i, which will vary from one set of sample stores to another. The second term arises from the fluctuations to be expected in the complete inventory X_i at Date I.

It remains to estimate σ^2. It is best to do this for each class separately. Since both x_{ij} and z_{ij} are assumed to be subject to the influence of chance fluctuations, we measure the residuals from each point perpendicularly to the line $z = b_i x$, and write

$$\sigma_i^2(ext) = \sum_{j=1}^{n_i} \frac{w_{ij} \, res_{ij}^2}{n_i - 1} \qquad \text{(Cf. Eq. 21, p. 28)} \qquad (59)$$

$$= \sum_{j=1}^{n_i} \frac{res_{ij}^2}{x_{ij}(n_i - 1)} \qquad (60)$$

The factor $n_i - 1$ arises from the reduction of n_i by unity for the single parameter b_i.

Perhaps the simplest way to evaluate the sum of the weighted squares of the residuals (the summation over j called for in the formula just written) is to measure each residual graphically, square it, and divide by the value of x_{ij} as read at the foot of the perpendicular dropped from the observed point to the line.

Another but theoretically less exact method of evaluating this summation would be simply to calculate the residuals from the line by the formula

$$\text{Residual} = z_{ij} - b_i x_{ij} \qquad (61)$$

as if they were measured in the vertical. The sum of the weighted squares calculated with vertical deviations will be about half the sum of the weighted squares calculated with perpendicular distances, and the factor 2 can be applied to compensate.

It will be sufficient for the purpose to set b_i in the brackets of Eq. 58 equal to unity, an assumption already made in the weights, and justified by the slopes in Fig. 23. With this simplification it is found that

$$\left(\frac{\sigma_Z}{Z}\right)^2 = \sum_{i=1}^{5} \sigma_i^2(ext) \left[\frac{2}{x_i} + \frac{1}{X_i}\right] \qquad (62)$$

The five terms called for in the summation over i on the right-hand side are the five separate values of $(\sigma_{Z_i}/Z_i)^2$ for the five inventories Z_1, Z_2, Z_3, Z_4, Z_5.

Fig. 23 shows a plot of the points for canned peas for the stores in the 2d, 3d, 4th, and 5th classes, in the state of New York. For this particular commodity, there was no store in the 1st class. The units of measurement are designated by the scales. The slopes of the four lines are b_2, b_3, b_4, and b_5. The scatter of the points is more than one might hope for, but the method gives useful results nevertheless.

Fig. 24 shows the points for the 5th class separately, with a wedge laid off each side of the line to show the width of two estimated standard errors. This wedge is indistinguishable from the 95 percent confidence band.

89. Summary of the errors to be considered; effect on sample designs.[9]   There are two kinds of problems that arise in sampling inventories, and we might designate them as Problem A and Problem B.   Problem A consists simply of sampling a pile of schedules. Every store in an area (e.g., New York state) has presumably sent in an itemized schedule showing the number of cans of peas and other commodities on hand at a certain date.   In the discussion that now confronts us, this date was Date II, but this is unimportant so far as the description of Problem A is concerned. The question is how to find, by sampling, a number (an estimate) that for purposes of action can be used in place of the total inventory of peas contained in the entire pile of schedules.   This is the problem, regardless of whether the responses written on the schedules are correct or not; and the error in the sample estimate will be the difference between that estimate and the actual count contained on the schedules, whether it be right or wrong.

The number of stores is large, perhaps in the thousands.   The reason for taking the sample would be to hasten the processing[10] of the data, and to get it done for less money.   The pile of inventories might be so big, and the deadline so short, that there is time

[9] The author is exceedingly indebted to Messrs. Hansen and Hurwitz, not only for permission to use their example, but more especially for assistance rendered in numerous discussions, during which the recognition and evaluation of the five different sources of errors were evolved.

[10] The term " processing of data " refers to office operations in the nature of editing, coding, transcribing, punching and tabulating, posting and consolidating, in the production of final tables or summaries.

to work with a sample, but not with the complete count. So far as Problem A is concerned here, there are two mutually exclusive sources of error, which may be outlined below.

i. The stores that are drawn into the sample are designated as the sample stores. In one particular sample survey these are a particular set of stores. But if the sample were redrawn from the same universe of stores, there would be a different set of sample stores, and another estimate Z of the total count. It follows that there is a sampling error in the estimated total count, and a sampling error in the calculated variances, arising from the selection of sample stores.

Messrs. Hansen and Hurwitz have made an approximate evaluation of this source of error, and their result is

$$\sigma_Z{}^2 \doteq \sum_{i=1}^{5} \frac{N_i - n_i}{N_i - 1} \frac{N_i}{n_i} \sum_{j=1}^{N_i} \left(z_{ij} - x_{ij} \frac{z_i}{x_i} \right)^2 \tag{63}$$

If the factor $(N_i - n_i)/(N_i - 1)$ is replaced by unity, this error is seen to be about half the fourth source of error mentioned below. This factor, incidentally, reduces the first source of error to zero when all the schedules of a class are processed, for then $N_i - n_i = 0$.

ii. The first source of error can be decreased by using an approximate relationship between x and z, provided one exists. An assumption is useful if it makes useful predictions. If some other set of assumptions turns out to be better for purposes of prediction, and if the extra cost involved in office procedure is not too great, a change might be warranted. A change in the assumption of a relationship will produce different results, not only in the estimated total inventories on Date II, but also in the estimated variance of that total inventory.

Sources i and ii do not both exist simultaneously. Messrs. Hansen and Hurwitz, in their evaluation of the sampling error (mentioned above), did not make use of any assumed relationship; hence their formula applies to source i only. There is no way of evaluating the second source of error analytically, even when it exists.

The effect of either or both of these two sources of error can be reduced to any desired degree by taking a big enough sample. Messrs. Hansen and Hurwitz wished particularly to reduce the error in the fifth class (the largest inventories); hence they took all of it. A 10 percent error in the fifth class would amount to as many cans of peas as a 50 percent error in one of the lower classes.

Problem B includes some other aspects that need to be considered when one takes into account the influences that affect the figures recorded on the schedules. In this problem, the inventories for Date II would ordinarily be collected on a sample basis, and the reports that have been received up to a certain deadline date would be processed. The action that is to be taken (policies in distribution) will affect all the stores in the area, those in the sample, and those not. A number of sources of error must be considered.

iii. Late reports introduce an error. It would of course be dangerous, if not folly, to assume that the late reports are a random sample of the universe. No attempt is made here to evaluate the bias arising from late reports.

In a sampling project, the total number of reporting stores may be so small that individual attention can be given to them, to reduce the proportion of late reports and the uncertainty introduced by them. For instance, one might send out telegrams just before the deadline to bring in some of the reports that threaten to be delinquent. Moreover, one might subsequently follow up some of the late reports, to decide, on the basis of empirical evidence, which way and how much the late reports affect the estimates.

iv. There are random errors in the responses of the sample stores, and there are fluctuations in their inventories owing to extraneous natural influences (such as the weather and freight tie-ups in and out), all of which throw the points away from whatever relationship may otherwise exist between the inventories on the two dates.

This source of error is the first term in the brackets of Eq. 58, and it is seen to be smaller as x_i increases, which is to say that the fourth source of error grows smaller as the sample grows bigger. This source of error, unlike the first and second, can not be reduced to zero by taking all the stores in any class.

The 2-sigma band in Fig. 24 is calculated from Eq. 57 and corresponds to the first term in the brackets of Eq. 62. This band shows how large a sample must be taken to reduce the fourth source of error to some desired degree. An assumed relationship other than the one adopted would lead to another band.

Deliberate errors of reporting are usually not random, and constitute an insidious problem of another kind. It is conceivable that under-reporting cancels out, as when X_i and x_i are both reported as just 50 percent of their true values; b_i would be twice as big, but Z_i would be unaffected.

v. Random errors of response, and extraneous natural influences are present, not only in the sample stores, but in the reported inventories of all the stores. As a consequence, the total inventory X_i of any class is affected. The effect of this error on the total inventory Z_i is evaluated by the second term in the brackets of Eq. 58.

vi. There is an error in Problem B arising from the assumption of a particular relationship and weighting. This corresponds to the second source of error, mentioned under Problem A. Again, there is no way of evaluating this source analytically.

APPENDIX

Tables for Making Random Observations for Class Illustration

Each number represents one observation.   The numbers may be taken out in any order — across, cornerwise, or in any systematic fashion that does not make use of the size of the number.

Part *A*: Normal Deviates Directly in Units of the Standard Error

(This table comes from a paper by Edward L. Dodd, *Boletin Matematico*, Buenos Aires, Año xv, 1942: pp. 76-7, with the kind permission of the author and editor.   These numbers were obtained from a transformation of the first two pages of Tippett's *Random Sampling Numbers*.)

−0.54	0.42	−0.26	2.04	0.83	0.23	−0.48	0.16
−0.21	1.67	−1.02	−1.08	0.58	0.09	−1.13	−0.61
−0.60	0.67	−0.41	−0.59	−0.37	−1.23	0.50	0.74
−1.59	0.06	−1.22	0.28	0.26	0.89	−0.19	1.16
−0.60	1.37	−1.08	1.30	0.53	0.28	1.18	0.37
0.22	−0.57	0.00	−0.97	−0.55	0.30	0.27	−0.59
1.45	−0.69	−0.41	0.11	1.14	0.26	0.01	−0.62
−0.84	0.79	−0.96	0.68	−1.72	1.01	1.15	0.56
1.72	−0.57	1.58	−0.34	−0.64	1.19	−0.86	0.39
0.93	−1.00	−0.87	0.01	−0.41	0.55	−0.26	0.57
0.17	−0.38	1.45	0.33	0.36	0.61	0.81	0.79
−1.27	0.49	−1.17	0.40	−0.77	0.00	−1.45	−0.70
0.48	0.03	0.17	−0.31	0.63	−0.40	0.97	0.37
−0.83	−0.77	−0.03	0.63	−0.56	−1.02	0.24	0.12
0.14	−0.06	−0.64	0.07	−0.89	0.38	0.19	1.72
−0.12	−0.91	−0.44	−0.26	1.63	−0.19	−0.57	2.62
−0.79	0.38	0.17	1.48	0.73	−0.97	0.11	0.73
0.50	−0.22	0.63	0.48	−1.19	0.59	−1.14	0.02
0.93	−0.22	−0.22	1.65	0.17	−0.27	0.24	−0.44
0.81	−0.33	0.24	1.98	−0.60	−0.20	0.00	1.11
1.54	0.56	−0.46	−1.45	−0.54	−1.27	0.35	−0.13
−0.40	0.33	0.26	1.54	−0.43	−1.24	−1.05	−0.05
1.34	−0.98	0.02	−1.50	0.39	−1.33	−0.10	−0.18
1.42	1.47	−0.58	0.55	−0.24	−0.82	0.33	−0.65
0.77	−0.32	−0.55	0.72	−2.36	0.53	−1.12	−0.86

1.95	1.87	0.63	−2.92	1.72	−0.90	−2.27	−0.88
1.57	1.41	1.17	1.53	−0.08	−1.75	0.44	0.14
−1.19	−0.37	0.25	−0.51	1.29	0.15	−0.72	0.89
−1.47	−0.25	−0.24	−1.02	−0.96	−1.09	0.06	−0.14
0.35	−0.25	−0.31	−0.78	0.91	−0.12	0.34	−0.39
−1.07	0.57	−0.34	−0.98	−1.52	−0.40	−0.14	−0.50
0.54	1.27	0.53	0.17	0.70	0.44	−0.92	−0.48
−0.46	−0.59	−1.38	1.31	1.21	0.04	1.01	1.35
0.81	−0.02	0.19	0.30	0.40	1.08	−0.41	1.33
1.16	−0.38	1.27	−1.42	0.35	−2.75	−0.64	0.25
−0.67	0.61	1.15	−3.89	−0.90	−0.70	−0.36	0.05
−2.01	−0.70	2.08	0.42	1.93	−0.97	1.38	−1.08
−0.52	1.04	0.60	1.56	−0.57	−1.46	−1.24	−0.49
0.67	−2.01	0.81	−0.72	−0.61	−0.02	−0.68	−0.29
0.05	−0.91	−0.77	1.54	−1.61	−0.87	−0.92	−0.81
−1.18	−0.66	−0.68	1.76	−2.47	−0.32	2.22	0.02
−0.28	−0.08	0.78	0.39	1.35	−0.48	−0.22	−0.35
−1.23	−0.76	−0.96	−0.74	−0.33	0.91	−1.11	−1.06
−0.91	0.75	0.15	0.57	1.66	−1.99	0.77	0.19
0.31	1.75	1.78	−0.80	0.75	−0.81	0.01	−1.59
−0.06	−0.12	−0.60	0.85	−0.09	−1.18	0.61	0.97
−1.66	0.52	−0.49	0.01	−0.03	−1.01	2.10	0.47
−0.01	−0.52	−1.06	−0.58	−1.05	−1.30	0.61	−0.31
−0.02	2.02	0.66	−0.25	−0.56	−1.59	−0.26	0.88
−0.72	−1.00	0.57	−1.95	−0.75	−0.23	−0.47	2.07
−1.15	−0.57	0.63	−0.25	−0.34	1.03	−0.64	0.12
0.11	−0.02	−1.33	0.56	−0.05	−1.12	1.13	−0.77
−0.45	−0.73	−0.22	2.25	−0.06	−0.12	−0.94	−0.65
0.78	−1.88	1.26	−0.79	0.77	−1.44	−1.16	0.58
0.49	−0.20	−0.36	0.02	−0.13	−0.50	−1.45	−0.01
1.39	−0.30	1.37	−0.80	0.45	1.81	0.88	−0.49
0.08	−1.29	−1.53	0.38	−0.04	1.13	1.19	1.07
−2.24	−0.06	0.85	1.42	−0.80	−0.76	0.01	1.10
−0.72	0.76	1.60	0.58	1.00	−0.26	−1.34	0.07
−1.80	0.07	−0.25	−1.94	1.44	0.20	0.18	−2.72
0.79	1.89	0.07	−0.19	2.25	−0.02	−1.29	1.35
−0.67	−0.19	−1.02	−2.01	−2.28	0.39	1.11	−0.07
0.42	−0.87	−0.49	1.37	0.29	0.23	−1.46	−0.28
0.46	−1.06	1.35	−0.06	2.34	−0.31	0.64	−0.60
−0.12	0.84	1.10	−0.42	0.82	−0.04	−0.17	1.79
0.18	2.27	−0.69	−1.34	−0.22	0.43	−1.41	0.29
−0.21	−1.06	−0.56	−1.46	−1.13	1.28	−1.02	−1.05
−0.12	−0.68	−0.36	0.08	0.72	0.56	−1.27	−0.70
−0.09	−1.54	2.16	−0.14	0.17	0.73	−1.18	−0.73
0.44	−0.37	2.12	1.40	−1.64	0.38	0.09	1.25
0.39	−1.84	0.81	0.92	−1.37	0.87	0.18	−0.86
−0.97	−0.18	−0.89	0.08	−0.38	1.27	0.66	−0.30
−1.12	−1.17	−0.43	1.22	−0.27	0.46	−0.95	−1.85
0.01	−0.25	−0.81	2.08	1.10	−0.44	0.58	0.29
0.79	−0.83	0.04	−0.84	−0.54	−1.98	0.73	−0.57
−0.85	1.28	−1.27	0.60	0.74	−0.21	0.89	0.60
2.54	−1.38	0.66	−0.27	0.84	−1.37	0.20	−0.13
−1.84	2.38	0.00	0.77	0.51	−1.36	−0.85	2.26
2.06	0.81	−0.22	0.48	−1.99	−1.11	0.65	1.20
−0.99	0.79	1.65	−0.23	−1.26	−0.53	0.27	−1.30

−0.81	−1.19	−0.31	0.32	−1.53	−1.48	−0.75	0.07
−1.63	−2.00	0.24	0.47	−1.08	0.71	−0.02	−0.08
−1.62	−0.24	1.37	0.35	−0.81	0.95	−0.36	0.39
0.64	0.64	0.40	−1.01	−0.21	−1.72	−0.39	−0.32
−0.44	−0.32	0.80	0.52	0.80	0.60	−0.10	1.74
0.49	−0.66	0.67	1.75	1.33	−0.61	−0.01	−1.00
1.27	−0.49	−0.35	−1.78	−1.25	0.34	1.27	−0.20
1.41	−0.72	−1.76	−0.47	−0.99	0.99	−0.15	−2.08
1.96	0.84	0.55	2.04	−1.02	0.89	−0.13	−0.88
−0.78	−0.80	−0.56	0.18	−1.01	0.76	−0.02	2.41
0.50	−0.50	−0.81	−0.43	−0.14	1.67	−1.84	1.80
−0.42	−0.37	−1.78	0.24	−0.27	0.60	1.07	0.22
2.00	0.14	−0.07	0.13	−0.32	−0.48	−0.34	−0.15
1.52	0.15	0.12	−2.07	0.61	0.52	−0.27	0.60
0.19	0.33	−0.37	0.31	−0.52	0.30	1.02	−0.83
0.48	0.89	−0.14	−0.54	2.55	1.86	−0.36	0.96
0.42	0.46	−0.02	−2.48	−1.76	1.23	−0.06	0.64
−0.63	−0.19	1.15	1.01	−0.17	1.28	−1.15	−1.60
0.48	−0.03	1.67	−0.38	0.40	0.74	2.52	1.02
−0.12	0.76	−0.28	0.60	−1.11	0.56	−0.03	0.42

PART B: NORMAL DISTRIBUTION OF THE NUMBERS FROM 0000 TO 9999. CLASS INTERVAL .2σ.

(This table is to be used in conjunction with Tippett's numbers, in circumstances where a longer series than that in Part A is required, or where it is desired to use pages of Tippett's numbers other than the first two.)

Interval Center	Limits	Cumulative area	Area of interval	Intervals for Tippett's numbers (0000–9999)	Center of interval
−3.8σ	− ∞	0			−3.8σ
−3.6	−3.7σ	0.000 1078	0.000 1078	0000	−3.6
−3.4	−3.5	.000 2326	.000 1248	0001	−3.4
−3.2	−3.3	.000 4834	.000 2508	0002–0004	−3.2
−3.0	−3.1	.000 9676	.000 4842	0005–0009	−3.0
−2.8	−2.9	.001 8658	.000 8982	0010–0018	−2.8
−2.6	−2.7	.003 4670	.001 6012	0019–0034	−2.6
−2.4	−2.5	.006 2097	.002 7427	0035–0061	−2.4
−2.2	−2.3	.010 7241	.004 5144	0062–0106	−2.2
−2.0	−2.1	.017 8644	.007 1403	0107–0178	−2.0
−1.8	−1.9	.028 7166	.010 8522	0179–0286	−1.8
−1.6	−1.7	.044 5655	.015 8489	0287–0445	−1.6
−1.4	−1.5	.066 8072	.022 2417	0446–0667	−1.4
−1.2	−1.3	.096 8005	.029 9933	0668–0967	−1.2
−1.0	−1.1	.135 6661	.038 8656	0968–1356	−1.0
−0.8	−0.9	.184 0601	.048 3940	1357–1840	−0.8
−0.6	−0.7	.241 9637	.057 9036	1841–2419	−0.6
−0.4	−0.5	.308 5375	.066 5738	2420–3084	−0.4
−0.2	−0.3	.382 0886	.073 5511	3085–3820	−0.2
0	−0.1	.460 1722	.078 0836	3821–4601	0
0.2	0.1	.539 8278	.079 6556	4602–5397	0.2
0.4	0.3	.617 9114	.078 0836	5398–6178	0.4
0.6	0.5	.691 4625	.073 5511	6179–6914	0.6
0.8	0.7	.758 0363	.066 5738	6915–7579	0.8
1.0	0.9	.815 9399	.057 9036	7580–8158	1.0
1.2	1.1	.864 3339	.048 3940	8159–8642	1.2
1.4	1.3	.903 1995	.038 8656	8643–9031	1.4
1.6	1.5	.933 1928	.029 9933	9032–9331	1.6
1.8	1.7	.955 4345	.022 2417	9332–9553	1.8
2.0	1.9	.971 2834	.015 8489	9554–9712	2.0
2.2	2.1	.982 1356	.010 8522	9713–9820	2.2
2.4	2.3	.989 2759	.007 1403	9821–9892	2.4
2.6	2.5	.993 7903	.004 5144	9893–9937	2.6
2.8	2.7	.996 5330	.002 7427	9938–9964	2.8
3.0	2.9	.998 1342	.001 6012	9965–9980	3.0
3.2	3.1	.999 0324	.000 8982	9981–9989	3.2
3.4	3.3	.999 5166	.000 4842	9990–9994	3.4
3.6	3.5	.999 7674	.000 2508	9995–9997	3.6
3.8	3.7	.999 8922	.000 1248	9998	3.8
	∞	1	.000 1078	9999	

INDEX

CATALOGUE OF DOVER BOOKS

MATHEMATICS—INTERMEDIATE TO ADVANCED

General

INTRODUCTION TO APPLIED MATHEMATICS, Francis D. Murnaghan. A practical and thoroughly sound introduction to a number of advanced branches of higher mathematics. Among the selected topics covered in detail are: vector and matrix analysis, partial and differential equations, integral equations, calculus of variations, Laplace transform theory, the vector triple product, linear vector functions, quadratic and bilinear forms, Fourier series, spherical harmonics, Bessel functions, the Heaviside expansion formula, and many others. Extremely useful book for graduate students in physics, engineering, chemistry, and mathematics. Index. 111 study exercises with answers. 41 illustrations. ix + 389pp. 5⅜ x 8½.
S1042 Paperbound **$2.00**

OPERATIONAL METHODS IN APPLIED MATHEMATICS, H. S. Carslaw and J. C. Jaeger. Explanation of the application of the Laplace Transformation to differential equations, a simple and effective substitute for more difficult and obscure operational methods. Of great practical value to engineers and to all workers in applied mathematics. Chapters on: Ordinary Linear Differential Equations with Constant Coefficients;; Electric Circuit Theory; Dynamical Applications; The Inversion Theorem for the Laplace Transformation; Conduction of Heat; Vibrations of Continuous Mechanical Systems; Hydrodynamics; Impulsive Functions; Chains of Differential Equations; and other related matters. 3 appendices. 153 problems, many with answers. 22 figures. xvi + 359pp. 5⅜ x 8½.
S1011 Paperbound **$2.25**

APPLIED MATHEMATICS FOR RADIO AND COMMUNICATIONS ENGINEERS, C. E. Smith. No extraneous material here!—only the theories, equations, and operations essential and immediately useful for radio work. Can be used as refresher, as handbook of applications and tables, or as full home-study course. Ranges from simplest arithmetic through calculus, series, and wave forms, hyperbolic trigonometry, simultaneous equations in mesh circuits, etc. Supplies applications right along with each math topic discussed. 22 useful tables of functions, formulas, logs, etc. Index. 166 exercises, 140 examples, all with answers. 95 diagrams. Bibliography. x + 336pp. 5⅜ x 8.
S141 Paperbound **$1.75**

Algebra, group theory, determinants, sets, matrix theory

ALGEBRAS AND THEIR ARITHMETICS, L. E. Dickson. Provides the foundation and background necessary to any advanced undergraduate or graduate student studying abstract algebra. Begins with elementary introduction to linear transformations, matrices, field of complex numbers; proceeds to order, basal units, modulus, quaternions, etc.; develops calculus of linears sets, describes various examples of algebras including invariant, difference, nilpotent, semi-simple. "Makes the reader marvel at his genius for clear and profound analysis," Amer. Mathematical Monthly. Index. xii + 241pp. 5⅜ x 8.
S616 Paperbound **$1.50**

THE THEORY OF EQUATIONS WITH AN INTRODUCTION TO THE THEORY OF BINARY ALGEBRAIC FORMS, W. S. Burnside and A. W. Panton. Extremely thorough and concrete discussion of the theory of equations, with extensive detailed treatment of many topics curtailed in later texts. Covers theory of algebraic equations, properties of polynomials, symmetric functions, derived functions, Horner's process, complex numbers and the complex variable, determinants and methods of elimination, invariant theory (nearly 100 pages), transformations, introduction to Galois theory, Abelian equations, and much more. Invaluable supplementary work for modern students and teachers. 759 examples and exercises. Index in each volume. Two volume set. Total of xxiv + 604pp. 5⅜ x 8.
S714 Vol I Paperbound **$1.85**
S715 Vol II Paperbound **$1.85**
The set **$3.70**

COMPUTATIONAL METHODS OF LINEAR ALGEBRA, V. N. Faddeeva, translated by **C. D. Benster.** First English translation of a unique and valuable work, the only work in English presenting a systematic exposition of the most important methods of linear algebra—classical and contemporary. Shows in detail how to derive numerical solutions of problems in mathematical physics which are frequently connected with those of linear algebra. Theory as well as individual practice. Part I surveys the mathematical background that is indispensable to what follows. Parts II and III, the conclusion, set forth the most important methods of solution, for both exact and iterative groups. One of the most outstanding and valuable features of this work is the 23 tables, double and triple checked for accuracy. These tables will not be found elsewhere. Author's preface. Translator's note. New bibliography and index. x + 252pp. 5⅜ x 8.
S424 Paperbound **$1.95**

ALGEBRAIC EQUATIONS, E. Dehn. Careful and complete presentation of Galois' theory of algebraic equations; theories of Lagrange and Galois developed in logical rather than historical form, with a more thorough exposition than in most modern texts. Many concrete applications and fully-worked-out examples. Discusses basic theory (very clear exposition of the symmetric group); isomorphic, transitive, and Abelian groups; applications of Lagrange's and Galois' theories; and much more. Newly revised by the author. Index. List of Theorems. xi + 208pp. 5⅜ x 8.
S697 Paperbound **$1.45**

Catalogue of Dover Books

ALGEBRAIC THEORIES, L. E. Dickson. Best thorough introduction to classical topics in higher algebra develops theories centering around matrices, invariants, groups. Higher algebra, Galois theory, finite linear groups, Klein's icosahedron, algebraic invariants, linear transformations, elementary divisors, invariant factors; quadratic, bi-linear, Hermitian forms, singly and in pairs. Proofs rigorous, detailed; topics developed lucidly, in close connection with their most frequent mathematical applications. Formerly "Modern Algebraic Theories." 155 problems. Bibliography. 2 indexes. 285pp. 5⅜ x 8.   S547 Paperbound **$1.50**

LECTURES ON THE ICOSAHEDRON AND THE SOLUTION OF EQUATIONS OF THE FIFTH DEGREE, Felix Klein. The solution of quintics in terms of rotation of a regular icosahedron around its axes of symmetry. A classic & indispensable source for those interested in higher algebra, geometry, crystallography. Considerable explanatory material included. 230 footnotes, mostly bibliographic. 2nd edition, xvi + 289pp. 5⅜ x 8.   S314 Paperbound **$2.25**

LINEAR GROUPS, WITH AN EXPOSITION OF THE GALOIS FIELD THEORY, L. E. Dickson. The classic exposition of the theory of groups, well within the range of the graduate student. Part I contains the most extensive and thorough presentation of the theory of Galois Fields available, with a wealth of examples and theorems. Part II is a full discussion of linear groups of finite order. Much material in this work is based on Dickson's own contributions. Also includes expositions of Jordan, Lie, Abel, Betti-Mathieu, Hermite, etc. "A milestone in the development of modern algebra," W. Magnus, in his historical introduction to this edition. Index. xv + 312pp. 5⅜ x 8.   S482 Paperbound **$1.95**

INTRODUCTION TO THE THEORY OF GROUPS OF FINITE ORDER, R. Carmichael. Examines fundamental theorems and their application. Beginning with sets, systems, permutations, etc., it progresses in easy stages through important types of groups: Abelian, prime power, permutation, etc. Except 1 chapter where matrices are desirable, no higher math needed. 783 exercises, problems. Index. xvi + 447pp. 5⅜ x 8.   S300 Paperbound **$2.25**

THEORY OF GROUPS OF FINITE ORDER, W. Burnside. First published some 40 years ago, this is still one of the clearest introductory texts. Partial contents: permutations, groups independent of representation, composition series of a group, isomorphism of a group with itself, Abelian groups, prime power groups, permutation groups, invariants of groups of linear substitution, graphical representation, etc. 45pp. of notes. Indexes. xxiv + 512pp. 5⅜ x 8.
S38 Paperbound **$2.75**

CONTINUOUS GROUPS OF TRANSFORMATIONS, L. P. Eisenhart. Intensive study of the theory and geometrical applications of continuous groups of transformations; a standard work on the subject, called forth by the revolution in physics in the 1920's. Covers tensor analysis, Riemannian geometry, canonical parameters, transitivity, imprimitivity, differential invariants, the algebra of constants of structure, differential geometry, contact transformations, etc. "Likely to remain one of the standard works on the subject for many years . . . principal theorems are proved clearly and concisely, and the arrangement of the whole is coherent," MATHEMATICAL GAZETTE. Index. 72-item bibliography. 185 exercises. ix + 301pp. 5⅜ x 8.
S781 Paperbound **$2.00**

THE THEORY OF GROUPS AND QUANTUM MECHANICS, H. Weyl. Discussions of Schroedinger's wave equation, de Broglie's waves of a particle, Jordan-Hoelder theorem, Lie's continuous groups of transformations, Pauli exclusion principle, quantization of Maxwell-Dirac field equations, etc. Unitary geometry, quantum theory, groups, application of groups to quantum mechanics, symmetry permutation group, algebra of symmetric transformation, etc. 2nd revised edition. Bibliography. Index. xxii + 422pp. 5⅜ x 8.   S269 Paperbound **$2.35**

APPLIED GROUP-THEORETIC AND MATRIX METHODS, Bryan Higman. The first systematic treatment of group and matrix theory for the physical scientist. Contains a comprehensive, easily-followed exposition of the basic ideas of group theory (realized through matrices) and its applications in the various areas of physics and chemistry: tensor analysis, relativity, quantum theory, molecular structure and spectra, and Eddington's quantum relativity. Includes rigorous proofs available only in works of a far more advanced character. 34 figures, numerous tables. Bibliography. Index. xiii + 454pp. 5⅜ x 8⅜.
S1147 Paperbound **$2.50**

THE THEORY OF GROUP REPRESENTATIONS, Francis D. Murnaghan. A comprehensive introduction to the theory of group representations. Particular attention is devoted to the groups—mainly the symmetric and rotation groups—which have proved to be of fundamental significance for quantum mechanics (esp. nuclear physics). Also a valuable contribution to the literature on matrices, since the usual representations of groups are groups of matrices. Covers the theory of group integration (as developed by Schur and Weyl), the theory of 2-valued or spin representations, the representations of the symmetric group, the crystallographic groups, the Lorentz group, reducibility (Schur's lemma, Burnside's Theorem, etc.), the alternating group, linear groups, the orthogonal group, etc. Index. List of references. xi + 369pp. 5⅜ x 8½.   S1112 Paperbound **$2.35**

THEORY OF SETS, E. Kamke. Clearest, amplest introduction in English, well suited for independent study. Subdivision of main theory, such as theory of sets of points, are discussed, but emphasis is on general theory. Partial contents: rudiments of set theory, arbitrary sets and their cardinal numbers, ordered sets and their order types, well-ordered sets and their cardinal numbers. Bibliography. Key to symbols. Index. vii + 144pp. 5⅜ x 8.
S141 Paperbound **$1.35**

THEORY AND APPLICATIONS OF FINITE GROUPS, G. A. Miller, H. F. Blichfeldt, L. E. Dickson.
Unusually accurate and authoritative work, each section prepared by a leading specialist: Miller on substitution and abstract groups, Blichfeldt on finite groups of linear homogeneous transformations, Dickson on applications of finite groups. Unlike more modern works, this gives the concrete basis from which abstract group theory arose. Includes Abelian groups, prime-power groups, isomorphisms, matrix forms of linear transformations, Sylow groups, Galois' theory of algebraic equations, duplication of a cube, trisection of an angle, etc. 2 Indexes. 267 problems. xvii + 390pp. 5⅜ x 8.   S216 Paperbound **$2.00**

THE THEORY OF DETERMINANTS, MATRICES, AND INVARIANTS, H. W. Turnbull. Important study includes all salient features and major theories. 7 chapters on determinants and matrices cover fundamental properties, Laplace identities, multiplication, linear equations, rank and differentiation, etc. Sections on invariants gives general properties, symbolic and direct methods of reduction, binary and polar forms, general linear transformation, first fundamental theorem, multilinear forms. Following chapters study development and proof of Hilbert's Basis Theorem, Gordan-Hilbert Finiteness Theorem, Clebsch's Theorem, and include discussions of apolarity, canonical forms, geometrical interpretations of algebraic forms, complete system of the general quadric, etc. New preface and appendix. Bibliography. xviii + 374pp. 5⅜ x 8.   S699 Paperbound **$2.25**

AN INTRODUCTION TO THE THEORY OF CANONICAL MATRICES, H. W. Turnbull and A. C. Aitken.
All principal aspects of the theory of canonical matrices, from definitions and fundamental properties of matrices to the practical applications of their reduction to canonical form. Beginning with matrix multiplications, reciprocals, and partitioned matrices, the authors go on to elementary transformations and bilinear and quadratic forms. Also covers such topics as a rational canonical form for the collineatory group, congruent and conjunctive transformation for quadratic and hermitian forms, unitary and orthogonal transformations, canonical reduction of pencils of matrices, etc. Index. Appendix. Historical notes at chapter ends. Bibliographies. 275 problems. xiv + 200pp. 5⅜ x 8.   S177 Paperbound **$1.55**

A TREATISE ON THE THEORY OF DETERMINANTS, T. Muir. Unequalled as an exhaustive compilation of nearly all the known facts about determinants up to the early 1930's. Covers notation and general properties, row and column transformation, symmetry, compound determinants, adjugates, rectangular arrays and matrices, linear dependence, gradients, Jacobians, Hessians, Wronskians, and much more. Invaluable for libraries of industrial and research organizations as well as for student, teacher, and mathematician; very useful in the field of computing machines. Revised and enlarged by W. H. Metzler. Index. 485 problems and scores of numerical examples. iv + 766pp. 5⅜ x 8.   S670 Paperbound **$3.00**

THEORY OF DETERMINANTS IN THE HISTORICAL ORDER OF DEVELOPMENT, Sir Thomas Muir.
Unabridged reprinting of this complete study of 1,859 papers on determinant theory written between 1693 and 1900. Most important and original sections reproduced, valuable commentary on each. No other work is necessary for determinant research: all types are covered— each subdivision of the theory treated separately; all papers dealing with each type are covered; you are told exactly what each paper is about and how important its contribution is. Each result, theory, extension, or modification is assigned its own identifying numeral so that the full history may be more easily followed. Includes papers on determinants in general, determinants and linear equations, symmetric determinants, alternants, recurrents, determinants having invariant factors, and all other major types. "A model of what such histories ought to be," NATURE. "Mathematicians must ever be grateful to Sir Thomas for his monumental work," AMERICAN MATH MONTHLY. Four volumes bound as two. Indices. Bibliographies. Total of lxxxiv + 1977pp. 5⅜ x 8.   S672-3 The set, Clothbound **$12.50**

Calculus and function theory, Fourier theory, infinite series, calculus of variations, real and complex functions

FIVE VOLUME "THEORY OF FUNCTIONS" SET BY KONRAD KNOPP

This five-volume set, prepared by Konrad Knopp, provides a complete and readily followed account of theory of functions. Proofs are given concisely, yet without sacrifice of completeness or rigor. These volumes are used as texts by such universities as M.I.T., University of Chicago, N. Y. City College, and many others. "Excellent introduction . . . remarkably readable, concise, clear, rigorous," JOURNAL OF THE AMERICAN STATISTICAL ASSOCIATION.

ELEMENTS OF THE THEORY OF FUNCTIONS, Konrad Knopp. This book provides the student with background for further volumes in this set, or texts on a similar level. Partial contents: foundations, system of complex numbers and the Gaussian plane of numbers, Riemann sphere of numbers, mapping by linear functions, normal forms, the logarithm, the cyclometric functions and binomial series. "Not only for the young student, but also for the student who knows all about what is in it," MATHEMATICAL JOURNAL. Bibliography. Index. 140pp. 5⅜ x 8.   S154 Paperbound **$1.35**

THEORY OF FUNCTIONS, PART I, Konrad Knopp. With volume II, this book provides coverage of basic concepts and theorems. Partial contents: numbers and points, functions of a complex variable, integral of a continuous function, Cauchy's integral theorem, Cauchy's integral formulae, series with variable terms, expansion of analytic functions in power series, analytic continuation and complete definition of analytic functions, entire transcendental functions, Laurent expansion, types of singularities. Bibliography. Index. vii + 146pp. 5⅜ x 8.
                                    S156 Paperbound **$1.35**

Differential equations, ordinary and partial; integral equations

INTRODUCTION TO THE DIFFERENTIAL EQUATIONS OF PHYSICS, L. Hopf. Especially valuable to the engineer with no math beyond elementary calculus. Emphasizing intuitive rather than formal aspects of concepts, the author covers an extensive territory. Partial contents: Law of causality, energy theorem, damped oscillations, coupling by friction, cylindrical and spherical coordinates, heat source, etc. Index. 48 figures. 160pp. 5⅜ x 8.
S120 Paperbound **$1.35**

INTRODUCTION TO THE THEORY OF LINEAR DIFFERENTIAL EQUATIONS, E. G. Poole. Authoritative discussions of important topics, with methods of solution more detailed than usual, for students with background of elementary course in differential equations. Studies existence theorems, linearly independent solutions; equations with constant coefficients; with uniform analytic coefficients; regular singularities; the hypergeometric equation; conformal representation; etc. Exercises. Index. 210pp. 5⅜ x 8.
S629 Paperbound **$1.65**

DIFFERENTIAL EQUATIONS FOR ENGINEERS, P. Franklin. Outgrowth of a course given 10 years at M. I. T. Makes most useful branch of pure math accessible for practical work. Theoretical basis of D.E.'s; solution of ordinary D.E.'s and partial derivatives arising from heat flow, steady-state temperature of a plate, wave equations; analytic functions; convergence of Fourier Series. 400 problems on electricity, vibratory systems, other topics. Formerly "Differential Equations for Electrical Engineers." Index 41 illus. 307pp. 5⅜ x 8.
S601 Paperbound **$1.65**

DIFFERENTIAL EQUATIONS, F. R. Moulton. A detailed, rigorous exposition of all the non-elementary processes of solving ordinary differential equations. Several chapters devoted to the treatment of practical problems, especially those of a physical nature, which are far more advanced than problems usually given as illustrations. Includes analytic differential equations; variations of a parameter; integrals of differential equations; analytic implicit functions; problems of elliptic motion; sine-amplitude functions; deviation of formal bodies; Cauchy-Lipschitz process; linear differential equations with periodic coefficients; differential equations in infinitely many variations; much more. Historical notes. 10 figures. 222 problems. Index. xv + 395pp. 5⅜ x 8.
S451 Paperbound **$2.00**

DIFFERENTIAL AND INTEGRAL EQUATIONS OF MECHANICS AND PHYSICS (DIE DIFFERENTIAL-UND INTEGRALGLEICHUNGEN DER MECHANIK UND PHYSIK), edited by P. Frank and R. von Mises. Most comprehensive and authoritative work on the mathematics of mathematical physics available today in the United States: the standard, definitive reference for teachers, physicists, engineers, and mathematicians—now published (in the original German) at a relatively inexpensive price for the first time! Every chapter in this 2,000-page set is by an expert in his field: Carathéodory, Courant, Frank, Mises, and a dozen others. Vol I, on mathematics, gives concise but complete coverages of advanced calculus, differential equations, integral equations, and potential, and partial differential equations. Index. xxiii + 916pp. Vol. II (physics): classical mechanics, optics, continuous mechanics, heat conduction and diffusion, the stationary and quasi-stationary electromagnetic field, electromagnetic oscillations, and wave mechanics. Index. xxiv + 1106pp. Two volume set. Each volume available separately. 5⅝ x 8⅜.
S787 Vol I Clothbound **$7.50**
S788 Vol II Clothbound **$7.50**
The set **$15.00**

LECTURES ON CAUCHY'S PROBLEM, J. Hadamard. Based on lectures given at Columbia, Rome, this discusses work of Riemann, Kirchhoff, Volterra, and the author's own research on the hyperbolic case in linear partial differential equations. It extends spherical and cylindrical waves to apply to all (normal) hyperbolic equations. Partial contents: Cauchy's problem, fundamental formula, equations with odd number, with even number of independent variables; method of descent. 32 figures. Index. iii + 316pp. 5⅜ x 8. S105 Paperbound **$1.75**

THEORY OF DIFFERENTIAL EQUATIONS, A. R. Forsyth. Out of print for over a decade, the complete 6 volumes (now bound as 3) of this monumental work represent the most comprehensive treatment of differential equations ever written. Historical presentation includes in 2500 pages every substantial development. Vol. 1, 2: EXACT EQUATIONS, PFAFF'S PROBLEM; ORDINARY EQUATIONS, NOT LINEAR: methods of Grassmann, Clebsch, Lie, Darboux; Cauchy's theorem; branch points; etc. Vol. 3, 4: ORDINARY EQUATIONS, NOT LINEAR; ORDINARY LINEAR EQUATIONS: Zeta Fuchsian functions, general theorems on algebraic integrals, Brun's theorem, equations with uniform periodic cofficients, etc. Vol. 4, 5: PARTIAL DIFFERENTIAL EQUATIONS: 2 existence-theorems, equations of theoretical dynamics, Laplace transformations, general transformation of equations of the 2nd order, much more. Indexes. Total of 2766pp. 5⅜ x 8. S576-7-8 Clothbound: the set **$15.00**

PARTIAL DIFFERENTIAL EQUATIONS OF MATHEMATICAL PHYSICS, A. G. Webster. A keystone work in the library of every mature physicist, engineer, researcher. Valuable sections on elasticity, compression theory, potential theory, theory of sound, heat conduction, wave propagation, vibration theory. Contents include: deduction of differential equations, vibrations, normal functions, Fourier's series, Cauchy's method, boundary problems, method of Riemann-Volterra. Spherical, cylindrical, ellipsoidal harmonics, applications, etc. 97 figures. vii + 440pp. 5⅜ x 8. S263 Paperbound **$2.25**

ORDINARY DIFFERENTIAL EQUATIONS, E. L. Ince. A most compendious analysis in real and complex domains. Existence and nature of solutions, continuous transformation groups, solutions in an infinite form, definite integrals, algebraic theory, Sturmian theory, boundary problems, existence theorems, 1st order, higher order, etc. "Deserves the highest praise, a notable addition to mathematical literature," BULLETIN, AM. MATH. SOC. Historical appendix. Bibliography. 18 figures. viii + 558pp. 5⅜ x 8. S349 Paperbound **$2.75**

INTRODUCTION TO NONLINEAR DIFFERENTIAL AND INTEGRAL EQUATIONS, Harold T. Davis. A thorough introduction to this important area, of increasing interest to mathematicians and scientists. First published by the United States Atomic Energy Commission, it includes chapters on the differential equation of the first order, the Riccati equation (as a bridge between linear and nonlinear equations), existence theorems, second order equations, elliptic integrals, elliptic functions, and theta functions, second order differential equations of polynomial class, continuous analytic continuation, the phase plane and its phenomena, nonlinear mechanics, the calculus of variations, etc. Appendices on Painlevé transcendents and Van der Pol and Volterra equations. Bibliography of 350 items. 137 problems. Index. xv + 566pp. 5⅜ x 8½. S971 Paperbound **$2.00**

THEORY OF FUNCTIONALS AND OF INTEGRAL AND INTEGRO-DIFFERENTIAL EQUATIONS, Vito Volterra. Unabridged republication of the only English translation. An exposition of the general theory of the functions depending on a continuous set of values of another function, based on the author's fundamental notion of the transition from a finite number of variables to a continually infinite number. Though dealing primarily with integral equations, much material on calculus of variations is included. The work makes no assumption of previous knowledge on the part of the reader. It begins with fundamental material and proceeds to Generalization of Analytic Functions, Integro-Differential Equations, Functional Derivative Equations, Applications, Other Directions of Theory of Functionals, etc. New introduction by G. C. Evans. Bibliography and criticism of Volterra's work by E. Whittaker. Bibliography. Index of authors cited. Index of subjects. xxxx + 226pp. 5⅜ x 8. S502 Paperbound **$1.75**

LINEAR INTEGRAL EQUATIONS, W. V. Lovitt. Systematic survey of general theory, with some application to differential equations, calculus of variations, problems of math, physics. Partial contents: integral equation of 2nd kind by successive substitutions; Fredholm's equation as ratio of 2 integral series in lambda, applications of the Fredholm theory, Hilbert-Schmidt theory of symmetric kernels, application, etc. Neumann, Dirichlet, vibratory problems. Index. ix + 253pp. 5⅜ x 8. S176 Paperbound **$2.00**

Foundations of mathematics

THE CONTINUUM AND OTHER TYPES OF SERIAL ORDER, E. V. Huntington. This famous book gives a systematic elementary account of the modern theory of the continuum as a type of serial order. Based on the Cantor-Dedekind ordinal theory, which requires no technical knowledge of higher mathematics, it offers an easily followed analysis of ordered classes, discrete and dense series, continuous series, Cantor's transfinite numbers. 2nd edition. Index. viii + 82pp. 5⅜ x 8. S130 Paperbound **$1.00**

CONTRIBUTIONS TO THE FOUNDING OF THE THEORY OF TRANSFINITE NUMBERS, Georg Cantor. These papers founded a new branch of mathematics. The famous articles of 1895-7 are translated, with an 82-page introduction by P. E. B. Jourdain dealing with Cantor, the background of his discoveries, their results, future possibilities. Bibliography. Index. Notes. ix + 211 pp. 5⅜ x 8. S45 Paperbound **$1.35**

ELEMENTARY MATHEMATICS FROM AN ADVANCED STANDPOINT, Felix Klein.

This classic text is an outgrowth of Klein's famous integration and survey course at Göttingen. Using one field of mathematics to interpret, adjust, illuminate another, it covers basic topics in each area, illustrating its discussion with extensive analysis. It is especially valuable in considering areas of modern mathematics. "Makes the reader feel the inspiration of . . . a great mathematician, inspiring teacher . . . with deep insight into the foundations and interrelations," BULLETIN, AMERICAN MATHEMATICAL SOCIETY.

Vol. 1. ARITHMETIC, ALGEBRA, ANALYSIS. Introducing the concept of function immediately, it enlivens abstract discussion with graphical and geometrically perceptual methods. Partial contents: natural numbers, extension of the notion of number, special properties, complex numbers. Real equations with real unknowns, complex quantities. Logarithmic, exponential functions, goniometric functions, infinitesimal calculus. Transcendence of e and pi, theory of assemblages. Index. 125 figures. ix + 274pp . 5⅜ x 8. S150 Paperbound **$1.85**

Vol. 2. GEOMETRY. A comprehensive view which accompanies the space perception inherent in geometry with analytic formulas which facilitate precise formulation. Partial contents: Simplest geometric manifolds: line segment, Grassmann determinant principles, classification of configurations of space, derivative manifolds. Geometric transformations: affine transformations, projective, higher point transformations, theory of the imaginary. Systematic discussion of geometry and its foundations. Indexes. 141 illustrations. ix + 214pp. 5⅜ x 8. S151 Paperbound **$1.75**

ESSAYS ON THE THEORY OF NUMBERS: 1. CONTINUITY AND IRRATIONAL NUMBERS; 2. THE NATURE AND MEANING OF NUMBERS, Richard Dedekind. The two most important essays on the logical foundations of the number system by the famous German mathematician. The first provides a purely arithmetic and perfectly rigorous foundation for irrational numbers and thereby a rigorous meaning to continuity in analysis. The second essay is an attempt to give a logical basis for transfinite numbers and properties of the natural numbers. Discusses the logical validity of mathematical induction. Authorized English translations by W. W. Beman of "Stetigkeit und irrationale Zahlen" and "Was sind und was sollen die Zahlen?" vii + 115pp. 5⅜ x 8. T1010 Paperbound **$1.00**

Geometry

THE FOUNDATIONS OF EUCLIDEAN GEOMETRY, H. G. Forder. The first rigorous account of Euclidean geometry, establishing propositions without recourse to empiricism, and without multiplying hypotheses. Corrects many traditional weaknesses of Euclidean proofs, and investigates the problems imposed on the axiom system by the discoveries of Bolyai and Lobachevsky. Some topics discussed are Classes and Relations; Axioms for Magnitudes; Congruence and Similarity; Algebra of Points; Hessenberg's Theorem; Continuity; Existence of Parallels; Reflections; Rotations; Isometries; etc. Invaluable for the light it throws on foundations of math. Lists: Axioms employed, Symbols, Constructions. 295pp. 5⅜ x 8. S481 Paperbound **$2.00**

ADVANCED EUCLIDEAN GEOMETRY, R. A. Johnson. For years the standard textbook on advanced Euclidean geometry, requires only high school geometry and trigonometry. Explores in unusual detail and gives proofs of hundreds of relatively recent theorems and corollaries, many formerly available only in widely scattered journals. Covers tangent circles, the theorem of Miquel, symmedian point, pedal triangles and circles, the Brocard configuration, and much more. Formerly "Modern Geometry." Index. 107 diagrams. xiii + 319pp. 5⅜ x 8. S669 Paperbound **$1.65**

HIGHER GEOMETRY: AN INTRODUCTION TO ADVANCED METHODS IN ANALYTIC GEOMETRY, F. S. Woods. Exceptionally thorough study of concepts and methods of advanced algebraic geometry (as distinguished from differential geometry). Exhaustive treatment of 1-, 2-, 3-, and 4-dimensional coordinate systems, leading to n-dimensional geometry in an abstract sense. Covers projectivity, tetracyclical coordinates, contact transformation, pentaspherical coordinates, much more. Based on M.I.T. lectures, requires sound preparation in analytic geometry and some knowledge of determinants. Index. Over 350 exercises. References. 60 figures. x + 423pp. 5⅜ x 8. S737 Paperbound **$2.00**

CONTEMPORARY GEOMETRY, André Delachet. Translated by Howard G. Bergmann. The recent developments in geometry covered in uncomplicated fashion. Clear discussions of modern thinking about the theory of groups, the concept of abstract geometry, projective geometry, algebraic geometry, vector spaces, new kinds of metric spaces, developments in differential geometry, etc. A large part of the book is devoted to problems, developments, and applications of topology. For advanced undergraduates and graduate students as well as mathematicians in other fields who want a brief introduction to current work in geometry. 39 figures. Index. xix + 94pp. 5⅜ x 8½. S988 Paperbound **$1.00**

ELEMENTS OF PROJECTIVE GEOMETRY, L. Cremona. Outstanding complete treatment of projective geometry by one of the foremost 19th century geometers. Detailed proofs of all fundamental principles, stress placed on the constructive aspects. Covers homology, law of duality, anharmonic ratios, theorems of Pascal and Brianchon, foci, polar reciprocal figures, etc. Only ordinary geometry necessary to understand this honored classic. Index. Over 150 fully worked out examples and problems. 252 diagrams. xx + 302pp. 5⅜ x 8. S668 Paperbound **$1.75**

AN INTRODUCTION TO PROJECTIVE GEOMETRY, R. M. Winger. One of the best introductory texts to an important area in modern mathematics. Contains full development of elementary concepts often omitted in other books. Employing the analytic method to capitalize on the student's collegiate training in algebra, analytic geometry and calculus, the author deals with such topics as Essential Constants, Duality, The Line at Infinity, Projective Properties and Double Ratio, Projective Coordinates, The Conic, Collineations and Involutions in One Dimension, Binary Forms, Algebraic Invariants, Analytic Treatment of the Conic, Collineations in the Plane, Cubic Involutions and the Rational Cubic Curve, and a clear discussion of Non-Euclidean Geometry. For senior-college students and graduates. "An excellent textbook . . . very clearly written . . . propositions stated concisely," A. Emch, Am. Math. Monthly. Corrected reprinting. 928 problems. Index. 116 figures. xii + 443pp. 5⅜ x 8. S949 Paperbound **$2.00**

ALGEBRAIC CURVES, Robert J. Walker, Professor of Mathematics, Cornell University. Fine introduction to algebraic geometry. Presents some of the recently developed algebraic methods of handling problems in algebraic geometry, shows how these methods are related to the older analytic and geometric problems, and applies them to those same geometric problems. Limited to the theory of curves, concentrating on birational transformations. Contents: Algebraic Preliminaries, Projective Spaces, Plane Algebraic Curves, Formal Power Series, Transformations of a Curve, Linear Series. 25 illustrations. Numerous exercises at ends of sections. Index. x + 201pp. 5⅜ x 8½. S336 Paperbound **$1.60**

THE ADVANCED GEOMETRY OF PLANE CURVES AND THEIR APPLICATIONS, C. Zwikker. An unusual study of many important curves, their geometrical properties and their applications, including discussions of many less well-known curves not often treated in textbooks on synthetic and analytic Euclidean geometry. Includes both algebraic and transcendental curves such as the conic sections, kinked curves, spirals, lemniscates, cycloids, etc. and curves generated as involutes, evolutes, anticaustics, pedals, envelopes and orthogonal trajectories. Dr. Zwikker represents the points of the curves by complex numbers instead of two real Cartesian coordinates, allowing direct and even elegant proofs. Formerly: "Advanced Plane Geometry." 273 figures. xii + 299pp. 5⅜ x 8½.   S1078 Paperbound **$2.00**

A TREATISE ON THE DIFFERENTIAL GEOMETRY OF CURVES AND SURFACES, L. P. Eisenhart. Introductory treatise especially for the graduate student, for years a highly successful textbook. More detailed and concrete in approach than most more recent books. Covers space curves, osculating planes, moving axes, Gauss' method, the moving trihedral, geodesics, conformal representation, etc. Last section deals with deformation of surfaces, rectilinear congruences, cyclic systems, etc. Index. 683 problems. 30 diagrams. xii + 474pp. 5⅜ x 8.
                                                                          S667 Paperbound **$2.75**

A TREATISE ON ALGEBRAIC PLANE CURVES, J. L. Coolidge. Unabridged reprinting of one of few full coverages in English, offering detailed introduction to theory of algebraic plane curves and their relations to geometry and analysis. Treats topological properties, Riemann-Roch theorem, all aspects of wide variety of curves including real, covariant, polar, containing series of a given sort, elliptic, polygonal, rational, the pencil, two parameter nets, etc. This volume will enable the reader to appreciate the symbolic notation of Aronhold and Clebsch. Bibliography. Index. 17 illustrations. xxiv + 513pp. 5⅜ x 8.   S543 Paperbound **$2.75**

AN INTRODUCTION TO THE GEOMETRY OF N DIMENSIONS, D. M. Y. Sommerville. An introduction presupposing no prior knowledge of the field, the only book in English devoted exclusively to higher dimensional geometry. Discusses fundamental ideas of incidence, parallelism, perpendicularity, angles between linear space; enumerative geometry; analytical geometry from projective and metric points of view; polytopes; elementary ideas in analysis situs; content of 'hyper-spacial figures. Bibliography. Index. 60 diagrams. 196pp. 5⅜ x 8.
                                                                          S494 Paperbound **$1.50**

GEOMETRY OF FOUR DIMENSIONS, H. P. Manning. Unique in English as a clear, concise introduction. Treatment is synthetic, and mostly Euclidean, although in hyperplanes and hyperspheres at infinity, non-Euclidean geometry is used. Historical introduction. Foundations of 4-dimensional geometry. Perpendicularity, simple angles. Angles of planes, higher order. Symmetry, order, motion; hyperpyramids, hypercones, hyperspheres; figures with parallel elements; volume, hypervolume in space; regular polyhedroids. Glossary. 78 figures. ix + 348pp. 5⅜ x 8.   S182 Paperbound **$2.00**

CONVEX FIGURES AND POLYHEDRA, L. A. Lyusternik. An excellent elementary discussion by a leading Russian mathematician. Beginning with the basic concepts of convex figures and bodies and their supporting lines and planes, the author covers such matters as centrally symmetric convex figures, theorems of Euler, Cauchy, Steinitz and Alexandrov on convex polyhedra, linear systems of convex bodies, planar sections of convex bodies, the Brunn-Minkowski inequality and its consequences, and many other related topics. No more than a high school background in mathematics needed for complete understanding. First English translation by T. J. Smith. 182 illustrations. Index. x + 176pp. 5⅜ x 8½.
                                                                          S1021 Paperbound **$1.50**

NON-EUCLIDEAN GEOMETRY, Roberto Bonola. The standard coverage of non-Euclidean geometry. It examines from both a historical and mathematical point of view the geometries which have arisen from a study of Euclid's 5th postulate upon parallel lines. Also included are complete texts, translated, of Bolyai's SCIENCE OF ABSOLUTE SPACE. Lobachevsky's THEORY OF PARALLELS. 180 diagrams. 431pp. 5⅜ x 8.   S27 Paperbound **$2.00**

ELEMENTS OF NON-EUCLIDEAN GEOMETRY, D. M. Y. Sommerville. Unique in proceeding step-by-step, in the manner of traditional geometry. Enables the student with only a good knowledge of high school algebra and geometry to grasp elementary hyperbolic, elliptic, analytic non-Euclidean geometries; space curvature and its philosophical implications; theory of radical axes; homothetic centres and systems of circles; parataxy and parallelism; absolute measure; Gauss' proof of the defect area theorem; geodesic representation; much more, all with exceptional clarity. 126 problems at chapter endings provide progressive practice and familiarity. 133 figures. Index. xvi + 274pp. 5⅜ x 8.   S460 Paperbound **$1.50**

INTRODUCTORY NON-EUCLIDEAN GEOMETRY, H. P. Manning. Sound elementary introduction to non-Euclidean geometry. The first two thirds (Pangeometry and the Hyperbolic Geometry) require a grasp of plane and solid geometry and trigonometry. The last sections (the Elliptic Geometry and Analytic Non-Euclidean Geometry) necessitate also basic college calculus for understanding the text. The book does not propose to investigate the foundations of geometry, but rather begins with the theorems common to Euclidean and non-Euclidean geometry and then takes up the specific differences between them. A simple and direct account of the bases of this important branch of mathematics for teachers and students. 94 figures. vii + 95pp. 5⅜ x 8.   S310 Paperbound **$1.00**

ELEMENTARY CONCEPTS OF TOPOLOGY, P. Alexandroff. First English translation of the famous brief introduction to topology for the beginner or for the mathematician not undertaking extensive study. This unusually useful intuitive approach deals primarily with the concepts of complex, cycle, and homology, and is wholly consistent with current investigations. Ranges from basic concepts of set-theoretic topology to the concept of Betti groups. "Glowing example of harmony between intuition and thought," David Hilbert. Translated by A. E. Farley. Introduction by D. Hilbert. Index. 25 figures. 73pp. 5⅜ x 8. **S747 Paperbound $1.00**

Number theory

INTRODUCTION TO THE THEORY OF NUMBERS, L. E. Dickson. Thorough, comprehensive approach with adequate coverage of classical literature, an introductory volume beginners can follow. Chapters on divisibility, congruences, quadratic residues & reciprocity, Diophantine equations, etc. Full treatment of binary quadratic forms without usual restriction to integral coefficients. Covers infinitude of primes, least residues, Fermat's theorem, Euler's phi function, Legendre's symbol, Gauss's lemma, automorphs, reduced forms, recent theorems of Thue & Siegel, many more. Much material not readily available elsewhere. 239 problems. Index. I figure. viii + 183pp. 5⅜ x 8. **S342 Paperbound $1.75**

ELEMENTS OF NUMBER THEORY, I. M. Vinogradov. Detailed 1st course for persons without advanced mathematics; 95% of this book can be understood by readers who have gone no farther than high school algebra. Partial contents: divisibility theory, important number theoretical functions, congruences, primitive roots and indices, etc. Solutions to both problems and exercises. Tables of primes, indices, etc. Covers almost every essential formula in elementary number theory! Translated from Russian. 233 problems, 104 exercises. viii + 227pp. 5⅜ x 8. **S259 Paperbound $1.75**

THEORY OF NUMBERS and DIOPHANTINE ANALYSIS, R. D. Carmichael. These two complete works in one volume form one of the most lucid introductions to number theory, requiring only a firm foundation in high school mathematics. "Theory of Numbers," partial contents: Eratosthenes' sieve, Euclid's fundamental theorem, G.C.F. and L.C.M. of two or more integers, linear congruences, etc "Diophantine Analysis": rational triangles, Pythagorean triangles, equations of third, fourth, higher degrees, method of functional equations, much more. "Theory of Numbers": 76 problems. Index. 94pp. "Diophantine Analysis": 222 problems. Index. 118pp. 5⅜ x 8. **S529 Paperbound $1.35**

Numerical analysis, tables

MATHEMATICAL TABLES AND FORMULAS, Compiled by Robert D. Carmichael and Edwin R. Smith. Valuable collection for students, etc. Contains all tables necessary in college algebra and trigonometry, such as five-place common logarithms, logarithmic sines and tangents of small angles, logarithmic trigonometric functions, natural trigonometric functions, four-place antilogarithms, tables for changing from sexagesimal to circular and from circular to sexagesimal measure of angles, etc. Also many tables and formulas not ordinarily accessible, including powers, roots, and reciprocals, exponential and hyperbolic functions, ten-place logarithms of prime numbers, and formulas and theorems from analytical and elementary geometry and from calculus. Explanatory introduction. viii + 269pp. 5⅜ x 8½. **S111 Paperbound $1.25**

MATHEMATICAL TABLES, H. B. Dwight. Unique for its coverage in one volume of almost every function of importance in applied mathematics, engineering, and the physical sciences. Three extremely fine tables of the three trig functions and their inverse functions to thousandths of radians; natural and common logarithms; squares, cubes; hyperbolic functions and the inverse hyperbolic functions; $(a^2 + b^2)$ exp. ½a; complete elliptic integrals of the 1st and 2nd kind; sine and cosine integrals; exponential integrals Ei(x) and Ei(— x); binomial coefficients; factorials to 250; surface zonal harmonics and first derivatives; Bernoulli and Euler numbers and their logs to base of 10; Gamma function; normal probability integral; over 60 pages of Bessel functions; the Riemann Zeta function. Each table with formulae generally used, sources of more extensive tables, interpolation data, etc. Over half have columns of differences, to facilitate interpolation. Introduction. Index. viii + 231pp. 5⅜ x 8. **S445 Paperbound $2.00**

TABLES OF FUNCTIONS WITH FORMULAE AND CURVES, E. Jahnke & F. Emde. The world's most comprehensive 1-volume English-text collection of tables, formulae, curves of transcendent functions. 4th corrected edition, new 76-page section giving tables, formulae for elementary functions—not in other English editions. Partial contents: sine, cosine, logarithmic integral; factorial function; error integral; theta functions; elliptic integrals, functions; Legendre, Bessel, Riemann, Mathieu, hypergeometric functions, etc. Supplementary books. Bibliography. Indexed. "Out of the way functions for which we know no other source," SCIENTIFIC COMPUTING SERVICE, Ltd. 212 figures. 400pp. 5⅜ x 8. **S133 Paperbound $2.00**

JACOBIAN ELLIPTIC FUNCTION TABLES, L. M. Milne-Thomson. An easy to follow, practical book which gives not only useful numerical tables, but also a complete elementary sketch of the application of elliptic functions. It covers Jacobian elliptic functions and a description of their principal properties; complete elliptic integrals; Fourier series and power series expansions; periods, zeros, poles, residues, formulas for special values of the argument; transformations, approximations, elliptic integrals, conformal mapping, factorization of cubic and quartic polynomials; application to the pendulum problem; etc. Tables and· graphs form the body of the book: Graph, 5 figure table of the elliptic function sn (u m); cn (u m); dn (u m). 8 figure table of complete elliptic integrals K, K′, E, E′, and the nome q. 7 figure table of the Jacobian zeta-function Z(u). 3 figures. xi + 123pp. 5⅜ x 8.
S194 Paperbound **$1.35**

TABLES OF INDEFINITE INTEGRALS, G. Petit Bois. Comprehensive and accurate, this orderly grouping of over 2500 of the most useful indefinite integrals will save you hours of laborious mathematical groundwork. After a list of 49 common transformations of integral expressions, with a wide variety of examples, the book takes up algebraic functions, irrational monomials, products and quotients of binomials, transcendental functions, natural logs, etc. You will rarely or never encounter an integral of an algebraic or transcendental function not included here; any more comprehensive set of tables costs at least $12 or $15. Index. 2544 integrals. xii + 154pp. 6⅛ x 9¼.
S225 Paperbound **$2.00**

SUMMATION OF SERIES, Collected by L. B. W. Jolley. Over 1100 common series collected, summed, and grouped for easy reference—for mathematicians, physicists, computer techni-cians, engineers, and students. Arranged for convenience into categories, such as arith-metical and geometrical progressions, powers and products of natural numbers, figurate and polygonal numbers, inverse natural numbers, exponential and logarithmic series, binomial expansions, simple inverse products, factorials, and trigonometric and hyperbolic expansions. Also included are series representing various Bessel functions, elliptic integrals; discussions of special series involving Legendre polynomials, the zeta function, Bernoulli's function, and similar expressions. Revised, enlarged second edition. New preface. xii + 251pp. 5⅜ x 8½.
S23 Paperbound **$2.25**

A TABLE OF THE INCOMPLETE ELLIPTIC INTEGRAL OF THE THIRD KIND, R. G. Selfridge, J. E. Maxfield. The first complete 6-place tables of values of the incomplete integral of the third kind, prepared under the auspices of the Research Department of the U.S. Naval Ordnance Test Station. Calculated on an IBM type 704 calculator and thoroughly verified by echo-checking and a check integral at the completion of each value of **a**. Of inestimable value in problems where the surface area of geometrical bodies can only be expressed in terms of the incomplete integral of the third and lower kinds; problems in aero-, fluid-, and thermodynamics involving processes where nonsymmetrical repetitive volumes must be determined; various types of seismological problems; problems of magnetic potentials due to circular current; etc. Foreword. Acknowledgment. Introduction. Use of table. xiv + 805pp. 5⅝ x 8⅜.
S501 Clothbound **$7.50**

PRACTICAL ANALYSIS, GRAPHICAL AND NUMERICAL METHODS, F. A. Willers. Translated by R. T. Beyer. Immensely practical handbook for engineers, showing how to interpolate, use various methods of numerical differentiation and integration, determine the roots of a single algebraic equation, system of linear equations, use empirical formulas, integrate differential equations, etc. Hundreds of shortcuts for arriving at numerical solutions. Special section on American calculating machines, by T. W. Simpson. 132 illustrations. 422pp. 5⅜ x 8.
S273 Paperbound **$2.00**

NUMERICAL INTEGRATION OF DIFFERENTIAL EQUATIONS, A. A. Bennett, W. E. Milne, H. Bateman. Republication of original monograph prepared for National Research Council. New methods of integration of differential equations developed by 3 leading mathematicians: THE INTERPOLATIONAL POLYNOMIAL and SUCCESSIVE APPROXIMATIONS by A. A. Bennett; STEP-BY-STEP METHODS OF INTEGRATION by W. W. Milne; METHODS FOR PARTIAL DIFFERENTIAL EQUATIONS by H. Bateman. Methods for partial differential equations, transition from differ-ence equations to differential equations, solution of differential equations to non-integral values of a parameter will interest mathematicians and physicists. 288 footnotes, mostly bibliographic; 235-item classified bibliography. 108pp. 5⅜ x 8.   S305 Paperbound **$1.35**

INTRODUCTION TO RELAXATION METHODS, F. S. Shaw. Fluid mechanics, design of electrical networks, forces in structural frameworks, stress distribution, buckling, etc. Solve linear simultaneous equations, linear ordinary differential equations, partial differential equations, Eigen-value problems by relaxation methods. Detailed examples throughout. Special tables for dealing with awkwardly-shaped boundaries. Indexes. 253 diagrams. 72 tables. 400pp. 5⅜ x 8.
S244 Paperbound **$2.45**

NUMERICAL SOLUTIONS OF DIFFERENTIAL EQUATIONS, H. Levy & E. A. Baggott. Comprehensive collection of methods for solving ordinary differential equations of first and higher order. All must pass 2 requirements: easy to grasp and practical, more rapid than school methods. Partial contents: graphical integration of differential equations, graphical methods for de-tailed solution. Numerical solution. Simultaneous equations and equations of 2nd and higher orders. "Should be in the hands of all in research in applied mathematics, teaching," NATURE. 21 figures. viii + 238pp. 5⅜ x 8.
S168 Paperbound **$1.75**

Probability theory and information theory

AN ELEMENTARY INTRODUCTION TO THE THEORY OF PROBABILITY, B. V. Gnedenko and A. Ya. Khinchin. Translated by Leo F. Boron. A clear, compact introduction designed to equip the reader with a fundamental grasp of the theory of probabiiity. It is thorough and authoritative within its purposely restricted range, yet the layman with a background in elementary mathematics will be able to follow it without difficulty. Covers such topics as the processes involved in the calculation of probabilities, conditional probabilities and the multiplication rule, Bayes's formula, Bernoulli's scheme and theorem, random variables and distribution laws, and dispersion and mean deviations. New translation of fifth (revised) Russian edition (1960)—the only translation checked and corrected by Gnedenko. New preface for Dover edition by B. V. Gnedenko. Index. Bibliography. Appendix: Table of values of function $\phi(a)$. xii + 130pp. 5⅜ x 8½. **T155 Paperbound $1.50**

AN INTRODUCTION TO MATHEMATICAL PROBABILITY, Julian Lowell Coolidge. A thorough introduction which presents the mathematical foundation of the theory of probability. A substantial body of material, yet can be understood with a knowledge of only elementary calculus. Contains: The Scope and Meaning of Mathematical Probability; Elementary Principles of Probability; Bernoulli's Theorem; Mean Value and Dispersion; Geometrical Probability; Probability of Causes; Errors of Observation; Errors in Many Variables; Indirect Observations; The Statistical Theory of Gases; and The Principles of Life Insurance. Six pages of logarithm tables. 4 diagrams. Subject and author indices. xii + 214pp. 5⅜ x 8½. **S258 Paperbound $1.35**

A GUIDE TO OPERATIONS RESEARCH, W. E. Duckworth. A brief nontechnical exposition of techniques and theories of operational research. A good introduction for the layman; also can provide the initiate with new understandings. No mathematical training needed, yet not an oversimplification. Covers game theory, mathematical analysis, information theory, linear programming, cybernetics, decision theory, etc. Also includes a discussion of the actual organization of an operational research program and an account of the uses of such programs in the oil, chemical, paper, and metallurgical industries, etc. Bibliographies at chapter ends. Appendices. 36 figures. 145pp. 5¼ x 8½. **T1129 Clothbound $3.50**

MATHEMATICAL FOUNDATIONS OF INFORMATION THEORY, A. I. Khinchin. For the first time mathematicians, statisticians, physicists, cyberneticists, and communications engineers are offered a complete and exact introduction to this relatively new field. Entropy as a measure of a finite scheme, applications to coding theory, study of sources, channels and codes, detailed proofs of both Shannon theorems for any ergodic source and any stationary channel with finite memory, and much more are covered. Bibliography. vii + 120pp. 5⅜ x 8. **S434 Paperbound $1.35**

SELECTED PAPERS ON NOISE AND STOCHASTIC PROCESS, edited by Prof. Nelson Wax, U. of Illinois. 6 basic papers for newcomers in the field, for those whose work involves noise characteristics. Chandrasekhar, Uhlenbeck & Ornstein, Uhlenbeck & Ming, Rice, Doob. Included is Kac's Chauvenet-Prize winning Random Walk. Extensive bibliography lists 200 articles, up through 1953. 21 figures. 337pp. 6⅛ x 9¼. **S262 Paperbound $2.50**

THEORY OF PROBABILITY, William Burnside. Synthesis, expansion of individual papers presents numerous problems in classical probability, offering many original views succinctly, effectively. Game theory, cards, selections from groups; geometrical probability in such areas as suppositions as to probability of position of point on a line, points on surface of sphere, etc. Includes methods of approximation, theory of errors, direct calculation of probabilities, etc. Index. 136pp. 5⅜ x 8. **S567 Paperbound $1.00**

Statistics

ELEMENTARY STATISTICS, WITH APPLICATIONS IN MEDICINE AND THE BIOLOGICAL SCIENCES, F. E. Croxton. A sound introduction to statistics for anyone in the physical sciences, assuming no prior acquaintance and requiring only a modest knowledge of math. All basic formulas carefully explained and illustrated; all necessary reference tables included. From basic terms and concepts, the study proceeds to frequency distribution, linear, non-linear, and multiple correlation, skewness, kurtosis, etc. A large section deals with reliability and significance of statistical methods. Containing concrete examples from medicine and biology, this book will prove unusually helpful to workers in those fields who increasingly must evaluate, check, and interpret statistics. Formerly titled "Elementary Statistics with Applications in Medicine." 101 charts. 57 tables. 14 appendices. Index. iv + 376pp. 5⅜ x 8. **S506 Paperbound $2.00**

ANALYSIS & DESIGN OF EXPERIMENTS, H. B. Mann. Offers a method for grasping the analysis of variance and variance design within a short time. Partial contents: Chi-square distribution and analysis of variance distribution, matrices, quadratic forms, likelihood ration tests and tests of linear hypotheses, power of analysis, Galois fields, non-orthogonal data, interblock estimates, etc. 15pp. of useful tables. x + 195pp. 5 x 7⅜. **S180 Paperbound $1.45**

METHODS OF STATISTICS, L. H. C. Tippett. A classic in its field, this unusually complete systematic introduction to statistical methods begins at beginner's level and progresses to advanced levels for experimenters and poll-takers in all fields of statistical research. Supplies fundamental knowledge of virtually all elementary methods in use today by sociologists, psychologists, biologists, engineers, mathematicians, etc. Explains logical and mathematical basis of each method described, with examples for each section. Covers frequency distributions and measures, inference from random samples, errors in large samples, simple analysis of variance, multiple and partial regression and correlation, etc. 4th revised (1952) edition. 16 charts. 5 significance tables. 152-item bibliography. 96 tables. 22 figures. 395pp. 6 x 9.
S228 Clothbound **$7.50**

STATISTICS MANUAL, E. L. Crow, F. A. Davis, M. W. Maxfield. Comprehensive collection of classical, modern statistics methods, prepared under auspices of U. S. Naval Ordnance Test Station, China Lake, Calif. Many examples from ordnance will be valuable to workers in all fields. Emphasis is on use, with information on fiducial limits, sign tests, Chi-square runs, sensitivity, quality control, much more. "Well written . . . excellent reference work," Operations Research. Corrected edition of NAVORD Report 3360 NOTS 948. Introduction. Appendix of 32 tables, charts. Index. Bibliography. 95 illustrations. 306pp. 5⅜ x 8.
S599 Paperbound **$1.75**

Symbolic logic

AN INTRODUCTION TO SYMBOLIC LOGIC, Susanne K. Langer. Probably the clearest book ever written on symbolic logic for the philosopher, general scientist and layman. It will be particularly appreciated by those who have been rebuffed by other introductory works because of insufficient mathematical training. No special knowledge of mathematics is required. Starting with the simplest symbols and conventions, you are led to a remarkable grasp of the Boole-Schroeder and Russell-Whitehead systems clearly and quickly. PARTIAL CONTENTS: Study of forms, Essentials of logical structure, Generalization, Classes, The deductive system of classes, The algebra of logic, Abstraction of interpretation, Calculus of propositions, Assumptions of PRINCIPIA MATHEMATICA, Logistics, Logic of the syllogism, Proofs of theorems. "One of the clearest and simplest introductions to a subject which is very much alive. The style is easy, symbolism is introduced gradually, and the intelligent non-mathematician should have no difficulty in following the argument," MATHEMATICS GAZETTE. Revised, expanded second edition. Truth-value tables. 368pp. 5⅜ x 8.
S164 Paperbound **$1.85**

A SURVEY OF SYMBOLIC LOGIC: THE CLASSIC ALGEBRA OF LOGIC, C. I. Lewis. Classic survey of the field, comprehensive and thorough. Indicates content of major systems, alternative methods of procedure, and relation of these to the Boole-Schroeder algebra and to one another. Contains historical summary, as well as full proofs and applications of the classic, or Boole-Schroeder, algebra of logic. Discusses diagrams for the logical relations of classes, the two-valued algebra, propositional functions of two or more variables, etc. Chapters 5 and 6 of the original edition, which contained material not directly pertinent, have been omitted in this edition at the author's request. Appendix. Bibliography. Index. viii + 352pp. 5⅝ x 8⅜.
S643 Paperbound **$2.00**

INTRODUCTION TO SYMBOLIC LOGIC AND ITS APPLICATIONS, R. Carnap. One of the clearest, most comprehensive, and rigorous introductions to modern symbolic logic by perhaps its greatest living master. Symbolic languages are analyzed and one constructed. Applications to math (symbolic representation of axiom systems for set theory, natural numbers, real numbers, topology, Dedekind and Cantor explanations of continuity), physics (the general analysis of concepts of determination, causality, space-time-topology, based on Einstein), biology (symbolic representation of an axiom system for basic concepts). "A masterpiece," Zentralblatt für Mathematik und ihre Grenzgebiete. Over 300 exercises. 5 figures. Bibliography. Index. xvi + 241pp. 5⅜ x 8.
S453 Paperbound **$1.85**
Clothbound **$4.00**

SYMBOLIC LOGIC, C. I. Lewis, C. H. Langford. Probably the most cited book in symbolic logic, this is one of the fullest treatments of paradoxes. A wide coverage of the entire field of symbolic logic, plus considerable material that has not appeared elsewhere. Basic to the entire volume is the distinction between the logic of extensions and of intensions. Considerable emphasis is placed on converse substitution, while the matrix system presents the supposition of a variety of non-Aristotelian logics. It has especially valuable sections on strict limitations, existence of terms, 2-valued algebra and its extension to propositional functions, truth value systems, the matrix method, implication and deductibility, general theory of propositions, propositions of ordinary discourse, and similar topics. "Authoritative, most valuable," TIMES, London. Bibliography. 506pp. 5⅜ x 8.
S170 Paperbound **$2.35**

THE ELEMENTS OF MATHEMATICAL LOGIC, Paul Rosenbloom. First publication in any language. This book is intended for readers who are mature mathematically, but have no previous training in symbolic logic. It does not limit itself to a single system, but covers the field as a whole. It is a development of lectures given at Lund University, Sweden, in 1948. Partial contents: Logic of classes, fundamental theorems, Boolean algebra, logic of propositions, logic of propositional functions, expressive languages, combinatory logics, development of mathematics within an object language, paradoxes, theorems of Post and Goedel, Church's theorem, and similar topics. iv + 214pp. 5⅜ x 8. S227 Paperbound **$1.45**

THE PRINCIPLES OF SCIENCE, A TREATISE ON LOGIC AND THE SCIENTIFIC METHOD, W. S. Jevons. Treating such topics as Inductive and Deductive Logic, the Theory of Number, Probability, and the Limits of Scientific Method, this milestone in the development of symbolic logic remains a stimulating contribution to the investigation of inferential validity in the natural and social sciences. It significantly advances Boole's logic, and contains a detailed introduction to the nature and methods of probability in physics, astronomy, everyday affairs, etc. In his introduction, Ernest Nagel of Columbia University says, "[Jevons] continues to be of interest as an attempt to articulate the logic of scientific inquiry." Index. liii + 786pp. 5⅜ x 8.   S446 Paperbound **$2.98**

Vector and tensor analysis

VECTOR AND TENSOR ANALYSIS, A. P. Wills. Covers the entire field of vector and tensor analysis from elementary notions to dyads and non-Euclidean manifolds (especially detailed), absolute differentiation, the Lamé operator, the Riemann-Christoffel and Ricci-Einstein tensors, and the calculation of the Gaussian curvature of a surface. Many illustrations from electrical engineering, relativity theory, astro-physics, quantum mechanics. Presupposes only a good working knowledge of calculus. Exercises at end of each chapter. Intended for physicists and engineers as well as pure mathematicians. 44 diagrams. 114 problems. Bibliography. Index. xxxii + 285pp. 5⅜ x 8.   S454 Paperbound **$1.75**

APPLICATIONS OF TENSOR ANALYSIS, A. J. McConnell. (Formerly APPLICATIONS OF THE ABSOLUTE DIFFERENTIAL CALCULUS.) An excellent text for understanding the application of tensor methods to familiar subjects such as dynamics, electricity, elasticity, and hydrodynamics. Explains the fundamental ideas and notation of tensor theory, the geometrical treatment of tensor algebra, the theory of differentiation of tensors, and includes a wealth of practical material. Bibliography. Index. 43 illustrations. 685 problems. xii + 381pp. 5⅜ x 8.   S373 Paperbound **$1.95**

VECTOR AND TENSOR ANALYSIS, G. E. Hay. One of the clearest introductions to this increasingly important subject. Start with simple definitions, finish the book with a sure mastery of oriented Cartesian vectors, Christoffel symbols, solenoidal tensors, and their applications. Complete breakdown of plane, solid, analytical, differential geometry. Separate chapters on application. All fundamental formulae listed & demonstrated. 195 problems, 66 figures. viii + 193pp. 5⅜ x 8.   S109 Paperbound **$1.85**

VECTOR ANALYSIS, FOUNDED UPON THE LECTURES OF J. WILLARD GIBBS, by E. B. Wilson. Still a first-rate introduction and supplementary text for students of mathematics and physics. Based on the pioneering lectures of Yale's great J. Willard Gibbs, can be followed by anyone who has had some calculus. Practical approach, stressing efficient use of combinations and functions of vectors. Worked examples from geometry, mechanics, hydrodynamics, gas theory, etc., as well as practice examples. Covers basic vector processes, differential and integral calculus in relation to vector functions, and theory of linear vector functions, forming an introduction to the study of multiple algebra and matrix theory. While the notation is not always modern, it is easily followed. xviii + 436pp. 5⅜ x 8.
S656 Paperbound **$2.25**

PROBLEMS AND WORKED SOLUTIONS IN VECTOR ANALYSIS, L. R. Shorter. More pages of fully-worked-out examples than any other text on vector analysis. A self-contained course for home study or a fine classroom supplement. 138 problems and examples begin with fundamentals, then cover systems of coordinates, relative velocity and acceleration, the commutative and distributive laws, axial and polar vectors, finite displacements, the calculus of vectors, curl and divergence, etc. Final chapter treats applications in dynamics and physics: kinematics of a rigid body, equipotential surfaces, etc. "Very helpful . . . very comprehensive. A handy book like this . . . will fill a great want," MATHEMATICAL GAZETTE. Index. List of 174 important equations. 158 figures. xiv + 356pp. 5⅜ x 8.   S135 Paperbound **$2.00**

Prices subject to change without notice.

Dover publishes books on art, music, philosophy, literature, languages, history, social sciences, psychology, handcrafts, orientalia, puzzles and entertainments, chess, pets and gardens, books explaining science, intermediate and higher mathematics, mathematical physics, engineering, biological sciences, earth sciences, classics of science, etc. Write to:

Dept. catrr.
Dover Publications, Inc.
180 Varick Street, N.Y. 14, N.Y.